PhET SIMULATIONS

Available in the Pearson eText and in the Study Area of MasteringPhysics

Extended Edition includes Chapters 1–44. Standard Edition includes Chapters 1–37.
Three-volume edition: Volume 1 includes Chapters 1–20, Volume 2 includes Chapters 21–37,
and Volume 3 includes Chapters 37–44.

*Indicates an associated tutorial available in the MasteringPhysics Item Library.

ActivPhysics OnLine™ ACTIVITIES

www.masteringphysics.com

Young and Freedman

Sears and Zemansky's
University Physics
With Modern Physics
Volume 2

Custom Edition for West Valley College

Taken from:
Sears and Zemansky's University Physics with Modern Physics,
Thirteenth Edition
by Hugh D. Young and Roger A. Freedman;
contributing author A. Lewis Ford

Cover Art: Courtesy of Photodisc/Getty Images

Taken from:

Sears and Zemansky's University Physics with Modern Physics, Thirteenth Edition
by Hugh D. Young and Roger A. Freedman; contributing author A. Lewis Ford
Copyright © 2012, 2008, 2004 by Pearson Education, Inc.
Published by Addison Wesley
Boston, Massachusetts 02116

This special edition published in cooperation with Pearson Learning Solutions.

All trademarks, service marks, registered trademarks, and registered service marks are the property of their respective owners and are used herein for identification purposes only.

Pearson Learning Solutions, 501 Boylston Street, Suite 900, Boston, MA 02116
A Pearson Education Company
www.pearsoned.com

Printed in the United States of America

1 2 3 4 5 6 7 8 9 10 V092 16 15 14 13 12 11

000200010270784046

AD

ISBN 10: 1-256-33608-4
ISBN 13: 978-1-256-33608-2

BRIEF CONTENTS

Build Skills

Learn basic and advanced skills that help solve a broad range of physics problems.

Problem-Solving Strategies coach students in how to approach specific types of problems.

▼

This text's **uniquely extensive set** of Examples enables students to explore problem-solving challenges in exceptional detail.

Consistent

The **Identify / Set Up / Execute / Evaluate** format, used in all Examples, encourages students to tackle problems thoughtfully rather than skipping to the math.

Focused

All Examples and Problem-Solving Strategies are revised to be more concise and focused.

Visual

Most Examples employ a diagram—often a **pencil sketch** that shows what a student should draw.

Problem-Solving Strategy 5.2 Newton's Second Law: Dynamics of Particles

IDENTIFY *the relevant concepts:* You have to use Newton's second law for *any* problem that involves forces acting on an accelerating

accelerate in different directions, you can use a different set of axes for each body.

Example 5.17 Toboggan ride with friction II

The same toboggan with the same coefficient of friction as in Example 5.16 *accelerates* down a steeper hill. Derive an expression for the acceleration in terms of g, α, μ_k, and w.

SOLUTION

IDENTIFY and SET UP: The toboggan is accelerating, so we must use Newton's second law as given in Eqs. (5.4). Our target variable is the downhill acceleration.

Our sketch and free-body diagram (Fig. 5.23) are almost the same as for Example 5.16. The toboggan's y-component of acceleration a_y is still zero but the x-component a_x is not, so we've drawn the downhill component of weight as a longer vector than the (uphill) friction force.

EXECUTE: It's convenient to express the weight as $w = mg$. Then Newton's second law in component form says

$$\sum F_x = mg \sin \alpha + (-f_k) = ma_x$$
$$\sum F_y = n + (-mg \cos \alpha) = 0$$

5.23 Our sketches for this problem.

(a) The situation   (b) Free-body diagram for toboggan

From the second equation and Eq. (5.5) we get an expression for f_k:

$$n = mg \cos \alpha$$
$$f_k = \mu_k n = \mu_k mg \cos \alpha$$

We substitute this into the x-component equation and solve for a_x:

$$mg \sin \alpha + (-\mu_k mg \cos \alpha) = ma_x$$
$$a_x = g(\sin \alpha - \mu_k \cos \alpha)$$

EVALUATE: As for the frictionless toboggan in Example 5.10, the acceleration doesn't depend on the mass m of the toboggan. That's because all of the forces that act on the toboggan (weight, normal force, and kinetic friction force) are proportional to m.

Let's check some special cases. If the hill is vertical ($\alpha = 90°$) so that $\sin \alpha = 1$ and $\cos \alpha = 0$, we have $a_x = g$ (the toboggan falls freely). For a certain value of α the acceleration is zero; this happens if

$$\sin \alpha = \mu_k \cos \alpha \qquad \text{and} \qquad \mu_k = \tan \alpha$$

This agrees with our result for the constant-velocity toboggan in Example 5.16. If the angle is even smaller, $\mu_k \cos \alpha$ is greater than $\sin \alpha$ and a_x is *negative;* if we give the toboggan an initial downhill push to start it moving, it will slow down and stop. Finally, if the hill is frictionless so that $\mu_k = 0$, we retrieve the result of Example 5.10: $a_x = g \sin \alpha$.

Notice that we started with a simple problem (Example 5.10) and extended it to more and more general situations. The general result we found in this example includes *all* the previous ones as special cases. Don't memorize this result, but do make sure you understand how we obtained it and what it means.

Suppose instead we give the toboggan an initial push *up* the hill. The direction of the kinetic friction force is now reversed, so the acceleration is different from the downhill value. It turns out that the expression for a_x is the same as for downhill motion except that the minus sign becomes plus. Can you show this?

Example 1.1 Converting speed units

The world land speed record is 763.0 mi/h, set on October 15, 1997, by Andy Green in the jet-engine car *Thrust SSC*. Express this speed in meters per second.

Identify. mi/h → m/s   mi → m
                          h → s

Set up: 1 mi = 1.609 km   1 km = 1000 m
        1 h = 3600 s

Execute
763.0 mi/h = $\left(763.0 \frac{mi}{h}\right)\left(\frac{1.609 km}{1 mi}\right)\left(\frac{1000 m}{1 km}\right)\left(\frac{1 h}{3600 s}\right)$

= 341.018611 m/s = <u>341.0 m/s</u>

NEW! Video Tutor Solution for Every Example
Each Example is explained and solved by an instructor in a Video Tutor solution provided in the Study Area of MasteringPhysics® and in the Pearson eText.

The Mathematics of Waves

Learning Goal: To qualitatively understand the formula for sine functions.

Consider a wave moving on a string. If you take a picture of the string at a specific time, then you get a graph of shape $y(x)$. If this is a simple sinusoidal wave (such as the standing wave harmonics found in musical instruments), then

The function $y = \sin(x)$ oscillates between a minimum value of $y = -1$ and a maximum value of $y = 1$. Multiplying this function by a number A changes the minimum and maximum values, increasing the magnitudes if $A > 1$ and decreasing the magnitudes if $A < 1$.

Part A

Give the minimum and maximum values of the function $y = 3\sin(x)$.

Give the minimum value followed by the maximum value, separated by a comma.

If you move to the right starting from $x = 0$, the function $y = \sin(x)$ begins to repeat itself when you reach $x = 2\pi$. This shows that the function $y = \sin(x)$ has a period of 2π. More formally, saying a function has a period of 2π means the value of the function at x is the same as the value at $x + 2\pi$, $x + 4\pi$, etc. (as well as at $x - 2\pi$, $x - 4\pi$, and so on).

If you change the function to $y = \sin(\omega x)$, then starting from $x = 0$, the function begins to repeat itself when $\omega x = 2\pi$. Solving for x, you can see that the period has changed from $T = 2\pi$ to $T = 2\pi/\omega$.

Part B

What is the period T of the function $y = 3\sin(4x)$?

Express your answer to three significant figures.

$T =$

NEW! Mathematics Review Tutorials
MasteringPhysics offers an extensive set of assignable mathematics review tutorials—covering differential and integral calculus as well as algebra and trigonometry.

Build **Confidence**

Develop problem-solving confidence through a range of practice options—from guided to unguided.

NEW! Bridging Problems

At the start of each problem set, a Bridging Problem helps students make the leap from routine exercises to challenging problems with confidence and ease.

Each Bridging Problem poses a moderately difficult, multi-concept problem, which often draws on earlier chapters. In place of a full solution, it provides a skeleton solution guide consisting of questions and hints.

A full solution is explained in a Video Tutor, provided in the Study Area of MasteringPhysics® and in the Pearson eText.

BRIDGING PROBLEM   Billiard Physics

A cue ball (a uniform solid sphere of mass m and radius R) is at rest on a level pool table. Using a pool cue, you give the ball a sharp, horizontal hit of magnitude F at a height h above the center of the ball (Fig. 10.37). The force of the hit is much greater than the friction force f that the table surface exerts on the ball. The hit lasts for a short time Δt. (a) For what value of h will the ball roll without slipping? (b) If you hit the ball dead center ($h = 0$), the ball will slide across the table for a while, but eventually it will roll without slipping. What will the speed of its center of mass be then?

SOLUTION GUIDE

See MasteringPhysics® study area for a Video Tutor solution.

IDENTIFY and SET UP

1. Draw a free-body diagram for the ball for the situation in part (a), including your choice of coordinate axes. Note that the cue exerts both an impulsive force on the ball and an impulsive torque around the center of mass.
2. The cue force applied for a time Δt gives the ball's center of mass a speed v_{cm}, and the cue torque applied for that same time gives the ball an angular speed ω. What must be the relationship between v_{cm} and ω for the ball to roll without slipping?

10.37

3. Draw two free-body diagrams for the ball in part (b): one showing the forces during the hit and the other showing the forces after the hit but before the ball is rolling without slipping.
4. What is the angular speed of the ball in part (b) just after the hit? While the ball is sliding, does v_{cm} increase or decrease? Does ω increase or decrease? What is the relationship between v_{cm} and ω when the ball is finally rolling without slipping?

EXECUTE

5. In part (a), use the impulse-momentum theorem to find the speed of the ball's center of mass immediately after the hit. Then use the rotational version of the impulse-momentum theorem to find the angular speed immediately after the hit. (*Hint:* To write down the rotational version of the impulse-momentum theorem, remember that the relationship between torque and angular momentum is the same as that between force and linear momentum.)
6. Use your results from step 5 to find the value of h that will cause the ball to roll without slipping immediately after the hit.
7. In part (b), again find the ball's center-of-mass speed and angular speed immediately after the hit. Then write Newton's second law for the translational motion and rotational motion of the ball as it is sliding. Use these equations to write expressions for v_{cm} and ω as functions of the elapsed time t since the hit.
8. Using your results from step 7, find the time t when v_{cm} and ω have the correct relationship for rolling without slipping. Then find the value of v_{cm} at this time.

EVALUATE

9. If you have access to a pool table, test out the results of parts (a) and (b) for yourself!
10. Can you show that if you used a hollow cylinder rather than a solid ball, you would have to hit the top of the cylinder to cause rolling without slipping as in part (a)?

Figure P14.95

14.95 · CP In Fig. P14.95 the upper ball is released from rest, collides with the stationary lower ball, and sticks to it. The strings are both 50.0 cm long. The upper ball has mass 2.00 kg, and it is initially 10.0 cm higher than the lower ball, which has mass 3.00 kg. Find the frequency and maximum angular displacement of the motion after the collision.

14.96 ·· CP BIO *T. rex.* Model the leg of the *T. rex* in Example 14.10 (Section 14.6) as two uniform rods, each 1.55 m long, joined rigidly end to end. Let the lower rod have mass M and the upper rod mass $2M$. The composite object is pivoted about the top of the upper rod. Compute the oscillation period of this object for small-amplitude oscillations. Compare your result to that of Example 14.10.

14.97 ·· CALC A slender, uniform, metal rod with mass M is pivoted without friction about an axis through its midpoint and perpendicular to the rod. A horizontal spring with force constant k is attached to the lower end of the rod, with the other end of the spring attached to a rigid support. If the rod is displaced by a small angle Θ from the vertical (Fig. P14.97) and released, show that it moves in angular SHM and calculate the period. (*Hint:* Assume that the angle Θ is small enough for the approximations $\sin \Theta \approx \Theta$ and $\cos \Theta \approx 1$ to be valid. The motion is simple harmonic if $d^2\theta/dt^2 = -\omega^2\theta$, and the period is then $T = 2\pi/\omega$.)

Figure P14.97

In response to professors, the Problem Sets now include more biomedically oriented problems (BIO), more difficult problems requiring calculus (CALC), and more cumulative problems that draw on earlier chapters (CP).

About 20% of problems are new or revised. These revisions are driven by detailed student-performance data gathered nationally through MasteringPhysics.

Problem difficulty is now indicated by a three-dot ranking system based on data from MasteringPhysics.

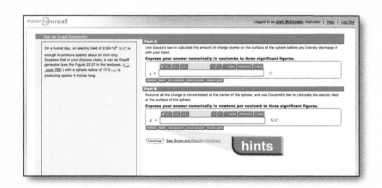

NEW! Enhanced End-of-Chapter Problems in MasteringPhysics
Select end-of-chapter problems will now offer additional support such as problem-solving strategy hints, relevant math review and practice, and links to the eText. These new enhanced problems bridge the gap between guided tutorials and traditional homework problems.

Bring Physics **to Life**

Deepen knowledge of physics by building connections to the real world.

NEW! Applications of Physics ▶
Throughout the text, free-standing captioned photos apply physics to real situations, with particular emphasis on applications of biomedical and general interest.

◀ NEW! PhET Simulations and Tutorials
Sixteen assignable PhET Tutorials enable students to make connections between real-life phenomena and the underlying physics. 76 PhET simulations are provided in the Study Area of MasteringPhysics® and in the Pearson eText.

The comprehensive library of ActivPhysics applets and applet-based tutorials is also available.

NEW! Video Tutor Demonstrations and Tutorials
"Pause and predict" demonstration videos of key physics concepts engage students by asking them to submit a prediction before seeing the outcome. These videos are available through the Study Area of MasteringPhysics and in the Pearson eText. A set of assignable tutorials based on these videos challenge students to transfer their understanding of the demonstration to a related problem situation.

Biomedically Based End-of-Chapter Problems ▶
To serve biosciences students, the text adds a substantial number of problems based on biological and biomedical situations.

Figure **E21.23**

21.24 •• **BIO** **Base Pairing in DNA, II.** Refer to Exercise 21.23. Figure E21.24 shows the bonding of the cytosine and guanine molecules. The $O-H$ and $H-N$ distances are each 0.110 nm. In this case, assume that the bonding is due only to the forces along the $O-H-O$, $N-H-N$, and $O-H-N$ combinations, and assume also that these three combinations are parallel to each other. Calculate the *net* force that cytosine exerts on guanine due to the preceding three combinations. Is this force attractive or repulsive?

Make a Difference with
MasteringPhysics®

www.masteringphysics.com

MasteringPhysics is the most effective and widely used online science tutorial, homework, and assessment system available.

NEW! Pre-Built Assignments

For every chapter in the book, MasteringPhysics now provides pre-built assignments that cover the material with a tested mix of tutorials and end-of-chapter problems of graded difficulty. Professors may use these assignments as-is or take them as a starting point for modification.

Gradebook

- Every assignment is graded automatically.
- Shades of red highlight vulnerable students and challenging assignments.

Class Performance on Assignment

Click on a problem to see which step your students struggled with most, and even their most common wrong answers. Compare results at every stage with the national average or with your previous class.

Gradebook Diagnostics

This screen provides your favorite weekly diagnostics. With a single click, charts summarize the most difficult problems, vulnerable students, grade distribution, and even improvement in scores over the course.

ABOUT THE AUTHORS

Hugh D. Young is Emeritus Professor of Physics at Carnegie Mellon University. He earned both his undergraduate and graduate degrees from that university. He earned his Ph.D. in fundamental particle theory under the direction of the late Richard Cutkosky. He joined the faculty of Carnegie Mellon in 1956 and retired in 2004. He also had two visiting professorships at the University of California, Berkeley.

Dr. Young's career has centered entirely on undergraduate education. He has written several undergraduate-level textbooks, and in 1973 he became a coauthor with Francis Sears and Mark Zemansky for their well-known introductory texts. In addition to his role on Sears and Zemansky's *University Physics,* he is also author of Sears and Zemansky's *College Physics.*

Dr. Young earned a bachelor's degree in organ performance from Carnegie Mellon in 1972 and spent several years as Associate Organist at St. Paul's Cathedral in Pittsburgh. He has played numerous organ recitals in the Pittsburgh area. Dr. Young and his wife, Alice, usually travel extensively in the summer, especially overseas and in the desert canyon country of southern Utah.

Roger A. Freedman is a Lecturer in Physics at the University of California, Santa Barbara. Dr. Freedman was an undergraduate at the University of California campuses in San Diego and Los Angeles, and did his doctoral research in nuclear theory at Stanford University under the direction of Professor J. Dirk Walecka. He came to UCSB in 1981 after three years teaching and doing research at the University of Washington.

At UCSB, Dr. Freedman has taught in both the Department of Physics and the College of Creative Studies, a branch of the university intended for highly gifted and motivated undergraduates. He has published research in nuclear physics, elementary particle physics, and laser physics. In recent years, he has worked to make physics lectures a more interactive experience through the use of classroom response systems.

In the 1970s Dr. Freedman worked as a comic book letterer and helped organize the San Diego Comic-Con (now the world's largest popular culture convention) during its first few years. Today, when not in the classroom or slaving over a computer, Dr. Freedman can be found either flying (he holds a commercial pilot's license) or driving with his wife, Caroline, in their 1960 Nash Metropolitan convertible.

A. Lewis Ford is Professor of Physics at Texas A&M University. He received a B.A. from Rice University in 1968 and a Ph.D. in chemical physics from the University of Texas at Austin in 1972. After a one-year postdoc at Harvard University, he joined the Texas A&M physics faculty in 1973 and has been there ever since. Professor Ford's research area is theoretical atomic physics, with a specialization in atomic collisions. At Texas A&M he has taught a variety of undergraduate and graduate courses, but primarily introductory physics.

HOW TO SUCCEED IN PHYSICS BY REALLY TRYING

Mark Hollabaugh *Normandale Community College*

Physics encompasses the large and the small, the old and the new. From the atom to galaxies, from electrical circuitry to aerodynamics, physics is very much a part of the world around us. You probably are taking this introductory course in calculus-based physics because it is required for subsequent courses you plan to take in preparation for a career in science or engineering. Your professor wants you to learn physics and to enjoy the experience. He or she is very interested in helping you learn this fascinating subject. That is part of the reason your professor chose this textbook for your course. That is also the reason Drs. Young and Freedman asked me to write this introductory section. We want you to succeed!

The purpose of this section of *University Physics* is to give you some ideas that will assist your learning. Specific suggestions on how to use the textbook will follow a brief discussion of general study habits and strategies.

Preparation for This Course

If you had high school physics, you will probably learn concepts faster than those who have not because you will be familiar with the language of physics. If English is a second language for you, keep a glossary of new terms that you encounter and make sure you understand how they are used in physics. Likewise, if you are farther along in your mathematics courses, you will pick up the mathematical aspects of physics faster. Even if your mathematics is adequate, you may find a book such as Arnold D. Pickar's *Preparing for General Physics: Math Skill Drills and Other Useful Help (Calculus Version)* to be useful. Your professor may actually assign sections of this math review to assist your learning.

Learning to Learn

Each of us has a different learning style and a preferred means of learning. Understanding your own learning style will help you to focus on aspects of physics that may give you difficulty and to use those components of your course that will help you overcome the difficulty. Obviously you will want to spend more time on those aspects that give you the most trouble. If you learn by hearing, lectures will be very important. If you learn by explaining, then working with other students will be useful to you. If solving problems is difficult for you, spend more time learning how to solve problems. Also, it is important to understand and develop good study habits. Perhaps the most important thing you can do for yourself is to set aside adequate, regularly scheduled study time in a distraction-free environment.

Answer the following questions for yourself:
- Am I able to use fundamental mathematical concepts from algebra, geometry and trigonometry? (If not, plan a program of review with help from your professor.)
- In similar courses, what activity has given me the most trouble? (Spend more time on this.) What has been the easiest for me? (Do this first; it will help to build your confidence.)

- Do I understand the material better if I read the book before or after the lecture? (You may learn best by skimming the material, going to lecture, and then undertaking an in-depth reading.)
- Do I spend adequate time in studying physics? (A rule of thumb for a class like this is to devote, on the average, 2.5 hours out of class for each hour in class. For a course meeting 5 hours each week, that means you should spend about 10 to 15 hours per week studying physics.)
- Do I study physics every day? (Spread that 10 to 15 hours out over an entire week!) At what time of the day am I at my best for studying physics? (Pick a specific time of the day and stick to it.)
- Do I work in a quiet place where I can maintain my focus? (Distractions will break your routine and cause you to miss important points.)

Working with Others

Scientists or engineers seldom work in isolation from one another but rather work cooperatively. You will learn more physics and have more fun doing it if you work with other students. Some professors may formalize the use of cooperative learning or facilitate the formation of study groups. You may wish to form your own informal study group with members of your class who live in your neighborhood or dorm. If you have access to e-mail, use it to keep in touch with one another. Your study group is an excellent resource when reviewing for exams.

Lectures and Taking Notes

An important component of any college course is the lecture. In physics this is especially important because your professor will frequently do demonstrations of physical principles, run computer simulations, or show video clips. All of these are learning activities that will help you to understand the basic principles of physics. Don't miss lectures, and if for some reason you do, ask a friend or member of your study group to provide you with notes and let you know what happened.

Take your class notes in outline form, and fill in the details later. It can be very difficult to take word for word notes, so just write down key ideas. Your professor may use a diagram from the textbook. Leave a space in your notes and just add the diagram later. After class, edit your notes, filling in any gaps or omissions and noting things you need to study further. Make references to the textbook by page, equation number, or section number.

Make sure you ask questions in class, or see your professor during office hours. Remember the only "dumb" question is the one that is not asked. Your college may also have teaching assistants or peer tutors who are available to help you with difficulties you may have.

Examinations

Taking an examination is stressful. But if you feel adequately prepared and are well-rested, your stress will be lessened. Preparing for an exam is a continual process; it begins the moment the last exam is over. You should immediately go over the exam and understand any mistakes you made. If you worked a problem and made substantial errors, try this: Take a piece of paper and divide it down the middle with a line from top to bottom. In one column, write the proper solution to the problem. In the other column, write what you did and why, if you know, and why your solution was incorrect. If you are uncertain why you made your mistake, or how to avoid making it again, talk with your professor. Physics continually builds on fundamental ideas and it is important to correct any misunderstandings immediately. *Warning:* While cramming at the last minute may get you through the present exam, you will not adequately retain the concepts for use on the next exam.

PREFACE

This book is the product of more than six decades of leadership and innovation in physics education. When the first edition of *University Physics* by Francis W. Sears and Mark W. Zemansky was published in 1949, it was revolutionary among calculus-based physics textbooks in its emphasis on the fundamental principles of physics and how to apply them. The success of *University Physics* with generations of several million students and educators around the world is a testament to the merits of this approach, and to the many innovations it has introduced subsequently.

In preparing this new Thirteenth Edition, we have further enhanced and developed *University Physics* to assimilate the best ideas from education research with enhanced problem-solving instruction, pioneering visual and conceptual pedagogy, the first systematically enhanced problems, and the most pedagogically proven and widely used online homework and tutorial system in the world.

New to This Edition

- Included in each chapter, **Bridging Problems** provide a transition between the single-concept Examples and the more challenging end-of-chapter problems. Each Bridging Problem poses a difficult, multiconcept problem, which often incorporates physics from earlier chapters. In place of a full solution, it provides a skeleton **Solution Guide** consisting of questions and hints, which helps train students to approach and solve challenging problems with confidence.
- **All Examples, Conceptual Examples, and Problem-Solving Strategies are revised** to enhance conciseness and clarity for today's students.
- The **core modern physics chapters** (Chapters 38–41) are revised extensively to provide a more idea-centered, less historical approach to the material. Chapters 42–44 are also revised significantly.
- **The fluid mechanics chapter now precedes the chapters on gravitation and periodic motion,** so that the latter immediately precedes the chapter on mechanical waves.
- **Additional bioscience applications** appear throughout the text, mostly in the form of marginal photos with explanatory captions, to help students see how physics is connected to many breakthroughs and discoveries in the biosciences.
- The **text has been streamlined** for tighter and more focused language.
- **Using data from MasteringPhysics, changes to the end-of-chapter content** include the following:
  - **15%–20% of problems are new.**
  - The number and level of **calculus-requiring problems** has been increased.
  - Most chapters include **five to seven biosciences-related problems.**
  - The number of **cumulative problems** (those incorporating physics from earlier chapters) has been increased.
- **Over 70 PhET simulations** are linked to the Pearson eText and provided in the Study Area of the MasteringPhysics website (with icons in the print text). These powerful simulations allow students to interact productively with the physics concepts they are learning. PhET clicker questions are also included on the Instructor Resource DVD.
- **Video Tutors bring key content to life throughout the text:**
  - **Dozens of Video Tutors feature "pause-and-predict" demonstrations of key physics concepts** and incorporate assessment as the student progresses to actively engage the student in understanding the key conceptual ideas underlying the physics principles.

Standard, Extended, and Three-Volume Editions

With MasteringPhysics:
- **Standard Edition:** Chapters 1–37 (ISBN 978-0-321-69688-5)
- **Extended Edition:** Chapters 1–44 (ISBN 978-0-321-67546-0)

Without MasteringPhysics:
- **Standard Edition:** Chapters 1–37 (ISBN 978-0-321-69689-2)
- **Extended Edition:** Chapters 1–44 (ISBN 978-0-321-69686-1)
- **Volume 1:** Chapters 1–20 (ISBN 978-0-321-73338-2)
- **Volume 2:** Chapters 21–37 (ISBN 978-0-321-75121-8)
- **Volume 3:** Chapters 37–44 (ISBN 978-0-321-75120-1)

- **Every Worked Example in the book is accompanied by a Video Tutor Solution** that walks students through the problem-solving process, providing a virtual teaching assistant on a round-the-clock basis.
- **All of these Video Tutors play directly through links within the Pearson eText.** Many also appear in the Study Area within MasteringPhysics.

Key Features of *University Physics*

- Deep and extensive **problem sets** cover a wide range of difficulty and exercise both physical understanding and problem-solving expertise. Many problems are based on complex real-life situations.
- This text offers a larger number of **Examples** and **Conceptual Examples** than any other leading calculus-based text, allowing it to explore problem-solving challenges not addressed in other texts.
- A research-based **problem-solving approach (Identify, Set Up, Execute, Evaluate)** is used not just in every Example but also in the Problem-Solving Strategies and throughout the Student and Instructor Solutions Manuals and the Study Guide. This consistent approach teaches students to tackle problems thoughtfully rather than cutting straight to the math.
- **Problem-Solving Strategies** coach students in how to approach specific types of problems.
- The **Figures** use a simplified graphical style to focus on the physics of a situation, and they incorporate **explanatory annotation.** Both techniques have been demonstrated to have a strong positive effect on learning.
- Figures that illustrate Example solutions often take the form of black-and-white **pencil sketches,** which directly represent what a student should draw in solving such a problem.
- The popular **Caution paragraphs** focus on typical misconceptions and student problem areas.
- End-of-section **Test Your Understanding** questions let students check their grasp of the material and use a multiple-choice or ranking-task format to probe for common misconceptions.
- **Visual Summaries** at the end of each chapter present the key ideas in words, equations, and thumbnail pictures, helping students to review more effectively.

Instructor Supplements

Note: For convenience, all of the following instructor supplements (except for the Instructor Resource DVD) can be downloaded from the Instructor Area, accessed via the left-hand navigation bar of MasteringPhysics (www.masteringphysics.com).

Instructor Solutions, prepared by A. Lewis Ford (Texas A&M University) and Wayne Anderson, contain complete and detailed solutions to all end-of-chapter problems. All solutions follow consistently the same Identify/Set Up/ Execute/Evaluate problem-solving framework used in the textbook. Download only from the MasteringPhysics Instructor Area or from the Instructor Resource Center (www.pearsonhighered.com/irc).

The cross-platform **Instructor Resource DVD** (ISBN 978-0-321-69661-8) provides a comprehensive library of more than 420 applets from ActivPhysics OnLine as well as all line figures from the textbook in JPEG format. In addition, all the key equations, problem-solving strategies, tables, and chapter summaries are provided in editable Word format. In-class weekly multiple-choice questions for use with various Classroom Response Systems (CRS) are also provided, based on the Test Your Understanding questions in the text. Lecture outlines in PowerPoint are also included along with over 70 PhET simulations.

MasteringPhysics® (www.masteringphysics.com) is the most advanced, educationally effective, and widely used physics homework and tutorial system in the world. Eight years in development, it provides instructors with a library of extensively pre-tested end-of-chapter problems and rich, multipart, multistep tutorials that incorporate a wide variety of answer types, wrong answer feedback, individualized help (comprising hints or simpler sub-problems upon request), all driven by the largest metadatabase of student problem-solving in the world. NSF-sponsored published research (and subsequent studies) show that Mastering-Physics has dramatic educational results. MasteringPhysics allows instructors to build wide-ranging homework assignments of just the right difficulty and length and provides them with efficient tools to analyze both class trends, and the work of any student in unprecedented detail.

MasteringPhysics routinely provides instant and individualized feedback and guidance to more than 100,000 students every day. A wide range of tools and support make MasteringPhysics fast and easy for instructors and students to learn to use. Extensive class tests show that by the end of their course, an unprecedented eight of nine students recommend MasteringPhysics as their preferred way to study physics and do homework.

MasteringPhysics enables instructors to:
- Quickly build homework assignments that combine regular end-of-chapter problems and tutoring (through additional multi-step tutorial problems that offer wrong-answer feedback and simpler problems upon request).
- Expand homework to include the widest range of automatically graded activities available—from numerical problems with randomized values, through algebraic answers, to free-hand drawing.
- Choose from a wide range of nationally pre-tested problems that provide accurate estimates of time to complete and difficulty.
- After an assignment is completed, quickly identify not only the problems that were the trickiest for students but the individual problem types where students had trouble.
- Compare class results against the system's worldwide average for each problem assigned, to identify issues to be addressed with just-in-time teaching.
- Check the work of an individual student in detail, including time spent on each problem, what wrong answers they submitted at each step, how much help they asked for, and how many practice problems they worked.

ActivPhysics OnLine™ (which is accessed through the Study Area within www.masteringphysics.com) provides a comprehensive library of more than 420 tried and tested ActivPhysics applets updated for web delivery using the latest online technologies. In addition, it provides a suite of highly regarded applet-based tutorials developed by education pioneers Alan Van Heuvelen and Paul D'Alessandris. Margin icons throughout the text direct students to specific exercises that complement the textbook discussion.

The online exercises are designed to encourage students to confront misconceptions, reason qualitatively about physical processes, experiment quantitatively, and learn to think critically. The highly acclaimed ActivPhysics OnLine companion workbooks help students work through complex concepts and understand them more clearly. More than 420 applets from the ActivPhysics OnLine library are also available on the Instructor Resource DVD for this text.

The **Test Bank** contains more than 2,000 high-quality problems, with a range of multiple-choice, true/false, short-answer, and regular homework-type questions. Test files are provided both in TestGen (an easy-to-use, fully networkable program for creating and editing quizzes and exams) and Word format. Download only from the MasteringPhysics Instructor Area or from the Instructor Resource Center (www.pearsonhighered.com/irc).

Five Easy Lessons: Strategies for Successful Physics Teaching (ISBN 978-0-805-38702-5) by Randall D. Knight (California Polytechnic State University, San Luis Obispo) is packed with creative ideas on how to enhance any physics course. It is an invaluable companion for both novice and veteran physics instructors.

Student Supplements

The **Study Guide** by Laird Kramer reinforces the text's emphasis on problem-solving strategies and student misconceptions. The *Study Guide for Volume 1* (ISBN 978-0-321-69665-6) covers Chapters 1–20, and the *Study Guide for Volumes 2 and 3* (ISBN 978-0-321-69669-4) covers Chapters 21–44.

The **Student Solutions Manual** by Lewis Ford (Texas A&M University) and Wayne Anderson contains detailed, step-by-step solutions to more than half of the odd-numbered end-of-chapter problems from the textbook. All solutions follow consistently the same Identify/Set Up/Execute/Evaluate problem-solving framework used in the textbook. The *Student Solutions Manual for Volume 1* (ISBN 978-0-321-69668-7) covers Chapters 1–20, and the *Student Solutions Manual for Volumes 2 and 3* (ISBN 978-0-321-69667-0) covers Chapters 21–44.

 MasteringPhysics® (www.masteringphysics.com) is a homework, tutorial, and assessment system based on years of research into how students work physics problems and precisely where they need help. Studies show that students who use MasteringPhysics significantly increase their scores compared to hand-written homework. MasteringPhysics achieves this improvement by providing students with instantaneous feedback specific to their wrong answers, simpler sub-problems upon request when they get stuck, and partial credit for their method(s). This individualized, 24/7 Socratic tutoring is recommended by nine out of ten students to their peers as the most effective and time-efficient way to study.

Pearson eText is available through MasteringPhysics, either automatically when MasteringPhysics is packaged with new books, or available as a purchased upgrade online. Allowing students access to the text wherever they have access to the Internet, Pearson eText comprises the full text, including figures that can be enlarged for better viewing. With eText, students are also able to pop up definitions and terms to help with vocabulary and the reading of the material. Students can also take notes in eText using the annotation feature at the top of each page.

Pearson Tutor Services (www.pearsontutorservices.com). Each student's subscription to MasteringPhysics also contains complimentary access to Pearson Tutor Services, powered by Smarthinking, Inc. By logging in with their MasteringPhysics ID and password, students will be connected to highly qualified e-instructors who provide additional interactive online tutoring on the major concepts of physics. Some restrictions apply; offer subject to change.

 ActivPhysics OnLine™ (which is accessed through the Study Area within www.masteringphysics.com) provides students with a suite of highly regarded applet-based tutorials (see above). The following workbooks help students work through complex concepts and understand them more clearly.

> **ActivPhysics OnLine Workbook, Volume 1: Mechanics * Thermal Physics * Oscillations & Waves** (978-0-805-39060-5)

> **ActivPhysics OnLine Workbook, Volume 2: Electricity & Magnetism * Optics * Modern Physics** (978-0-805-39061-2)

Acknowledgments

We would like to thank the hundreds of reviewers and colleagues who have offered valuable comments and suggestions over the life of this textbook. The continuing success of *University Physics* is due in large measure to their contributions.

Edward Adelson (Ohio State University), Ralph Alexander (University of Missouri at Rolla), J. G. Anderson, R. S. Anderson, Wayne Anderson (Sacramento City College), Alex Azima (Lansing Community College), Dilip Balamore (Nassau Community College), Harold Bale (University of North Dakota), Arun Bansil (Northeastern University), John Barach (Vanderbilt University), J. D. Barnett, H. H. Barschall, Albert Bartlett (University of Colorado), Marshall Bartlett (Hollins University), Paul Baum (CUNY, Queens College), Frederick Becchetti (University of Michigan), B. Bederson, David Bennum (University of Nevada, Reno), Lev I. Berger (San Diego State University), Robert Boeke (William Rainey Harper College), S. Borowitz, A. C. Braden, James Brooks (Boston University), Nicholas E. Brown (California Polytechnic State University, San Luis Obispo), Tony Buffa (California Polytechnic State University, San Luis Obispo), A. Capecelatro, Michael Cardamone (Pennsylvania State University), Duane Carmony (Purdue University), Troy Carter (UCLA), P. Catranides, John Cerne (SUNY at Buffalo), Tim Chupp (University of Michigan), Shinil Cho (La Roche College), Roger Clapp (University of South Florida), William M. Cloud (Eastern Illinois University), Leonard Cohen (Drexel University), W. R. Coker (University of Texas, Austin), Malcolm D. Cole (University of Missouri at Rolla), H. Conrad, David Cook (Lawrence University), Gayl Cook (University of Colorado), Hans Courant (University of Minnesota), Bruce A. Craver (University of Dayton), Larry Curtis (University of Toledo), Jai Dahiya (Southeast Missouri State University), Steve Detweiler (University of Florida), George Dixon (Oklahoma State University), Donald S. Duncan, Boyd Edwards (West Virginia University), Robert Eisenstein (Carnegie Mellon University), Amy Emerson Missourn (Virginia Institute of Technology), William Faissler (Northeastern University), William Fasnacht (U.S. Naval Academy), Paul Feldker (St. Louis Community College), Carlos Figueroa (Cabrillo College), L. H. Fisher, Neil Fletcher (Florida State University), Robert Folk, Peter Fong (Emory University), A. Lewis Ford (Texas A&M University), D. Frantszog, James R. Gaines (Ohio State University), Solomon Gartenhaus (Purdue University), Ron Gautreau (New Jersey Institute of Technology), J. David Gavenda (University of Texas, Austin), Dennis Gay (University of North Florida), James Gerhart (University of Washington), N. S. Gingrich, J. L. Glathart, S. Goodwin, Rich Gottfried (Frederick Community College), Walter S. Gray (University of Michigan), Paul Gresser (University of Maryland), Benjamin Grinstein (UC San Diego), Howard Grotch (Pennsylvania State University), John Gruber (San Jose State University), Graham D. Gutsche (U.S. Naval Academy), Michael J. Harrison (Michigan State University), Harold Hart (Western Illinois University), Howard Hayden (University of Connecticut), Carl Helrich (Goshen College), Laurent Hodges (Iowa State University), C. D. Hodgman, Michael Hones (Villanova University), Keith Honey (West Virginia Institute of Technology), Gregory Hood (Tidewater Community College), John Hubisz (North Carolina State University), M. Iona, John Jaszczak (Michigan Technical University), Alvin Jenkins (North Carolina State University), Robert P. Johnson (UC Santa Cruz), Lorella Jones (University of Illinois), John Karchek (GMI Engineering & Management Institute), Thomas Keil (Worcester Polytechnic Institute), Robert Kraemer (Carnegie Mellon University), Jean P. Krisch (University of Michigan), Robert A. Kromhout, Andrew Kunz (Marquette University), Charles Lane (Berry College), Thomas N. Lawrence (Texas State University), Robert J. Lee, Alfred Leitner (Rensselaer Polytechnic University), Gerald P. Lietz (De Paul University), Gordon Lind (Utah State University), S. Livingston, Elihu Lubkin (University of Wisconsin, Milwaukee), Robert Luke (Boise State University), David Lynch (Iowa State University), Michael Lysak (San Bernardino Valley College), Jeffrey Mallow (Loyola University), Robert Mania (Kentucky State University), Robert Marchina (University of Memphis), David Markowitz (University of Connecticut), R. J. Maurer, Oren Maxwell (Florida International University), Joseph L. McCauley (University of Houston), T. K. McCubbin, Jr. (Pennsylvania State University), Charles McFarland (University of Missouri at Rolla), James Mcguire (Tulane University), Lawrence McIntyre (University of Arizona), Fredric Messing (Carnegie-Mellon University), Thomas Meyer (Texas A&M University), Andre Mirabelli (St. Peter's College, New Jersey), Herbert Muether (S.U.N.Y., Stony Brook), Jack Munsee (California State University, Long Beach), Lorenzo Narducci (Drexel University), Van E. Neie (Purdue University), David A. Nordling (U. S. Naval Academy), Benedict Oh (Pennsylvania State University), L. O. Olsen, Jim Pannell (DeVry Institute of Technology), W. F. Parks (University of Missouri), Robert Paulson (California State University, Chico), Jerry Peacher (University of Missouri at Rolla), Arnold Perlmutter (University of Miami), Lennart Peterson (University of Florida), R. J. Peterson (University of Colorado, Boulder), R. Pinkston, Ronald Poling (University of Minnesota), J. G. Potter, C. W. Price (Millersville University), Francis Prosser (University of Kansas), Shelden H. Radin, Roberto Ramos (Drexel University), Michael Rapport (Anne Arundel Community College), R. Resnick, James A. Richards, Jr., John S. Risley (North Carolina State University), Francesc Roig (University of California, Santa Barbara), T. L. Rokoske, Richard Roth (Eastern Michigan University), Carl Rotter (University of West Virginia), S. Clark Rowland (Andrews University), Rajarshi Roy (Georgia Institute of Technology), Russell A. Roy (Santa Fe Community College), Dhiraj Sardar (University of Texas, San Antonio), Bruce Schumm (UC Santa Cruz), Melvin Schwartz (St. John's University), F. A. Scott, L. W. Seagondollar, Paul Shand (University of Northern Iowa), Stan Shepherd (Pennsylvania State University), Douglas Sherman (San Jose State), Bruce Sherwood (Carnegie Mellon University), Hugh Siefkin (Greenville College), Tomasz Skwarnicki (Syracuse University), C. P. Slichter, Charles W. Smith (University of Maine, Orono), Malcolm Smith (University of Lowell), Ross Spencer (Brigham Young University), Julien Sprott (University of Wisconsin), Victor Stanionis (Iona College), James Stith (American Institute of Physics), Chuck Stone (North Carolina A&T State

University), Edward Strother (Florida Institute of Technology), Conley Stutz (Bradley University), Albert Stwertka (U.S. Merchant Marine Academy), Kenneth Szpara-DeNisco (Harrisburg Area Community College), Martin Tiersten (CUNY, City College), David Toot (Alfred University), Somdev Tyagi (Drexel University), F. Verbrugge, Helmut Vogel (Carnegie Mellon University), Robert Webb (Texas A & M), Thomas Weber (Iowa State University), M. Russell Wehr, (Pennsylvania State University), Robert Weidman (Michigan Technical University), Dan Whalen (UC San Diego), Lester V. Whitney, Thomas Wiggins (Pennsylvania State University), David Willey (University of Pittsburgh, Johnstown), George Williams (University of Utah), John Williams (Auburn University), Stanley Williams (Iowa State University), Jack Willis, Suzanne Willis (Northern Illinois University), Robert Wilson (San Bernardino Valley College), L. Wolfenstein, James Wood (Palm Beach Junior College), Lowell Wood (University of Houston), R. E. Worley, D. H. Ziebell (Manatee Community College), George O. Zimmerman (Boston University)

In addition, we both have individual acknowledgments we would like to make.

I want to extend my heartfelt thanks to my colleagues at Carnegie Mellon, especially Professors Robert Kraemer, Bruce Sherwood, Ruth Chabay, Helmut Vogel, and Brian Quinn, for many stimulating discussions about physics pedagogy and for their support and encouragement during the writing of several successive editions of this book. I am equally indebted to the many generations of Carnegie Mellon students who have helped me learn what good teaching and good writing are, by showing me what works and what doesn't. It is always a joy and a privilege to express my gratitude to my wife Alice and our children Gretchen and Rebecca for their love, support, and emotional sustenance during the writing of several successive editions of this book. May all men and women be blessed with love such as theirs. — H. D. Y.

I would like to thank my past and present colleagues at UCSB, including Rob Geller, Carl Gwinn, Al Nash, Elisabeth Nicol, and Francesc Roig, for their whole-hearted support and for many helpful discussions. I owe a special debt of gratitude to my early teachers Willa Ramsay, Peter Zimmerman, William Little, Alan Schwettman, and Dirk Walecka for showing me what clear and engaging physics teaching is all about, and to Stuart Johnson for inviting me to become a co-author of *University Physics* beginning with the 9th edition. I want to express special thanks to the editorial staff at Addison-Wesley and their partners: to Nancy Whilton for her editorial vision; to Margot Otway for her superb graphic sense and careful development of this edition; to Peter Murphy for his contributions to the worked examples; to Jason J. B. Harlow for his careful reading of the page proofs; and to Chandrika Madhavan, Steven Le, and Cindy Johnson for keeping the editorial and production pipeline flowing. Most of all, I want to express my gratitude and love to my wife Caroline, to whom I dedicate my contribution to this book. Hey, Caroline, the new edition's done at last — let's go flying! — R. A. F.

Please Tell Us What You Think!

We welcome communications from students and professors, especially concerning errors or deficiencies that you find in this edition. We have devoted a lot of time and effort to writing the best book we know how to write, and we hope it will help you to teach and learn physics. In turn, you can help us by letting us know what still needs to be improved! Please feel free to contact us either electronically or by ordinary mail. Your comments will be greatly appreciated.

December 2010

Hugh D. Young
Department of Physics
Carnegie Mellon University
Pittsburgh, PA 15213
hdy@andrew.cmu.edu

Roger A. Freedman
Department of Physics
University of California, Santa Barbara
Santa Barbara, CA 93106-9530
airboy@physics.ucsb.edu
http://www.physics.ucsb.edu/~airboy/

DETAILED CONTENTS

ELECTRIC CHARGE AND ELECTRIC FIELD

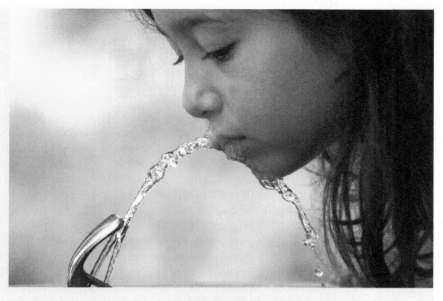

? Water makes life possible: The cells of your body could not function without water in which to dissolve essential biological molecules. What electrical properties of water make it such a good solvent?

LEARNING GOALS

By studying this chapter, you will learn:

- The nature of electric charge, and how we know that electric charge is conserved.

- How objects become electrically charged.

- How to use Coulomb's law to calculate the electric force between charges.

- The distinction between electric force and electric field.

- How to calculate the electric field due to a collection of charges.

- How to use the idea of electric field lines to visualize and interpret electric fields.

- How to calculate the properties of electric dipoles.

In Chapter 5 we mentioned the four kinds of fundamental forces. To this point the only one of these forces that we have examined in any detail is gravity. Now we are ready to examine the force of *electromagnetism,* which encompasses both electricity and magnetism. Electromagnetic phenomena will occupy our attention for most of the remainder of this book.

Electromagnetic interactions involve particles that have a property called *electric charge,* an attribute that is as fundamental as mass. Just as objects with mass are accelerated by gravitational forces, so electrically charged objects are accelerated by electric forces. The shock you feel when you scuff your shoes across a carpet and then reach for a metal doorknob is due to charged particles leaping between your finger and the doorknob. Electric currents are simply streams of charged particles flowing within wires in response to electric forces. Even the forces that hold atoms together to form solid matter, and that keep the atoms of solid objects from passing through each other, are fundamentally due to electric interactions between the charged particles within atoms.

We begin our study of electromagnetism in this chapter by examining the nature of electric charge. We'll find that charge is quantized and obeys a conservation principle. When charges are at rest in our frame of reference, they exert *electrostatic* forces on each other. These forces are of tremendous importance in chemistry and biology and have many technological applications. Electrostatic forces are governed by a simple relationship known as *Coulomb's law* and are most conveniently described by using the concept of *electric field.* In later chapters we'll expand our discussion to include electric charges in motion. This will lead us to an understanding of magnetism and, remarkably, of the nature of light.

While the key ideas of electromagnetism are conceptually simple, applying them to practical problems will make use of many of your mathematical skills, especially your knowledge of geometry and integral calculus. For this reason you may find this chapter and those that follow to be more mathematically demanding than earlier chapters. The reward for your extra effort will be a deeper understanding of principles that are at the heart of modern physics and technology.

21.1 Electric Charge

The ancient Greeks discovered as early as 600 B.C. that after they rubbed amber with wool, the amber could attract other objects. Today we say that the amber has acquired a net **electric charge,** or has become *charged.* The word "electric" is derived from the Greek word *elektron,* meaning amber. When you scuff your shoes across a nylon carpet, you become electrically charged, and you can charge a comb by passing it through dry hair.

Plastic rods and fur (real or fake) are particularly good for demonstrating **electrostatics,** the interactions between electric charges that are at rest (or nearly so). After we charge both plastic rods in Fig. 21.1a by rubbing them with the piece of fur, we find that the rods repel each other.

When we rub glass rods with silk, the glass rods also become charged and repel each other (Fig. 21.1b). But a charged plastic rod *attracts* a charged glass rod; furthermore, the plastic rod and the fur attract each other, and the glass rod and the silk attract each other (Fig. 21.1c).

These experiments and many others like them have shown that there are exactly two kinds of electric charge: the kind on the plastic rod rubbed with fur and the kind on the glass rod rubbed with silk. Benjamin Franklin (1706–1790) suggested calling these two kinds of charge *negative* and *positive,* respectively, and these names are still used. The plastic rod and the silk have negative charge; the glass rod and the fur have positive charge.

> **Two positive charges or two negative charges repel each other. A positive charge and a negative charge attract each other.**

CAUTION **Electric attraction and repulsion** The attraction and repulsion of two charged objects are sometimes summarized as "Like charges repel, and opposite charges attract." But keep in mind that the phrase "like charges" does *not* mean that the two charges are exactly identical, only that both charges have the same algebraic *sign* (both positive or both negative). "Opposite charges" means that both objects have an electric charge, and those charges have different signs (one positive and the other negative).

21.1 Experiments in electrostatics. **(a)** Negatively charged objects repel each other. **(b)** Positively charged objects repel each other. **(c)** Positvely charged objects and negatively charged objects attract each other.

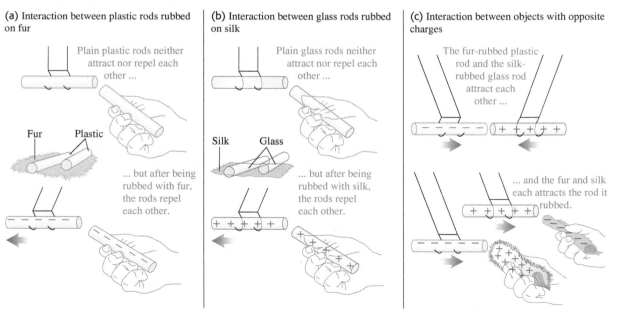

(a) Interaction between plastic rods rubbed on fur

Plain plastic rods neither attract nor repel each other ...

Fur   Plastic

... but after being rubbed with fur, the rods repel each other.

(b) Interaction between glass rods rubbed on silk

Plain glass rods neither attract nor repel each other ...

Silk   Glass

... but after being rubbed with silk, the rods repel each other.

(c) Interaction between objects with opposite charges

The fur-rubbed plastic rod and the silk-rubbed glass rod attract each other ...

... and the fur and silk each attracts the rod it rubbed.

21.2 Schematic diagram of the operation of a laser printer.

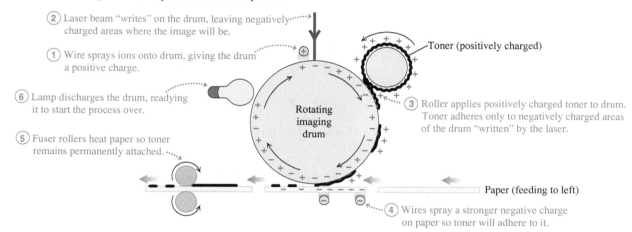

② Laser beam "writes" on the drum, leaving negatively charged areas where the image will be.

① Wire sprays ions onto drum, giving the drum a positive charge.

⑥ Lamp discharges the drum, readying it to start the process over.

⑤ Fuser rollers heat paper so toner remains permanently attached.

Toner (positively charged)

Rotating imaging drum

③ Roller applies positively charged toner to drum. Toner adheres only to negatively charged areas of the drum "written" by the laser.

Paper (feeding to left)

④ Wires spray a stronger negative charge on paper so toner will adhere to it.

One application of forces between charged bodies is in a laser printer (Fig. 21.2). The printer's light-sensitive imaging drum is given a positive charge. As the drum rotates, a laser beam shines on selected areas of the drum, leaving those areas with a *negative* charge. Positively charged particles of toner adhere only to the areas of the drum "written" by the laser. When a piece of paper is placed in contact with the drum, the toner particles stick to the paper and form an image.

Electric Charge and the Structure of Matter

When you charge a rod by rubbing it with fur or silk as in Fig. 21.1, there is no visible change in the appearance of the rod. What, then, actually happens to the rod when you charge it? To answer this question, we must look more closely at the structure of atoms, the building blocks of ordinary matter.

The structure of atoms can be described in terms of three particles: the negatively charged **electron**, the positively charged **proton,** and the uncharged **neutron** (Fig. 21.3). The proton and neutron are combinations of other entities called *quarks,* which have charges of $\pm\frac{1}{3}$ and $\pm\frac{2}{3}$ times the electron charge. Isolated quarks have not been observed, and there are theoretical reasons to believe that it is impossible in principle to observe a quark in isolation.

The protons and neutrons in an atom make up a small, very dense core called the **nucleus,** with dimensions of the order of 10^{-15} m. Surrounding the nucleus are the electrons, extending out to distances of the order of 10^{-10} m from the nucleus. If an atom were a few kilometers across, its nucleus would be the size of a tennis ball. The negatively charged electrons are held within the atom by the attractive electric forces exerted on them by the positively charged nucleus. (The protons and neutrons are held within stable atomic nuclei by an attractive interaction, called the *strong nuclear force,* that overcomes the electric repulsion of the protons. The strong nuclear force has a short range, and its effects do not extend far beyond the nucleus.)

The masses of the individual particles, to the precision that they are presently known, are

$$\text{Mass of electron} = m_e = 9.10938215(45) \times 10^{-31}\ \text{kg}$$

$$\text{Mass of proton} = m_p = 1.672621637(83) \times 10^{-27}\ \text{kg}$$

$$\text{Mass of neutron} = m_n = 1.674927211(84) \times 10^{-27}\ \text{kg}$$

The numbers in parentheses are the uncertainties in the last two digits. Note that the masses of the proton and neutron are nearly equal and are roughly 2000 times

21.3 The structure of an atom. The particular atom depicted here is lithium (see Fig. 21.4a).

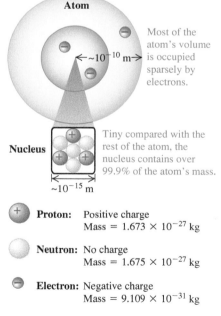

Atom

Most of the atom's volume is occupied sparsely by electrons.

$\leftarrow\!10^{-10}\ \text{m}\!\rightarrow$

Nucleus

Tiny compared with the rest of the atom, the nucleus contains over 99.9% of the atom's mass.

$\sim\!10^{-15}\ \text{m}$

⊕ **Proton:** Positive charge
Mass $= 1.673 \times 10^{-27}\ \text{kg}$

Neutron: No charge
Mass $= 1.675 \times 10^{-27}\ \text{kg}$

⊖ **Electron:** Negative charge
Mass $= 9.109 \times 10^{-31}\ \text{kg}$

The charges of the electron and proton are equal in magnitude.

21.4 (a) A neutral atom has as many electrons as it does protons. (b) A positive ion has a deficit of electrons. (c) A negative ion has an excess of electrons. (The electron "shells" are a schematic representation of the actual electron distribution, a diffuse cloud many times larger than the nucleus.)

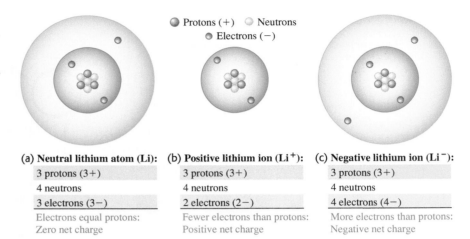

Protons (+)   Neutrons
Electrons (−)

(a) Neutral lithium atom (Li):
3 protons (3+)
4 neutrons
3 electrons (3−)
Electrons equal protons:
Zero net charge

(b) Positive lithium ion (Li⁺):
3 protons (3+)
4 neutrons
2 electrons (2−)
Fewer electrons than protons:
Positive net charge

(c) Negative lithium ion (Li⁻):
3 protons (3+)
4 neutrons
4 electrons (4−)
More electrons than protons:
Negative net charge

the mass of the electron. Over 99.9% of the mass of any atom is concentrated in its nucleus.

The negative charge of the electron has (within experimental error) *exactly* the same magnitude as the positive charge of the proton. In a neutral atom the number of electrons equals the number of protons in the nucleus, and the net electric charge (the algebraic sum of all the charges) is exactly zero (Fig. 21.4a). The number of protons or electrons in a neutral atom of an element is called the **atomic number** of the element. If one or more electrons are removed from an atom, what remains is called a **positive ion** (Fig. 21.4b). A **negative ion** is an atom that has *gained* one or more electrons (Fig. 21.4c). This gain or loss of electrons is called **ionization.**

When the total number of protons in a macroscopic body equals the total number of electrons, the total charge is zero and the body as a whole is electrically neutral. To give a body an excess negative charge, we may either *add negative* charges to a neutral body or *remove positive* charges from that body. Similarly, we can create an excess positive charge by either *adding positive* charge or *removing negative* charge. In most cases, negatively charged (and highly mobile) electrons are added or removed, and a "positively charged body" is one that has lost some of its normal complement of electrons. When we speak of the charge of a body, we always mean its *net* charge. The net charge is always a very small fraction (typically no more than 10^{-12}) of the total positive charge or negative charge in the body.

Electric Charge Is Conserved

Implicit in the foregoing discussion are two very important principles. First is the **principle of conservation of charge:**

> **The algebraic sum of all the electric charges in any closed system is constant.**

If we rub together a plastic rod and a piece of fur, both initially uncharged, the rod acquires a negative charge (since it takes electrons from the fur) and the fur acquires a positive charge of the *same* magnitude (since it has lost as many electrons as the rod has gained). Hence the total electric charge on the two bodies together does not change. In any charging process, charge is not created or destroyed; it is merely *transferred* from one body to another.

Conservation of charge is thought to be a *universal* conservation law. No experimental evidence for any violation of this principle has ever been observed. Even in high-energy interactions in which particles are created and destroyed, such as the creation of electron–positron pairs, the total charge of any closed system is exactly constant.

The second important principle is:

The magnitude of charge of the electron or proton is a natural unit of charge.

Every observable amount of electric charge is always an integer multiple of this basic unit. We say that charge is *quantized*. A familiar example of quantization is money. When you pay cash for an item in a store, you have to do it in one-cent increments. Cash can't be divided into amounts smaller than one cent, and electric charge can't be divided into amounts smaller than the charge of one electron or proton. (The quark charges, $\pm\frac{1}{3}$ and $\pm\frac{2}{3}$ of the electron charge, are probably not observable as isolated charges.) Thus the charge on any macroscopic body is always either zero or an integer multiple (negative or positive) of the electron charge.

Understanding the electric nature of matter gives us insight into many aspects of the physical world (Fig. 21.5). The chemical bonds that hold atoms together to form molecules are due to electric interactions between the atoms. They include the strong ionic bonds that hold sodium and chlorine atoms together to make table salt and the relatively weak bonds between the strands of DNA that record your body's genetic code. The normal force exerted on you by the chair in which you're sitting arises from electric forces between charged particles in the atoms of your seat and in the atoms of your chair. The tension force in a stretched string and the adhesive force of glue are likewise due to the electric interactions of atoms.

Test Your Understanding of Section 21.1 (a) Strictly speaking, does the plastic rod in Fig. 21.1 weigh more, less, or the same after rubbing it with fur? (b) What about the glass rod after rubbing it with silk? What about (c) the fur and (d) the silk? ❙

21.2 Conductors, Insulators, and Induced Charges

21.5 Most of the forces on this water skier are electric. Electric interactions between adjacent molecules give rise to the force of the water on the ski, the tension in the tow rope, and the resistance of the air on the skier's body. Electric interactions also hold the atoms of the skier's body together. Only one wholly nonelectric force acts on the skier: the force of gravity.

Mastering**PHYSICS**

PhET: Balloons and Static Electricity
PhET: John Travoltage

Some materials permit electric charge to move easily from one region of the material to another, while others do not. For example, Fig. 21.6a shows a copper wire supported by a nylon thread. Suppose you touch one end of the wire to a charged plastic rod and attach the other end to a metal ball that is initially uncharged; you then remove the charged rod and the wire. When you bring another charged body up close to the ball (Figs. 21.6b and 21.6c), the ball is attracted or repelled, showing that the ball has become electrically charged. Electric charge has been transferred through the copper wire between the ball and the surface of the plastic rod.

The copper wire is called a **conductor** of electricity. If you repeat the experiment using a rubber band or nylon thread in place of the wire, you find that *no* charge is transferred to the ball. These materials are called **insulators.** Conductors permit the easy movement of charge through them, while insulators do not. (The supporting nylon threads shown in Fig. 21.6 are insulators, which prevents charge from leaving the metal ball and copper wire.)

As an example, carpet fibers on a dry day are good insulators. As you walk across a carpet, the rubbing of your shoes against the fibers causes charge to build up on you, and this charge remains on you because it can't flow through the insulating fibers. If you then touch a conducting object such as a doorknob, a rapid charge transfer takes place between your finger and the doorknob, and you feel a shock. One way to prevent this is to wind some of the carpet fibers around conducting cores so that any charge that builds up on you can be transferred harmlessly to the carpet. Another solution is to coat the carpet fibers with an anti-static layer that does not easily transfer electrons to or from your shoes; this prevents any charge from building up on you in the first place.

21.6 Copper is a good conductor of electricity; nylon is a good insulator. **(a)** The copper wire conducts charge between the metal ball and the charged plastic rod to charge the ball negatively. Afterward, the metal ball is **(b)** repelled by a negatively charged plastic rod and **(c)** attracted to a positively charged glass rod.

(a)

The wire conducts charge from the negatively charged plastic rod to the metal ball.

(b)

(c)

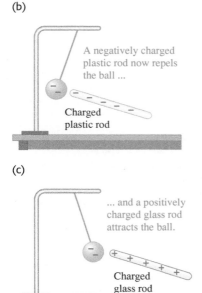

Most metals are good conductors, while most nonmetals are insulators. Within a solid metal such as copper, one or more outer electrons in each atom become detached and can move freely throughout the material, just as the molecules of a gas can move through the spaces between the grains in a bucket of sand. The other electrons remain bound to the positively charged nuclei, which themselves are bound in nearly fixed positions within the material. In an insulator there are no, or very few, free electrons, and electric charge cannot move freely through the material. Some materials called *semiconductors* are intermediate in their properties between good conductors and good insulators.

Charging by Induction

We can charge a metal ball using a copper wire and an electrically charged plastic rod, as in Fig. 21.6a. In this process, some of the excess electrons on the rod are transferred from it to the ball, leaving the rod with a smaller negative charge. But there is a different technique in which the plastic rod can give another body a charge of *opposite* sign without losing any of its own charge. This process is called charging by **induction.**

Figure 21.7 shows an example of charging by induction. An uncharged metal ball is supported on an insulating stand (Fig. 21.7a). When you bring a negatively charged rod near it, without actually touching it (Fig. 21.7b), the free electrons in the metal ball are repelled by the excess electrons on the rod, and they shift toward the right, away from the rod. They cannot escape from the ball because the supporting stand and the surrounding air are insulators. So we get excess negative charge at the right surface of the ball and a deficiency of negative charge (that is, a net positive charge) at the left surface. These excess charges are called **induced charges.**

Not all of the free electrons move to the right surface of the ball. As soon as any induced charge develops, it exerts forces toward the *left* on the other free electrons. These electrons are repelled by the negative induced charge on the right and attracted toward the positive induced charge on the left. The system reaches an equilibrium state in which the force toward the right on an electron, due to the charged rod, is just balanced by the force toward the left due to the induced charge. If we remove the charged rod, the free electrons shift back to the left, and the original neutral condition is restored.

What happens if, while the plastic rod is nearby, you touch one end of a conducting wire to the right surface of the ball and the other end to the earth (Fig. 21.7c)? The earth is a conductor, and it is so large that it can act as a practically infinite source of extra electrons or sink of unwanted electrons. Some of the negative charge flows through the wire to the earth. Now suppose you disconnect the wire (Fig. 21.7d) and then remove the rod (Fig. 21.7e); a net positive charge is left on the ball. The charge on the negatively charged rod has not changed during this process. The earth acquires a negative charge that is equal in magnitude to the induced positive charge remaining on the ball.

21.7 Charging a metal ball by induction.

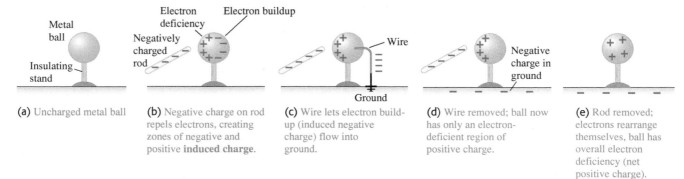

(a) Uncharged metal ball

(b) Negative charge on rod repels electrons, creating zones of negative and positive **induced charge**.

(c) Wire lets electron build-up (induced negative charge) flow into ground.

(d) Wire removed; ball now has only an electron-deficient region of positive charge.

(e) Rod removed; electrons rearrange themselves, ball has overall electron deficiency (net positive charge).

21.8 The charges within the molecules of an insulating material can shift slightly. As a result, a comb with either sign of charge attracts a neutral insulator. By Newton's third law the neutral insulator exerts an equal-magnitude attractive force on the comb.

(a) A charged comb picking up uncharged pieces of plastic

(b) How a negatively charged comb attracts an insulator

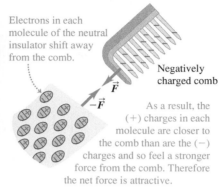

Electrons in each molecule of the neutral insulator shift away from the comb.

Negatively charged comb

$\vec{F}$

$-\vec{F}$

As a result, the (+) charges in each molecule are closer to the comb than are the (−) charges and so feel a stronger force from the comb. Therefore the net force is attractive.

(c) How a positively charged comb attracts an insulator

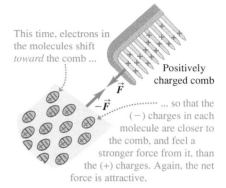

This time, electrons in the molecules shift *toward* the comb ...

Positively charged comb

$\vec{F}$

$-\vec{F}$

... so that the (−) charges in each molecule are closer to the comb, and feel a stronger force from it, than the (+) charges. Again, the net force is attractive.

Electric Forces on Uncharged Objects

Finally, we note that a charged body can exert forces even on objects that are *not* charged themselves. If you rub a balloon on the rug and then hold the balloon against the ceiling, it sticks, even though the ceiling has no net electric charge. After you electrify a comb by running it through your hair, you can pick up uncharged bits of paper or plastic with the comb (Fig. 21.8a). How is this possible?

This interaction is an induced-charge effect. Even in an insulator, electric charges can shift back and forth a little when there is charge nearby. This is shown in Fig. 21.8b; the negatively charged plastic comb causes a slight shifting of charge within the molecules of the neutral insulator, an effect called *polarization.* The positive and negative charges in the material are present in equal amounts, but the positive charges are closer to the plastic comb and so feel an attraction that is stronger than the repulsion felt by the negative charges, giving a net attractive force. (In Section 21.3 we will study how electric forces depend on distance.) Note that a neutral insulator is also attracted to a *positively* charged comb (Fig. 21.8c). Now the charges in the insulator shift in the opposite direction; the negative charges in the insulator are closer to the comb and feel an attractive force that is stronger than the repulsion felt by the positive charges in the insulator. Hence a charged object of *either* sign exerts an attractive force on an uncharged insulator. Figure 21.9 shows an industrial application of this effect.

Test Your Understanding of Section 21.2   You have two lightweight metal spheres, each hanging from an insulating nylon thread. One of the spheres has a net negative charge, while the other sphere has no net charge. (a) If the spheres are close together but do not touch, will they (i) attract each other, (ii) repel each other, or (iii) exert no force on each other? (b) You now allow the two spheres to touch. Once they have touched, will the two spheres (i) attract each other, (ii) repel each other, or (iii) exert no force on each other? ❙

21.3 Coulomb's Law

Charles Augustin de Coulomb (1736–1806) studied the interaction forces of charged particles in detail in 1784. He used a torsion balance (Fig. 21.10a) similar to the one used 13 years later by Cavendish to study the much weaker gravitational interaction, as we discussed in Section 13.1. For **point charges,** charged

21.9 The electrostatic painting process (compare Figs. 21.7b and 21.7c). A metal object to be painted is connected to the earth ("ground"), and the paint droplets are given an electric charge as they exit the sprayer nozzle. Induced charges of the opposite sign appear in the object as the droplets approach, just as in Fig. 21.7b, and they attract the droplets to the surface. This process minimizes overspray from clouds of stray paint particles and gives a particularly smooth finish.

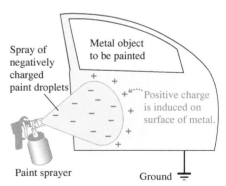

Spray of negatively charged paint droplets

Metal object to be painted

Positive charge is induced on surface of metal.

Paint sprayer

Ground

Mastering**PHYSICS**

ActivPhysics 11.1: Electric Force: Coulomb's Law
ActivPhysics 11.2: Electric Force: Superposition Principle
ActivPhysics 11.3: Electric Force: Superposition (Quantitative)

Application Electric Forces, Sweat, and Cystic Fibrosis

Application Electric Forces, Sweat, and Cystic Fibrosis

One way to test for the genetic disease cystic fibrosis (CF) is by measuring the salt content of a person's sweat. Sweat is a mixture of water and ions, including the sodium (Na^+) and chloride (Cl^-) ions that make up ordinary salt (NaCl). When sweat is secreted by epithelial cells, some of the Cl^- ions flow from the sweat back into these cells (a process called reabsorption). The electric attraction between negative and positive charges pulls Na^+ ions along with the Cl^-. Water molecules cannot flow back into the epithelial cells, so sweat on the skin has a low salt content. However, in persons with CF the reabsorption of Cl^- ions is blocked. Hence the sweat of persons with CF is unusually salty, with up to four times the normal concentration of Cl^- and Na^+.

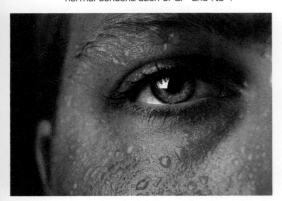

bodies that are very small in comparison with the distance r between them, Coulomb found that the electric force is proportional to $1/r^2$. That is, when the distance r doubles, the force decreases to one-quarter of its initial value; when the distance is halved, the force increases to four times its initial value.

The electric force between two point charges also depends on the quantity of charge on each body, which we will denote by q or Q. To explore this dependence, Coulomb divided a charge into two equal parts by placing a small charged spherical conductor into contact with an identical but uncharged sphere; by symmetry, the charge is shared equally between the two spheres. (Note the essential role of the principle of conservation of charge in this procedure.) Thus he could obtain one-half, one-quarter, and so on, of any initial charge. He found that the forces that two point charges q_1 and q_2 exert on each other are proportional to each charge and therefore are proportional to the *product* q_1q_2 of the two charges.

Thus Coulomb established what we now call **Coulomb's law:**

> **The magnitude of the electric force between two point charges is directly proportional to the product of the charges and inversely proportional to the square of the distance between them.**

In mathematical terms, the magnitude F of the force that each of two point charges q_1 and q_2 a distance r apart exerts on the other can be expressed as

$$F = k\frac{|q_1q_2|}{r^2} \qquad (21.1)$$

where k is a proportionality constant whose numerical value depends on the system of units used. The absolute value bars are used in Eq. (21.1) because the charges q_1 and q_2 can be either positive or negative, while the force magnitude F is always positive.

The directions of the forces the two charges exert on each other are always along the line joining them. When the charges q_1 and q_2 have the same sign, either both positive or both negative, the forces are repulsive; when the charges have opposite signs, the forces are attractive (Fig. 21.10b). The two forces obey Newton's third law; they are always equal in magnitude and opposite in direction, even when the charges are not equal in magnitude.

21.10 (a) Measuring the electric force between point charges. (b) The electric forces between point charges obey Newton's third law: $\vec{F}_{1 \text{ on } 2} = -\vec{F}_{2 \text{ on } 1}$.

(a) A torsion balance of the type used by Coulomb to measure the electric force

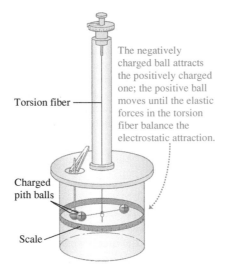

Torsion fiber

The negatively charged ball attracts the positively charged one; the positive ball moves until the elastic forces in the torsion fiber balance the electrostatic attraction.

Charged pith balls

Scale

(b) Interactions between point charges

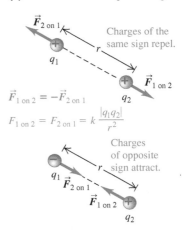

$\vec{F}_{2 \text{ on } 1}$

Charges of the same sign repel.

q_1

$\vec{F}_{1 \text{ on } 2}$

q_2

$\vec{F}_{1 \text{ on } 2} = -\vec{F}_{2 \text{ on } 1}$

$F_{1 \text{ on } 2} = F_{2 \text{ on } 1} = k\dfrac{|q_1q_2|}{r^2}$

Charges of opposite sign attract.

q_1

$\vec{F}_{2 \text{ on } 1}$

$\vec{F}_{1 \text{ on } 2}$

q_2

The proportionality of the electric force to $1/r^2$ has been verified with great precision. There is no reason to suspect that the exponent is different from precisely 2. Thus the form of Eq. (21.1) is the same as that of the law of gravitation. But electric and gravitational interactions are two distinct classes of phenomena. Electric interactions depend on electric charges and can be either attractive or repulsive, while gravitational interactions depend on mass and are always attractive (because there is no such thing as negative mass).

Fundamental Electric Constants

The value of the proportionality constant k in Coulomb's law depends on the system of units used. In our study of electricity and magnetism we will use SI units exclusively. The SI electric units include most of the familiar units such as the volt, the ampere, the ohm, and the watt. (There is *no* British system of electric units.) The SI unit of electric charge is called one **coulomb** (1 C). In SI units the constant k in Eq. (21.1) is

$$k = 8.987551787 \times 10^9 \, \text{N} \cdot \text{m}^2/\text{C}^2 \cong 8.988 \times 10^9 \, \text{N} \cdot \text{m}^2/\text{C}^2$$

The value of k is known to such a large number of significant figures because this value is closely related to the speed of light in vacuum. (We will show this in Chapter 32 when we study electromagnetic radiation.) As we discussed in Section 1.3, this speed is *defined* to be exactly $c = 2.99792458 \times 10^8$ m/s. The numerical value of k is defined in terms of c to be precisely

$$k = (10^{-7} \, \text{N} \cdot \text{s}^2/\text{C}^2)c^2$$

You should check this expression to confirm that k has the right units.

In principle we can measure the electric force F between two equal charges q at a measured distance r and use Coulomb's law to determine the charge. Thus we could regard the value of k as an operational definition of the coulomb. For reasons of experimental precision it is better to define the coulomb instead in terms of a unit of electric *current* (charge per unit time), the *ampere,* equal to 1 coulomb per second. We will return to this definition in Chapter 28.

In SI units we usually write the constant k in Eq. (21.1) as $1/4\pi\epsilon_0$, where ϵ_0 ("epsilon-nought" or "epsilon-zero") is another constant. This appears to complicate matters, but it actually simplifies many formulas that we will encounter in later chapters. From now on, we will usually write Coulomb's law as

$$F = \frac{1}{4\pi\epsilon_0} \frac{|q_1 q_2|}{r^2} \qquad \text{(Coulomb's law: force between two point charges)} \qquad (21.2)$$

The constants in Eq. (21.2) are approximately

$$\epsilon_0 = 8.854 \times 10^{-12} \, \text{C}^2/\text{N} \cdot \text{m}^2 \quad \text{and} \quad \frac{1}{4\pi\epsilon_0} = k = 8.988 \times 10^9 \, \text{N} \cdot \text{m}^2/\text{C}^2$$

In examples and problems we will often use the approximate value

$$\frac{1}{4\pi\epsilon_0} = 9.0 \times 10^9 \, \text{N} \cdot \text{m}^2/\text{C}^2$$

which is within about 0.1% of the correct value.

As we mentioned in Section 21.1, the most fundamental unit of charge is the magnitude of the charge of an electron or a proton, which is denoted by e. The most precise value available as of the writing of this book is

$$e = 1.602176487(40) \times 10^{-19} \, \text{C}$$

One coulomb represents the negative of the total charge of about 6×10^{18} electrons. For comparison, a copper cube 1 cm on a side contains about 2.4×10^{24}

electrons. About 10^{19} electrons pass through the glowing filament of a flashlight bulb every second.

In electrostatics problems (that is, problems that involve charges at rest), it's very unusual to encounter charges as large as 1 coulomb. Two 1-C charges separated by 1 m would exert forces on each other of magnitude 9×10^9 N (about 1 million tons)! The total charge of all the electrons in a copper one-cent coin is even greater, about 1.4×10^5 C, which shows that we can't disturb electric neutrality very much without using enormous forces. More typical values of charge range from about 10^{-9} to about 10^{-6} C. The microcoulomb ($1 \ \mu C = 10^{-6}$ C) and the nanocoulomb ($1 \ nC = 10^{-9}$ C) are often used as practical units of charge.

Example 21.1   Electric force versus gravitational force

An α particle (the nucleus of a helium atom) has mass $m = 6.64 \times 10^{-27}$ kg and charge $q = +2e = 3.2 \times 10^{-19}$ C. Compare the magnitude of the electric repulsion between two α ("alpha") particles with that of the gravitational attraction between them.

SOLUTION

IDENTIFY and SET UP: This problem involves Newton's law for the gravitational force F_g between particles (see Section 13.1) and Coulomb's law for the electric force F_e between point charges. To compare these forces, we make our target variable the ratio F_e/F_g. We use Eq. (21.2) for F_e and Eq. (13.1) for F_g.

21.11 Our sketch for this problem.

$$q = 3.2 \times 10^{-19} \ C$$
$$m = 6.64 \times 10^{-27} kg$$

EXECUTE: Figure 21.11 shows our sketch. From Eqs. (21.2) and (13.1),

$$F_e = \frac{1}{4\pi\epsilon_0} \frac{q^2}{r^2} \qquad F_g = G\frac{m^2}{r^2}$$

These are both inverse-square forces, so the r^2 factors cancel when we take the ratio:

$$\frac{F_e}{F_g} = \frac{1}{4\pi\epsilon_0 G} \frac{q^2}{m^2}$$

$$= \frac{9.0 \times 10^9 \ N \cdot m^2/C^2}{6.67 \times 10^{-11} \ N \cdot m^2/kg^2} \frac{(3.2 \times 10^{-19} \ C)^2}{(6.64 \times 10^{-27} \ kg)^2}$$

$$= 3.1 \times 10^{35}$$

EVALUATE: This astonishingly large number shows that the gravitational force in this situation is completely negligible in comparison to the electric force. This is always true for interactions of atomic and subnuclear particles. But within objects the size of a person or a planet, the positive and negative charges are nearly equal in magnitude, and the net electric force is usually much *smaller* than the gravitational force.

Superposition of Forces

Coulomb's law as we have stated it describes only the interaction of two *point* charges. Experiments show that when two charges exert forces simultaneously on a third charge, the total force acting on that charge is the *vector sum* of the forces that the two charges would exert individually. This important property, called the **principle of superposition of forces,** holds for any number of charges. By using this principle, we can apply Coulomb's law to *any* collection of charges. Two of the examples at the end of this section use the superposition principle.

Strictly speaking, Coulomb's law as we have stated it should be used only for point charges *in a vacuum.* If matter is present in the space between the charges, the net force acting on each charge is altered because charges are induced in the molecules of the intervening material. We will describe this effect later. As a practical matter, though, we can use Coulomb's law unaltered for point charges in air. At normal atmospheric pressure, the presence of air changes the electric force from its vacuum value by only about one part in 2000.

Problem-Solving Strategy 21.1   Coulomb's Law

IDENTIFY *the relevant concepts:* Coulomb's law describes the electric force between charged particles.

SET UP *the problem* using the following steps:
1. Sketch the locations of the charged particles and label each particle with its charge.
2. If the charges do not all lie on a single line, set up an *xy*-coordinate system.
3. The problem will ask you to find the electric force on one or more particles. Identify which these are.

EXECUTE *the solution* as follows:
1. For each particle that exerts an electric force on a given particle of interest, use Eq. (21.2) to calculate the magnitude of that force.
2. Using those magnitudes, sketch a free-body diagram showing the electric force vectors acting on each particle of interest. The force exerted by particle 1 on particle 2 points from particle 2 toward particle 1 if the charges have opposite signs, but points from particle 2 directly away from particle 1 if the charges have the same sign.
3. Use the principle of superposition to calculate the total electric force—a *vector* sum—on each particle of interest. (Review the vector algebra in Sections 1.7 through 1.9. The method of components is often helpful.)
4. Use consistent units; SI units are completely consistent. With $1/4\pi\epsilon_0 = 9.0 \times 10^9 \text{ N} \cdot \text{m}^2/\text{C}^2$, distances must be in meters, charges in coulombs, and forces in newtons.
5. Some examples and problems in this and later chapters involve *continuous* distributions of charge along a line, over a surface, or throughout a volume. In these cases the vector sum in step 3 becomes a vector *integral*. We divide the charge distribution into infinitesimal pieces, use Coulomb's law for each piece, and integrate to find the vector sum. Sometimes this can be done without actual integration.
6. Exploit any symmetries in the charge distribution to simplify your problem solving. For example, two identical charges q exert zero net electric force on a charge Q midway between them, because the forces on Q have equal magnitude and opposite direction.

EVALUATE *your answer:* Check whether your numerical results are reasonable. Confirm that the direction of the net electric force agrees with the principle that charges of the same sign repel and charges of opposite sign attract.

Example 21.2   Force between two point charges

Two point charges, $q_1 = +25$ nC and $q_2 = -75$ nC, are separated by a distance $r = 3.0$ cm (Fig. 21.12a). Find the magnitude and direction of the electric force (a) that q_1 exerts on q_2 and (b) that q_2 exerts on q_1.

SOLUTION

IDENTIFY and SET UP: This problem asks for the electric forces that two charges exert on each other. We use Coulomb's law, Eq. (21.2), to calculate the magnitudes of the forces. The signs of the charges will determine the directions of the forces.

EXECUTE: (a) After converting the units of r to meters and the units of q_1 and q_2 to coulombs, Eq. (21.2) gives us

$$F_{1 \text{ on } 2} = \frac{1}{4\pi\epsilon_0}\frac{|q_1 q_2|}{r^2}$$

$$= (9.0 \times 10^9 \text{ N} \cdot \text{m}^2/\text{C}^2)\frac{|(+25 \times 10^{-9} \text{ C})(-75 \times 10^{-9} \text{ C})|}{(0.030 \text{ m})^2}$$

$$= 0.019 \text{ N}$$

The charges have opposite signs, so the force is attractive (to the left in Fig. 21.12b); that is, the force that acts on q_2 is directed toward q_1 along the line joining the two charges.

21.12 What force does q_1 exert on q_2, and what force does q_2 exert on q_1? Gravitational forces are negligible.

(a) The two charges   (b) Free-body diagram for charge q_2 (c) Free-body diagram for charge q_1

(b) Proceeding as in part (a), we have

$$F_{1 \text{ on } 2} = \frac{1}{4\pi\epsilon_0}\frac{|q_2 q_1|}{r^2} = F_{2 \text{ on } 1} = 0.019 \text{ N}$$

The attractive force that acts on q_1 is to the right, toward q_2 (Fig. 21.12c).

EVALUATE: Newton's third law applies to the electric force. Even though the charges have different magnitudes, the magnitude of the force that q_2 exerts on q_1 is the same as the magnitude of the force that q_1 exerts on q_2, and these two forces are in opposite directions.

Example 21.3   Vector addition of electric forces on a line

Two point charges are located on the *x*-axis of a coordinate system: $q_1 = 1.0$ nC is at $x = +2.0$ cm, and $q_2 = -3.0$ nC is at $x = +4.0$ cm. What is the total electric force exerted by q_1 and q_2 on a charge $q_3 = 5.0$ nC at $x = 0$?

SOLUTION

IDENTIFY and SET UP: Figure 21.13a shows the situation. To find the total force on q_3, our target variable, we find the vector sum of the two electric forces on it.

Continued

EXECUTE: Figure 21.13b is a free-body diagram for q_3, which is repelled by q_1 (which has the same sign) and attracted to q_2 (which has the opposite sign): $\vec{F}_{1 \text{ on } 3}$ is in the $-x$-direction and $\vec{F}_{2 \text{ on } 3}$ is in the $+x$-direction. After unit conversions, we have from Eq. (21.2)

$$F_{1 \text{ on } 3} = \frac{1}{4\pi\epsilon_0} \frac{|q_1 q_3|}{r_{13}^2}$$

$$= (9.0 \times 10^9 \text{ N} \cdot \text{m}^2/\text{C}^2) \frac{(1.0 \times 10^{-9} \text{ C})(5.0 \times 10^{-9} \text{C})}{(0.020 \text{ m})^2}$$

$$= 1.12 \times 10^{-4} \text{ N} = 112 \ \mu\text{N}$$

In the same way you can show that $F_{2 \text{ on } 3} = 84 \ \mu\text{N}$. We thus have $\vec{F}_{1 \text{ on } 3} = (-112 \ \mu\text{N})\hat{\imath}$ and $\vec{F}_{2 \text{ on } 3} = (84 \ \mu\text{N})\hat{\imath}$. The net force on q_3 is

$$\vec{F}_3 = \vec{F}_{1 \text{ on } 3} + \vec{F}_{2 \text{ on } 3} = (-112 \ \mu\text{N})\hat{\imath} + (84 \ \mu\text{N})\hat{\imath} = (-28 \ \mu\text{N})\hat{\imath}$$

21.13 Our sketches for this problem.

(a) Our diagram of the situation

(b) Free-body diagram for q_3

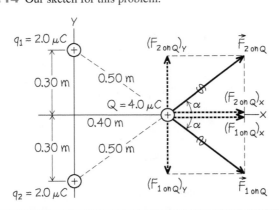

EVALUATE: As a check, note that the magnitude of q_2 is three times that of q_1, but q_2 is twice as far from q_3 as q_1. Equation (21.2) then says that $F_{2 \text{ on } 3}$ must be $3/2^2 = 3/4 = 0.75$ as large as $F_{1 \text{ on } 3}$. This agrees with our calculated values: $F_{2 \text{ on } 3}/F_{1 \text{ on } 3} = (84 \ \mu\text{N})/(112 \ \mu\text{N}) = 0.75$. Because $F_{2 \text{ on } 3}$ is the weaker force, the direction of the net force is that of $\vec{F}_{1 \text{ on } 3}$—that is, in the negative x-direction.

Example 21.4   Vector addition of electric forces in a plane

Two equal positive charges $q_1 = q_2 = 2.0 \ \mu\text{C}$ are located at $x = 0$, $y = 0.30$ m and $x = 0$, $y = -0.30$ m, respectively. What are the magnitude and direction of the total electric force that q_1 and q_2 exert on a third charge $Q = 4.0 \ \mu\text{C}$ at $x = 0.40$ m, $y = 0$?

SOLUTION

IDENTIFY and SET UP: As in Example 21.3, we must compute the force that each charge exerts on Q and then find the vector sum of those forces. Figure 21.14 shows the situation. Since the three charges do not all lie on a line, the best way to calculate the forces is to use components.

21.14 Our sketch for this problem.

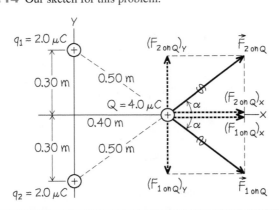

EXECUTE: Figure 21.14 shows the forces $\vec{F}_{1 \text{ on } Q}$ and $\vec{F}_{2 \text{ on } Q}$ due to the identical charges q_1 and q_2, which are at equal distances from Q. From Coulomb's law, both forces have magnitude

$$F_{1 \text{ or } 2 \text{ on } Q} = (9.0 \times 10^9 \text{ N} \cdot \text{m}^2/\text{C}^2)$$
$$\times \frac{(4.0 \times 10^{-6} \text{ C})(2.0 \times 10^{-6} \text{ C})}{(0.50 \text{ m})^2} = 0.29 \text{ N}$$

The x-components of the two forces are equal:

$$(F_{1 \text{ or } 2 \text{ on } Q})_x = (F_{1 \text{ or } 2 \text{ on } Q})\cos \alpha = (0.29 \text{ N}) \frac{0.40 \text{ m}}{0.50 \text{ m}} = 0.23 \text{ N}$$

From symmetry we see that the y-components of the two forces are equal and opposite. Hence their sum is zero and the total force $\vec{F}$ on Q has only an x-component $F_x = 0.23$ N $+$ 0.23 N $=$ 0.46 N. The total force on Q is in the $+x$-direction, with magnitude 0.46 N.

EVALUATE: The total force on Q points neither directly away from q_1 nor directly away from q_2. Rather, this direction is a compromise that points away from the *system* of charges q_1 and q_2. Can you see that the total force would *not* be in the $+x$-direction if q_1 and q_2 were not equal or if the geometrical arrangement of the changes were not so symmetric?

Test Your Understanding of Section 21.3 Suppose that charge q_2 in Example 21.4 were $-2.0 \ \mu\text{C}$. In this case, the total electric force on Q would be (i) in the positive x-direction; (ii) in the negative x-direction; (iii) in the positive y-direction; (iv) in the negative y-direction; (v) zero; (vi) none of these.

21.4 Electric Field and Electric Forces

When two electrically charged particles in empty space interact, how does each one know the other is there? We can begin to answer this question, and at the same time reformulate Coulomb's law in a very useful way, by using the concept of *electric field*.

Electric Field

To introduce this concept, let's look at the mutual repulsion of two positively charged bodies A and B (Fig. 21.15a). Suppose B has charge q_0, and let $\vec{F}_0$ be the electric force of A on B. One way to think about this force is as an "action-at-a-distance" force—that is, as a force that acts across empty space without needing any matter (such as a push rod or a rope) to transmit it through the intervening space. (Gravity can also be thought of as an "action-at-a-distance" force.) But a more fruitful way to visualize the repulsion between A and B is as a two-stage process. We first envision that body A, as a result of the charge that it carries, somehow *modifies the properties of the space around it*. Then body B, as a result of the charge that *it* carries, senses how space has been modified at its position. The response of body B is to experience the force $\vec{F}_0$.

To elaborate how this two-stage process occurs, we first consider body A by itself: We remove body B and label its former position as point P (Fig. 21.15b). We say that the charged body A produces or causes an **electric field** at point P (and at all other points in the neighborhood). This electric field is present at P even if there is no charge at P; it is a consequence of the charge on body A only. If a point charge q_0 is then placed at point P, it experiences the force $\vec{F}_0$. We take the point of view that this force is exerted on q_0 *by the field* at P (Fig. 21.15c). Thus the electric field is the intermediary through which A communicates its presence to q_0. Because the point charge q_0 would experience a force at *any* point in the neighborhood of A, the electric field that A produces exists at all points in the region around A.

We can likewise say that the point charge q_0 produces an electric field in the space around it and that this electric field exerts the force $-\vec{F}_0$ on body A. For each force (the force of A on q_0 and the force of q_0 on A), one charge sets up an electric field that exerts a force on the second charge. We emphasize that this is an *interaction* between *two* charged bodies. A single charge produces an electric field in the surrounding space, but this electric field cannot exert a net force on the charge that created it; as we discussed in Section 4.3, a body cannot exert a net force on itself. (If this wasn't true, you would be able to lift yourself to the ceiling by pulling up on your belt!)

> **The electric force on a charged body is exerted by the electric field created by *other* charged bodies.**

To find out experimentally whether there is an electric field at a particular point, we place a small charged body, which we call a **test charge,** at the point (Fig. 21.15c). If the test charge experiences an electric force, then there is an electric field at that point. This field is produced by charges other than q_0.

Force is a vector quantity, so electric field is also a vector quantity. (Note the use of vector signs as well as boldface letters and plus, minus, and equals signs in the following discussion.) We define the *electric field* $\vec{E}$ at a point as the electric force $\vec{F}_0$ experienced by a test charge q_0 at the point, divided by the charge q_0. That is, the electric field at a certain point is equal to the *electric force per unit charge* experienced by a charge at that point:

$$\vec{E} = \frac{\vec{F}_0}{q_0} \quad \text{(definition of electric field as electric force per unit charge)} \tag{21.3}$$

In SI units, in which the unit of force is 1 N and the unit of charge is 1 C, the unit of electric field magnitude is 1 newton per coulomb (1 N/C).

If the field $\vec{E}$ at a certain point is known, rearranging Eq. (21.3) gives the force $\vec{F}_0$ experienced by a point charge q_0 placed at that point. This force is just equal to the electric field $\vec{E}$ produced at that point by charges other than q_0, multiplied by the charge q_0:

$$\vec{F}_0 = q_0\vec{E} \quad \text{(force exerted on a point charge q_0 by an electric field $\vec{E}$)} \tag{21.4}$$

21.15 A charged body creates an electric field in the space around it.

(a) *A and B exert electric forces on each other.*

(b) *Remove body B ...*
... and label its former position as P.

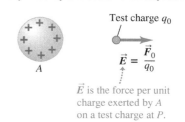
(c) *Body A sets up an electric field $\vec{E}$ at point P.*

Test charge q_0

$$\vec{E} = \frac{\vec{F}_0}{q_0}$$

$\vec{E}$ is the force per unit charge exerted by A on a test charge at P.

Application Sharks and the "Sixth Sense"

Sharks have the ability to locate prey (such as flounder and other bottom-dwelling fish) that are completely hidden beneath the sand at the bottom of the ocean. They do this by sensing the weak electric fields produced by muscle contractions in their prey. Sharks derive their sensitivity to electric fields (a "sixth sense") from jelly-filled canals in their bodies. These canals end in pores on the shark's skin (shown in this photograph). An electric field as weak as 5×10^{-7} N/C causes charge flow within the canals and triggers a signal in the shark's nervous system. Because the shark has canals with different orientations, it can measure different components of the electric-field vector and hence determine the direction of the field.

21.16 The force $\vec{F}_0 = q_0\vec{E}$ exerted on a point charge q_0 placed in an electric field $\vec{E}$.

The force on a positive test charge q_0 points in the direction of the electric field.

The force on a negative test charge q_0 points opposite to the electric field.

ActivPhysics 11.4: Electric Field: Point Charge
ActivPhysics 11.9: Motion of a Charge in an Electric Field: Introduction
ActivPhysics 11.10: Motion in an Electric Field: Problems

The charge q_0 can be either positive or negative. If q_0 is *positive*, the force $\vec{F}_0$ experienced by the charge is the same direction as $\vec{E}$; if q_0 is *negative*, $\vec{F}_0$ and $\vec{E}$ are in opposite directions (Fig. 21.16).

While the electric field concept may be new to you, the basic idea—that one body sets up a field in the space around it and a second body responds to that field—is one that you've actually used before. Compare Eq. (21.4) to the familiar expression for the gravitational force $\vec{F}_g$ that the earth exerts on a mass m_0:

$$\vec{F}_g = m_0\vec{g} \qquad (21.5)$$

In this expression, $\vec{g}$ is the acceleration due to gravity. If we divide both sides of Eq. (21.5) by the mass m_0, we obtain

$$\vec{g} = \frac{\vec{F}_g}{m_0}$$

Thus $\vec{g}$ can be regarded as the gravitational force per unit mass. By analogy to Eq. (21.3), we can interpret $\vec{g}$ as the *gravitational field*. Thus we treat the gravitational interaction between the earth and the mass m_0 as a two-stage process: The earth sets up a gravitational field $\vec{g}$ in the space around it, and this gravitational field exerts a force given by Eq. (21.5) on the mass m_0 (which we can regard as a *test mass*). The gravitational field $\vec{g}$, or gravitational force per unit mass, is a useful concept because it does not depend on the mass of the body on which the gravitational force is exerted; likewise, the electric field $\vec{E}$, or electric force per unit charge, is useful because it does not depend on the charge of the body on which the electric force is exerted.

CAUTION $\vec{F}_0 = q_0\vec{E}_0$ **is for *point* test charges only** The electric force experienced by a test charge q_0 can vary from point to point, so the electric field can also be different at different points. For this reason, Eq. (21.4) can be used only to find the electric force on a *point* charge. If a charged body is large enough in size, the electric field $\vec{E}$ may be noticeably different in magnitude and direction at different points on the body, and calculating the net electric force on the body can become rather complicated. ▌

Electric Field of a Point Charge

If the source distribution is a point charge q, it is easy to find the electric field that it produces. We call the location of the charge the **source point,** and we call the point P where we are determining the field the **field point.** It is also useful to introduce a *unit vector* $\hat{r}$ that points along the line from source point to field point (Fig. 21.17a). This unit vector is equal to the displacement vector $\vec{r}$ from the source point to the field point, divided by the distance $r = |\vec{r}|$ between these two points; that is, $\hat{r} = \vec{r}/r$. If we place a small test charge q_0 at the field point P, at a

21.17 The electric field $\vec{E}$ produced at point P by an isolated point charge q at S. Note that in both (b) and (c), $\vec{E}$ is *produced* by q [see Eq. (21.7)] but *acts* on the charge q_0 at point P [see Eq. (21.4)].

(a)

Unit vector $\hat{r}$ points from source point S to field point P.

(b)

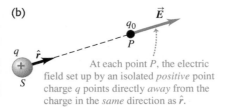

At each point P, the electric field set up by an isolated *positive* point charge q points directly *away* from the charge in the *same* direction as $\hat{r}$.

(c)

At each point P, the electric field set up by an isolated *negative* point charge q points directly *toward* the charge in the *opposite* direction from $\hat{r}$.

distance r from the source point, the magnitude F_0 of the force is given by Coulomb's law, Eq. (21.2):

$$F_0 = \frac{1}{4\pi\epsilon_0} \frac{|qq_0|}{r^2}$$

From Eq. (21.3) the magnitude E of the electric field at P is

$$E = \frac{1}{4\pi\epsilon_0} \frac{|q|}{r^2} \quad \text{(magnitude of electric field of a point charge)} \quad (21.6)$$

Using the unit vector $\hat{r}$, we can write a *vector* equation that gives both the magnitude and direction of the electric field $\vec{E}$:

$$\vec{E} = \frac{1}{4\pi\epsilon_0} \frac{q}{r^2}\hat{r} \quad \text{(electric field of a point charge)} \quad (21.7)$$

By definition, the electric field of a point charge always points *away from* a positive charge (that is, in the same direction as $\hat{r}$; see Fig. 21.17b) but *toward* a negative charge (that is, in the direction opposite $\hat{r}$; see Fig. 21.17c).

We have emphasized calculating the electric field $\vec{E}$ at a certain point. But since $\vec{E}$ can vary from point to point, it is not a single vector quantity but rather an *infinite* set of vector quantities, one associated with each point in space. This is an example of a **vector field.** Figure 21.18 shows a number of the field vectors produced by a positive or negative point charge. If we use a rectangular (x, y, z) coordinate system, each component of $\vec{E}$ at any point is in general a function of the coordinates (x, y, z) of the point. We can represent the functions as $E_x(x, y, z)$, $E_y(x, y, z)$, and $E_z(x, y, z)$. Vector fields are an important part of the language of physics, not just in electricity and magnetism. One everyday example of a vector field is the velocity $\vec{v}$ of wind currents; the magnitude and direction of $\vec{v}$, and hence its vector components, vary from point to point in the atmosphere.

In some situations the magnitude and direction of the field (and hence its vector components) have the same values everywhere throughout a certain region; we then say that the field is *uniform* in this region. An important example of this is the electric field inside a *conductor.* If there is an electric field within a conductor, the field exerts a force on every charge in the conductor, giving the free charges a net motion. By definition an electrostatic situation is one in which the charges have *no* net motion. We conclude that *in electrostatics the electric field at every point within the material of a conductor must be zero.* (Note that we are not saying that the field is necessarily zero in a *hole* inside a conductor.)

In summary, our description of electric interactions has two parts. First, a given charge distribution acts as a source of electric field. Second, the electric field exerts a force on any charge that is present in the field. Our analysis often has two corresponding steps: first, calculating the field caused by a source charge distribution; second, looking at the effect of the field in terms of force and motion. The second step often involves Newton's laws as well as the principles of electric interactions. In the next section we show how to calculate fields caused by various source distributions, but first here are three examples of calculating the field due to a point charge and of finding the force on a charge due to a given field $\vec{E}$.

21.18 A point charge q produces an electric field $\vec{E}$ at *all* points in space. The field strength decreases with increasing distance.

(a) The field produced by a positive point charge points *away from* the charge.

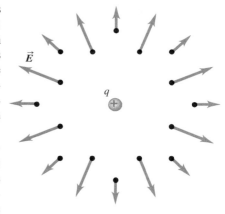

(b) The field produced by a negative point charge points *toward* the charge.

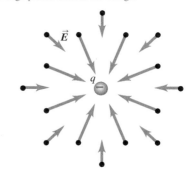

Example 21.5   **Electric-field magnitude for a point charge**

What is the magnitude of the electric field $\vec{E}$ at a field point 2.0 m from a point charge $q = 4.0$ nC?

SOLUTION

IDENTIFY and SET UP: This problem concerns the electric field due to a point charge. We are given the magnitude of the charge

Continued

and the distance from the charge to the field point, so we use Eq. (21.6) to calculate the field magnitude E.

EXECUTE: From Eq. (21.6),

$$E = \frac{1}{4\pi\epsilon_0}\frac{|q|}{r^2} = (9.0 \times 10^9 \text{ N} \cdot \text{m}^2/\text{C}^2)\frac{4.0 \times 10^{-9} \text{ C}}{(2.0 \text{ m})^2}$$

$$= 9.0 \text{ N/C}$$

EVALUATE: Our result $E = 9.0$ N/C means that if we placed a 1.0-C charge at a point 2.0 m from q, it would experience a 9.0-N force. The force on a 2.0-C charge at that point would be $(2.0 \text{ C})(9.0 \text{ N/C}) = 18$ N, and so on.

Example 21.6 Electric-field vector for a point charge

A point charge $q = -8.0$ nC is located at the origin. Find the electric-field vector at the field point $x = 1.2$ m, $y = -1.6$ m.

SOLUTION

IDENTIFY and SET UP: We must find the electric-field *vector* $\vec{E}$ due to a point charge. Figure 21.19 shows the situation. We use Eq. (21.7); to do this, we must find the distance r from the source point S (the position of the charge q, which in this example is at the origin O) to the field point P, and we must obtain an expression for the unit vector $\hat{r} = \vec{r}/r$ that points from S to P.

EXECUTE: The distance from S to P is

$$r = \sqrt{x^2 + y^2} = \sqrt{(1.2 \text{ m})^2 + (-1.6 \text{ m})^2} = 2.0 \text{ m}$$

The unit vector $\hat{r}$ is then

$$\hat{r} = \frac{\vec{r}}{r} = \frac{x\hat{i} + y\hat{j}}{r}$$

$$= \frac{(1.2 \text{ m})\hat{i} + (-1.6 \text{ m})\hat{j}}{2.0 \text{ m}} = 0.60\hat{i} - 0.80\hat{j}$$

Then, from Eq. (21.7),

$$\vec{E} = \frac{1}{4\pi\epsilon_0}\frac{q}{r^2}\hat{r}$$

$$= (9.0 \times 10^9 \text{ N} \cdot \text{m}^2/\text{C}^2)\frac{(-8.0 \times 10^{-9} \text{ C})}{(2.0 \text{ m})^2}(0.60\hat{i} - 0.80\hat{j})$$

$$= (-11 \text{ N/C})\hat{i} + (14 \text{ N/C})\hat{j}$$

21.19 Our sketch for this problem.

EVALUATE: Since q is negative, $\vec{E}$ points from the field point to the charge (the source point), in the direction opposite to $\hat{r}$ (compare Fig. 21.17c). We leave the calculation of the magnitude and direction of $\vec{E}$ to you (see Exercise 21.36).

Example 21.7 Electron in a uniform field

When the terminals of a battery are connected to two parallel conducting plates with a small gap between them, the resulting charges on the plates produce a nearly uniform electric field $\vec{E}$ between the plates. (In the next section we'll see why this is.) If the plates are 1.0 cm apart and are connected to a 100-volt battery as shown in Fig. 21.20, the field is vertically upward and has magnitude $E = 1.00 \times 10^4$ N/C. (a) If an electron (charge $-e = -1.60 \times 10^{-9}$ C, mass $m = 9.11 \times 10^{-31}$ kg) is released from rest at the upper plate, what is its acceleration? (b) What speed and kinetic energy does it acquire while traveling 1.0 cm to the lower plate? (c) How long does it take to travel this distance?

SOLUTION

IDENTIFY and SET UP: This example involves the relationship between electric field and electric force. It also involves the relationship between force and acceleration, the definition of kinetic energy, and the kinematic relationships among acceleration, distance, velocity, and time. Figure 21.20 shows our coordinate system. We are given the electric field, so we use Eq. (21.4) to find the force on the electron and Newton's second law to find its acceleration. Because the field is uniform, the force is constant and we can use the constant-acceleration formulas from Chapter 2 to find the electron's velocity and travel time. We find the kinetic energy using $K = \frac{1}{2}mv^2$.

21.20 A uniform electric field between two parallel conducting plates connected to a 100-volt battery. (The separation of the plates is exaggerated in this figure relative to the dimensions of the plates.)

The thin arrows represent the uniform electric field.

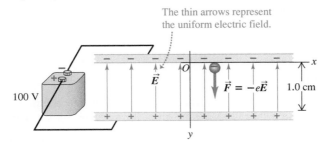

EXECUTE: (a) Although $\vec{E}$ is upward (in the $+y$-direction), $\vec{F}$ is downward (because the electron's charge is negative) and so F_y is negative. Because F_y is constant, the electron's acceleration is constant:

$$a_y = \frac{F_y}{m} = \frac{-eE}{m} = \frac{(-1.60 \times 10^{-19} \text{ C})(1.00 \times 10^4 \text{ N/C})}{9.11 \times 10^{-31} \text{ kg}}$$

$$= -1.76 \times 10^{15} \text{ m/s}^2$$

(b) The electron starts from rest, so its motion is in the y-direction only (the direction of the acceleration). We can find the electron's speed at any position y using the constant-acceleration Eq. (2.13), $v_y^2 = v_{0y}^2 + 2a_y(y - y_0)$. We have $v_{0y} = 0$ and $y_0 = 0$, so at $y = -1.0$ cm $= -1.0 \times 10^{-2}$ m we have

$$|v_y| = \sqrt{2a_y y} = \sqrt{2(-1.76 \times 10^{15} \text{ m/s}^2)(-1.0 \times 10^{-2} \text{ m})}$$

$$= 5.9 \times 10^6 \text{ m/s}$$

The velocity is downward, so $v_y = -5.9 \times 10^6$ m/s. The electron's kinetic energy is

$$K = \tfrac{1}{2}mv^2 = \tfrac{1}{2}(9.11 \times 10^{-31} \text{ kg})(5.9 \times 10^6 \text{ m/s})^2$$

$$= 1.6 \times 10^{-17} \text{ J}$$

(c) From Eq. (2.8) for constant acceleration, $v_y = v_{0y} + a_y t$,

$$t = \frac{v_y - v_{0y}}{a_y} = \frac{(-5.9 \times 10^6 \text{ m/s}) - (0 \text{ m/s})}{-1.76 \times 10^{15} \text{ m/s}^2}$$

$$= 3.4 \times 10^{-9} \text{ s}$$

EVALUATE: Our results show that in problems concerning subatomic particles such as electrons, many quantities—including acceleration, speed, kinetic energy, and time—will have *very* different values from those typical of everyday objects such as baseballs and automobiles.

Test Your Understanding of Section 21.4 (a) A negative point charge moves along a straight-line path directly toward a stationary positive point charge. Which aspect(s) of the electric force on the negative point charge will remain constant as it moves? (i) magnitude; (ii) direction; (iii) both magnitude and direction; (iv) neither magnitude nor direction. (b) A negative point charge moves along a circular orbit around a positive point charge. Which aspect(s) of the electric force on the negative point charge will remain constant as it moves? (i) magnitude; (ii) direction; (iii) both magnitude and direction; (iv) neither magnitude nor direction. |

21.5 Electric-Field Calculations

ActivPhysics 11.5: Electric Field Due to a Dipole
ActivPhysics 11.6: Electric Field: Problems

Equation (21.7) gives the electric field caused by a single point charge. But in most realistic situations that involve electric fields and forces, we encounter charge that is *distributed* over space. The charged plastic and glass rods in Fig. 21.1 have electric charge distributed over their surfaces, as does the imaging drum of a laser printer (Fig. 21.2). In this section we'll learn to calculate electric fields caused by various distributions of electric charge. Calculations of this kind are of tremendous importance for technological applications of electric forces. To determine the trajectories of atomic nuclei in an accelerator for cancer radiotherapy or of charged particles in a semiconductor electronic device, you have to know the detailed nature of the electric field acting on the charges.

The Superposition of Electric Fields

To find the field caused by a charge distribution, we imagine the distribution to be made up of many point charges $q_1, q_2, q_3, \ldots$. (This is actually quite a realistic description, since we have seen that charge is carried by electrons and protons that are so small as to be almost pointlike.) At any given point P, each point charge produces its own electric field $\vec{E}_1, \vec{E}_2, \vec{E}_3, \ldots$, so a test charge q_0 placed at P experiences a force $\vec{F}_1 = q_0\vec{E}_1$ from charge q_1, a force $\vec{F}_2 = q_0\vec{E}_2$ from charge q_2, and so on. From the principle of superposition of forces discussed in Section 21.3, the *total* force $\vec{F}_0$ that the charge distribution exerts on q_0 is the vector sum of these individual forces:

$$\vec{F}_0 = \vec{F}_1 + \vec{F}_2 + \vec{F}_3 + \cdots = q_0\vec{E}_1 + q_0\vec{E}_2 + q_0\vec{E}_3 + \cdots$$

The combined effect of all the charges in the distribution is described by the *total* electric field $\vec{E}$ at point P. From the definition of electric field, Eq. (21.3), this is

$$\vec{E} = \frac{\vec{F}_0}{q_0} = \vec{E}_1 + \vec{E}_2 + \vec{E}_3 + \cdots$$

21.21 Illustrating the principle of superposition of electric fields.

The total electric field $\vec{E}$ at point P is the vector sum of $\vec{E}_1$ and $\vec{E}_2$.

The total electric field at P is the vector sum of the fields at P due to each point charge in the charge distribution (Fig. 21.21). This is the **principle of superposition of electric fields.**

When charge is distributed along a line, over a surface, or through a volume, a few additional terms are useful. For a line charge distribution (such as a long, thin, charged plastic rod), we use λ (the Greek letter lambda) to represent the **linear charge density** (charge per unit length, measured in C/m). When charge is distributed over a surface (such as the surface of the imaging drum of a laser printer), we use σ (sigma) to represent the **surface charge density** (charge per unit area, measured in C/m^2). And when charge is distributed through a volume, we use ρ (rho) to represent the **volume charge density** (charge per unit volume, C/m^3).

Some of the calculations in the following examples may look fairly intricate. After you've worked through the examples one step at a time, the process will seem less formidable. We will use many of the calculational techniques in these examples in Chapter 28 to calculate the *magnetic* fields caused by charges in motion.

Problem-Solving Strategy 21.2 | **Electric-Field Calculations**

IDENTIFY *the relevant concepts:* Use the principle of superposition to calculate the electric field due to a discrete or continuous charge distribution.

SET UP *the problem* using the following steps:
1. Make a drawing showing the locations of the charges and your choice of coordinate axes.
2. On your drawing, indicate the position of the *field point P* (the point at which you want to calculate the electric field $\vec{E}$).

EXECUTE *the solution* as follows:
1. Use consistent units. Distances must be in meters and charge must be in coulombs. If you are given centimeters or nanocoulombs, don't forget to convert.
2. Distinguish between the source point S and the field point P. The field produced by a point charge always points from S to P if the charge is positive, and from P to S if the charge is negative.
3. Use *vector* addition when applying the principle of superposition; review the treatment of vector addition in Chapter 1 if necessary.

4. Simplify your calculations by exploiting any symmetries in the charge distribution.
5. If the charge distribution is continuous, define a small element of charge that can be considered as a point, find its electric field at P, and find a way to add the fields of all the charge elements by doing an integral. Usually it is easiest to do this for each component of $\vec{E}$ separately, so you may need to evaluate more than one integral. Ensure that the limits on your integrals are correct; especially when the situation has symmetry, don't count a charge twice.

EVALUATE *your answer:* Check that the direction of $\vec{E}$ is reasonable. If your result for the electric-field magnitude E is a function of position (say, the coordinate x), check your result in any limits for which you know what the magnitude should be. When possible, check your answer by calculating it in a different way.

Example 21.8 | **Field of an electric dipole**

Point charges $q_1 = +12$ nC and $q_2 = -12$ nC are 0.100 m apart (Fig. 21.22). (Such pairs of point charges with equal magnitude and opposite sign are called *electric dipoles*.) Compute the electric field caused by q_1, the field caused by q_2, and the total field (a) at point a; (b) at point b; and (c) at point c.

SOLUTION

IDENTIFY and SET UP: We must find the total electric field at various points due to two point charges. We use the principle of superposition: $\vec{E} = \vec{E}_1 + \vec{E}_2$. Figure 21.22 shows the coordinate system and the locations of the field points a, b, and c.

EXECUTE: At each field point, $\vec{E}$ depends on $\vec{E}_1$ and $\vec{E}_2$ there; we first calculate the magnitudes E_1 and E_2 at each field point. At a the magnitude of the field $\vec{E}_{1a}$ caused by q_1 is

$$E_{1a} = \frac{1}{4\pi\epsilon_0}\frac{|q_1|}{r^2} = (9.0 \times 10^9 \text{ N} \cdot \text{m}^2/\text{C}^2)\frac{12 \times 10^{-9} \text{ C}}{(0.060 \text{ m})^2}$$

$$= 3.0 \times 10^4 \text{ N/C}$$

We calculate the other field magnitudes in a similar way. The results are

$$E_{1a} = 3.0 \times 10^4 \text{ N/C} \qquad E_{1b} = 6.8 \times 10^4 \text{ N/C}$$
$$E_{1c} = 6.39 \times 10^3 \text{ N/C}$$
$$E_{2a} = 6.8 \times 10^4 \text{ N/C} \qquad E_{2b} = 0.55 \times 10^4 \text{ N/C}$$
$$E_{2c} = E_{1c} = 6.39 \times 10^3 \text{ N/C}$$

The *directions* of the corresponding fields are in all cases *away* from the positive charge q_1 and *toward* the negative charge q_2.

21.22 Electric field at three points, a, b, and c, set up by charges q_1 and q_2, which form an electric dipole.

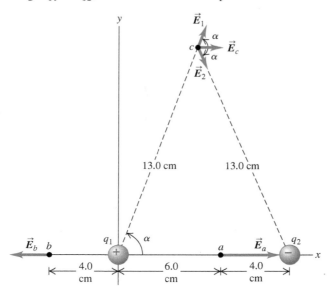

(a) At a, $\vec{E}_{1a}$ and $\vec{E}_{2a}$ are both directed to the right, so

$$\vec{E}_a = E_{1a}\hat{\imath} + E_{2a}\hat{\imath} = (9.8 \times 10^4 \text{ N/C})\hat{\imath}$$

(b) At b, $\vec{E}_{1b}$ is directed to the left and $\vec{E}_{2b}$ is directed to the right, so

$$\vec{E}_b = -E_{1b}\hat{\imath} + E_{2b}\hat{\imath} = (-6.2 \times 10^4 \text{ N/C})\hat{\imath}$$

(c) Figure 21.22 shows the directions of $\vec{E}_1$ and $\vec{E}_2$ at c. Both vectors have the same x-component:

$$E_{1cx} = E_{2cx} = E_{1c}\cos\alpha = (6.39 \times 10^3 \text{ N/C})\left(\tfrac{5}{13}\right)$$
$$= 2.46 \times 10^3 \text{ N/C}$$

From symmetry, E_{1y} and E_{2y} are equal and opposite, so their sum is zero. Hence

$$\vec{E}_c = 2(2.46 \times 10^3 \text{ N/C})\hat{\imath} = (4.9 \times 10^3 \text{ N/C})\hat{\imath}$$

EVALUATE: We can also find $\vec{E}_c$ using Eq. (21.7) for the field of a point charge. The displacement vector $\vec{r}_1$ from q_1 to point c is $\vec{r}_1 = r\cos\alpha\,\hat{\imath} + r\sin\alpha\,\hat{\jmath}$. Hence the unit vector that points from q_1 to point c is $\hat{r}_1 = \vec{r}_1/r = \cos\alpha\,\hat{\imath} + \sin\alpha\,\hat{\jmath}$. By symmetry, the unit vector that points from q_2 to point c has the opposite x-component but the same y-component: $\hat{r}_2 = -\cos\alpha\,\hat{\imath} + \sin\alpha\,\hat{\jmath}$. We can now use Eq. (21.7) to write the fields $\vec{E}_{1c}$ and $\vec{E}_{2c}$ at c in vector form, then find their sum. Since $q_2 = -q_1$ and the distance r to c is the same for both charges,

$$\vec{E}_c = \vec{E}_{1c} + \vec{E}_{2c} = \frac{1}{4\pi\epsilon_0}\frac{q_1}{r^2}\hat{r}_1 + \frac{1}{4\pi\epsilon_0}\frac{q_2}{r^2}\hat{r}_2$$

$$= \frac{1}{4\pi\epsilon_0 r^2}(q_1\hat{r}_1 + q_2\hat{r}_2) = \frac{q_1}{4\pi\epsilon_0 r^2}(\hat{r}_1 - \hat{r}_2)$$

$$= \frac{1}{4\pi\epsilon_0}\frac{q_1}{r^2}(2\cos\alpha\,\hat{\imath})$$

$$= 2(9.0 \times 10^9 \text{ N}\cdot\text{m}^2/\text{C}^2)\frac{12 \times 10^{-9} \text{ C}}{(0.13 \text{ m})^2}\left(\tfrac{5}{13}\right)\hat{\imath}$$

$$= (4.9 \times 10^3 \text{ N/C})\hat{\imath}$$

This is the same as we calculated in part (c).

Example 21.9   **Field of a ring of charge**

Charge Q is uniformly distributed around a conducting ring of radius a (Fig. 21.23). Find the electric field at a point P on the ring axis at a distance x from its center.

SOLUTION

IDENTIFY and SET UP: This is a problem in the superposition of electric fields. Each bit of charge around the ring produces an electric field at an arbitrary point on the x-axis; our target variable is the total field at this point due to all such bits of charge.

21.23 Calculating the electric field on the axis of a ring of charge. In this figure, the charge is assumed to be positive.

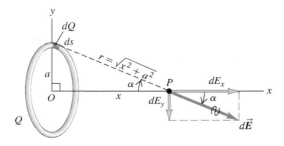

EXECUTE: We divide the ring into infinitesimal segments ds as shown in Fig. 21.23. In terms of the linear charge density $\lambda = Q/2\pi a$, the charge in a segment of length ds is $dQ = \lambda\,ds$. Consider two identical segments, one as shown in the figure at $y = a$ and another halfway around the ring at $y = -a$. From Example 21.4, we see that the net force $d\vec{F}$ they exert on a point test charge at P, and thus their net field $d\vec{E}$, are directed along the x-axis. The same is true for any such pair of segments around the ring, so the *net* field at P is along the x-axis: $\vec{E} = E_x\hat{\imath}$.

To calculate E_x, note that the square of the distance r from a single ring segment to the point P is $r^2 = x^2 + a^2$. Hence the magnitude of this segment's contribution $d\vec{E}$ to the electric field at P is

$$dE = \frac{1}{4\pi\epsilon_0}\frac{dQ}{x^2 + a^2}$$

The x-component of this field is $dE_x = dE\cos\alpha$. We know $dQ = \lambda\,ds$ and Fig. 21.23 shows that $\cos\alpha = x/r = x/(x^2 + a^2)^{1/2}$, so

$$dE_x = dE\cos\alpha = \frac{1}{4\pi\epsilon_0}\frac{dQ}{x^2 + a^2}\frac{x}{\sqrt{x^2 + a^2}}$$

$$= \frac{1}{4\pi\epsilon_0}\frac{\lambda x}{(x^2 + a^2)^{3/2}}ds$$

Continued

To find E_x we integrate this expression over the entire ring—that is, for s from 0 to $2\pi a$ (the circumference of the ring). The integrand has the same value for all points on the ring, so it can be taken outside the integral. Hence we get

$$E_x = \int dE_x = \frac{1}{4\pi\epsilon_0}\frac{\lambda x}{(x^2 + a^2)^{3/2}}\int_0^{2\pi a} ds$$

$$= \frac{1}{4\pi\epsilon_0}\frac{\lambda x}{(x^2 + a^2)^{3/2}}(2\pi a)$$

$$\vec{E} = E_x\hat{i} = \frac{1}{4\pi\epsilon_0}\frac{Qx}{(x^2 + a^2)^{3/2}}\hat{i} \qquad (21.8)$$

EVALUATE: Equation (21.8) shows that $\vec{E} = 0$ at the center of the ring ($x = 0$). This makes sense; charges on opposite sides of the ring push in opposite directions on a test charge at the center, and the vector sum of each such pair of forces is zero. When the field point P is much farther from the ring than the ring's radius, we have $x \gg a$ and the denominator in Eq. (21.8) becomes approximately equal to x^3. In this limit the electric field at P is

$$\vec{E} = \frac{1}{4\pi\epsilon_0}\frac{Q}{x^2}\hat{i}$$

That is, when the ring is so far away that its radius is negligible in comparison to the distance x, its field is the same as that of a point charge.

Example 21.10 Field of a charged line segment

Positive charge Q is distributed uniformly along the y-axis between $y = -a$ and $y = +a$. Find the electric field at point P on the x-axis at a distance x from the origin.

SOLUTION

IDENTIFY and SET UP: Figure 21.24 shows the situation. As in Example 21.9, we must find the electric field due to a continuous distribution of charge. Our target variable is an expression for the electric field at P as a function of x. The x-axis is a perpendicular bisector of the segment, so we can use a symmetry argument.

EXECUTE: We divide the line charge of length $2a$ into infinitesimal segments of length dy. The linear charge density is $\lambda = Q/2a$, and the charge in a segment is $dQ = \lambda\,dy = (Q/2a)dy$. The distance r from a segment at height y to the field point P is $r = (x^2 + y^2)^{1/2}$, so the magnitude of the field at P due to the segment at height y is

$$dE = \frac{1}{4\pi\epsilon_0}\frac{dQ}{r^2} = \frac{1}{4\pi\epsilon_0}\frac{Q}{2a}\frac{dy}{(x^2 + y^2)}$$

Figure 21.24 shows that the x- and y-components of this field are $dE_x = dE\cos\alpha$ and $dE_y = -dE\sin\alpha$, where $\cos\alpha = x/r$ and $\sin\alpha = y/r$. Hence

$$dE_x = \frac{1}{4\pi\epsilon_0}\frac{Q}{2a}\frac{x\,dy}{(x^2 + y^2)^{3/2}}$$

$$dE_y = \frac{1}{4\pi\epsilon_0}\frac{Q}{2a}\frac{y\,dy}{(x^2 + y^2)^{3/2}}$$

To find the total field at P, we must sum the fields from all segments along the line—that is, we must integrate from $y = -a$ to $y = +a$. You should work out the details of the integration (a table of integrals will help). The results are

$$E_x = \frac{1}{4\pi\epsilon_0}\frac{Q}{2a}\int_{-a}^{+a}\frac{x\,dy}{(x^2 + y^2)^{3/2}} = \frac{Q}{4\pi\epsilon_0}\frac{1}{x\sqrt{x^2 + a^2}}$$

$$E_y = \frac{1}{4\pi\epsilon_0}\frac{Q}{2a}\int_{-a}^{+a}\frac{y\,dy}{(x^2 + y^2)^{3/2}} = 0$$

or, in vector form,

$$\vec{E} = \frac{1}{4\pi\epsilon_0}\frac{Q}{x\sqrt{x^2 + a^2}}\hat{i} \qquad (21.9)$$

21.24 Our sketch for this problem.

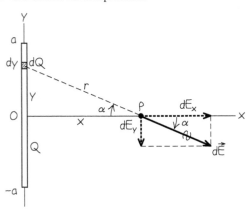

$\vec{E}$ points away from the line of charge if λ is positive and toward the line of charge if λ is negative.

EVALUATE: Using a symmetry argument as in Example 21.9, we could have guessed that E_y would be zero; if we place a positive test charge at P, the upper half of the line of charge pushes downward on it, and the lower half pushes up with equal magnitude. Symmetry also tells us that the upper and lower halves of the segment contribute equally to the total field at P.

If the segment is very *short* (or the field point is very far from the segment) so that $x \gg a$, we can neglect a in the denominator of Eq. (21.9). Then the field becomes that of a point charge, just as in Example 21.9:

$$\vec{E} = \frac{1}{4\pi\epsilon_0}\frac{Q}{x^2}\hat{i}$$

To see what happens if the segment is very *long* (or the field point is very close to it) so that $a \gg x$, we first rewrite Eq. (21.9) slightly:

$$\vec{E} = \frac{1}{2\pi\epsilon_0}\frac{\lambda}{x\sqrt{(x^2/a^2) + 1}}\hat{i} \qquad (21.10)$$

In the limit $a \gg x$ we can neglect x^2/a^2 in the denominator of Eq. (21.10), so

$$\vec{E} = \frac{\lambda}{2\pi\epsilon_0 x}\hat{i}$$

This is the field of an *infinitely long* line of charge. At any point P at a perpendicular distance r from the line in *any* direction, $\vec{E}$ has magnitude

$$E = \frac{\lambda}{2\pi\epsilon_0 r} \qquad \text{(infinite line of charge)}$$

Note that this field is proportional to $1/r$ rather than to $1/r^2$ as for a point charge.

There's really no such thing in nature as an infinite line of charge. But when the field point is close enough to the line, there's very little difference between the result for an infinite line and the real-life finite case. For example, if the distance r of the field point from the center of the line is 1% of the length of the line, the value of E differs from the infinite-length value by less than 0.02%.

Example 21.11 Field of a uniformly charged disk

A nonconducting disk of radius R has a uniform positive surface charge density σ. Find the electric field at a point along the axis of the disk a distance x from its center. Assume that x is positive.

SOLUTION

IDENTIFY and SET UP: Figure 21.25 shows the situation. We represent the charge distribution as a collection of concentric rings of charge dQ. In Example 21.9 we obtained Eq. (21.8) for the field on the axis of a single uniformly charged ring, so all we need do here is integrate the contributions of our rings.

EXECUTE: A typical ring has charge dQ, inner radius r, and outer radius $r + dr$. Its area is approximately equal to its width dr times its circumference $2\pi r$, or $dA = 2\pi r\, dr$. The charge per unit area is $\sigma = dQ/dA$, so the charge of the ring is $dQ = \sigma\, dA = 2\pi\sigma r\, dr$. We use dQ in place of Q in Eq. (21.8), the expression for the field due to a ring that we found in Example 21.9, and replace the ring radius a with r. Then the field component dE_x at point P due to this ring is

$$dE_x = \frac{1}{4\pi\epsilon_0} \frac{2\pi\sigma r x\, dr}{(x^2 + r^2)^{3/2}}$$

21.25 Our sketch for this problem.

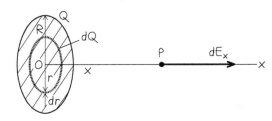

To find the total field due to all the rings, we integrate dE_x over r from $r = 0$ to $r = R$ (*not* from $-R$ to R):

$$E_x = \int_0^R \frac{1}{4\pi\epsilon_0} \frac{(2\pi\sigma r\, dr)x}{(x^2 + r^2)^{3/2}} = \frac{\sigma x}{4\epsilon_0} \int_0^R \frac{2r\, dr}{(x^2 + r^2)^{3/2}}$$

You can evaluate this integral by making the substitution $t = x^2 + r^2$ (which yields $dt = 2r\, dr$); you can work out the details. The result is

$$E_x = \frac{\sigma x}{2\epsilon_0} \left[-\frac{1}{\sqrt{x^2 + R^2}} + \frac{1}{x} \right]$$

$$= \frac{\sigma}{2\epsilon_0} \left[1 - \frac{1}{\sqrt{(R^2/x^2) + 1}} \right] \qquad (21.11)$$

EVALUATE: If the disk is very large (or if we are very close to it), so that $R \gg x$, the term $1/\sqrt{(R^2/x^2) + 1}$ in Eq. (21.11) is very much less than 1. Then Eq. (21.11) becomes

$$E = \frac{\sigma}{2\epsilon_0} \qquad (21.12)$$

Our final result does not contain the distance x from the plane. Hence the electric field produced by an *infinite* plane sheet of charge is *independent of the distance from the sheet.* The field direction is everywhere perpendicular to the sheet, away from it. There is no such thing as an infinite sheet of charge, but if the dimensions of the sheet are much larger than the distance x of the field point P from the sheet, the field is very nearly given by Eq. (21.12).

If P is to the *left* of the plane ($x < 0$), the result is the same except that the direction of $\vec{E}$ is to the left instead of the right. If the surface charge density is negative, the directions of the fields on both sides of the plane are toward it rather than away from it.

Example 21.12 Field of two oppositely charged infinite sheets

Two infinite plane sheets with uniform surface charge densities $+\sigma$ and $-\sigma$ are placed parallel to each other with separation d (Fig. 21.26). Find the electric field between the sheets, above the upper sheet, and below the lower sheet.

SOLUTION

IDENTIFY and SET UP: Equation (21.12) gives the electric field due to a single infinite plane sheet of charge. To find the field due to *two* such sheets, we combine the fields using the principle of superposition (Fig. 21.26).

21.26 Finding the electric field due to two oppositely charged infinite sheets. The sheets are seen edge-on; only a portion of the infinite sheets can be shown!

Continued

EXECUTE: From Eq. (21.12), both $\vec{E}_1$ and $\vec{E}_2$ have the same magnitude at all points, independent of distance from either sheet:

$$E_1 = E_2 = \frac{\sigma}{2\epsilon_0}$$

From Example 21.11, $\vec{E}_1$ is everywhere directed away from sheet 1, and $\vec{E}_2$ is everywhere directed toward sheet 2.

Between the sheets, $\vec{E}_1$ and $\vec{E}_2$ reinforce each other; above the upper sheet and below the lower sheet, they cancel each other. Thus the total field is

$$\vec{E} = \vec{E}_1 + \vec{E}_2 = \begin{cases} 0 & \text{above the upper sheet} \\ \dfrac{\sigma}{\epsilon_0}\hat{j} & \text{between the sheets} \\ 0 & \text{below the lower sheet} \end{cases}$$

EVALUATE: Because we considered the sheets to be infinite, our result does not depend on the separation d. Our result shows that the field between oppositely charged plates is essentially uniform if the plate separation is much smaller than the dimensions of the plates. We actually used this result in Example 21.7 (Section 21.4).

CAUTION **Electric fields are not "flows"** You may have thought that the field $\vec{E}_1$ of sheet 1 would be unable to "penetrate" sheet 2, and that field $\vec{E}_2$ caused by sheet 2 would be unable to "penetrate" sheet 1. You might conclude this if you think of the electric field as some kind of physical substance that "flows" into or out of charges. But in fact there is no such substance, and the electric fields $\vec{E}_1$ and $\vec{E}_2$ depend only on the individual charge distributions that create them. The *total* field at every point is just the vector sum of $\vec{E}_1$ and $\vec{E}_2$.

Test Your Understanding of Section 21.5 Suppose that the line of charge in Fig. 21.25 (Example 21.11) had charge $+Q$ distributed uniformly between $y = 0$ and $y = +a$ and had charge $-Q$ distributed uniformly between $y = 0$ and $y = -a$. In this situation, the electric field at P would be (i) in the positive x-direction; (ii) in the negative x-direction; (iii) in the positive y-direction; (iv) in the negative y-direction; (v) zero; (vi) none of these.

21.6 Electric Field Lines

21.27 The direction of the electric field at any point is tangent to the field line through that point.

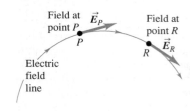

MasteringPHYSICS

PhET: Charges and Fields
PhET: Electric Field of Dreams
PhET: Electric Field Hockey

The concept of an electric field can be a little elusive because you can't see an electric field directly. Electric field *lines* can be a big help for visualizing electric fields and making them seem more real. An **electric field line** is an imaginary line or curve drawn through a region of space so that its tangent at any point is in the direction of the electric-field vector at that point. Figure 21.27 shows the basic idea. (We used a similar concept in our discussion of fluid flow in Section 12.5. A *streamline* is a line or curve whose tangent at any point is in the direction of the velocity of the fluid at that point. However, the similarity between electric field lines and fluid streamlines is a mathematical one only; there is nothing "flowing" in an electric field.) The English scientist Michael Faraday (1791–1867) first introduced the concept of field lines. He called them "lines of force," but the term "field lines" is preferable.

Electric field lines show the direction of $\vec{E}$ at each point, and their spacing gives a general idea of the *magnitude* of $\vec{E}$ at each point. Where $\vec{E}$ is strong, we draw lines bunched closely together; where $\vec{E}$ is weaker, they are farther apart. At any particular point, the electric field has a unique direction, so only one field line can pass through each point of the field. In other words, *field lines never intersect.*

Figure 21.28 shows some of the electric field lines in a plane containing (a) a single positive charge; (b) two equal-magnitude charges, one positive and one negative (a dipole); and (c) two equal positive charges. Diagrams such as these are sometimes called *field maps;* they are cross sections of the actual three-dimensional patterns. The direction of the total electric field at every point in each diagram is along the tangent to the electric field line passing through the point. Arrowheads indicate the direction of the $\vec{E}$-field vector along each field line. The actual field vectors have been drawn at several points in each pattern. Notice that in general, the magnitude of the electric field is different at different points on a given field line; a field line is *not* a curve of constant electric-field magnitude!

Figure 21.28 shows that field lines are directed *away* from positive charges (since close to a positive point charge, $\vec{E}$ points away from the charge) and

21.28 Electric field lines for three different charge distributions. In general, the magnitude of $\vec{E}$ is different at different points along a given field line.

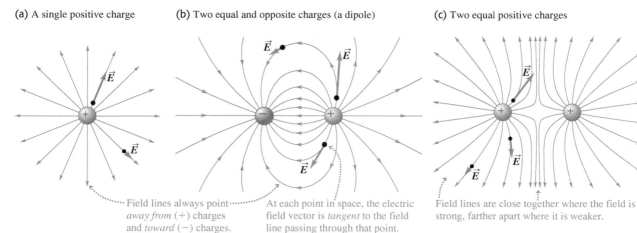

(a) A single positive charge

(b) Two equal and opposite charges (a dipole)

(c) Two equal positive charges

Field lines always point *away from* (+) charges and *toward* (−) charges.

At each point in space, the electric field vector is *tangent* to the field line passing through that point.

Field lines are close together where the field is strong, farther apart where it is weaker.

toward negative charges (since close to a negative point charge, $\vec{E}$ points toward the charge). In regions where the field magnitude is large, such as between the positive and negative charges in Fig. 21.28b, the field lines are drawn close together. In regions where the field magnitude is small, such as between the two positive charges in Fig. 21.28c, the lines are widely separated. In a *uniform* field, the field lines are straight, parallel, and uniformly spaced, as in Fig. 21.20.

Figure 21.29 is a view from above of a demonstration setup for visualizing electric field lines. In the arrangement shown here, the tips of two positively charged wires are inserted in a container of insulating liquid, and some grass seeds are floated on the liquid. The grass seeds are electrically neutral insulators, but the electric field of the two charged wires causes *polarization* of the grass seeds; there is a slight shifting of the positive and negative charges within the molecules of each seed, like that shown in Fig. 21.8. The positively charged end of each grass seed is pulled in the direction of $\vec{E}$ and the negatively charged end is pulled opposite $\vec{E}$. Hence the long axis of each grass seed tends to orient parallel to the electric field, in the direction of the field line that passes through the position of the seed (Fig. 21.29b).

CAUTION Electric field lines are not the same as trajectories It's a common misconception that if a charged particle of charge q is in motion where there is an electric field, the particle must move along an electric field line. Because $\vec{E}$ at any point is tangent to the field line that passes through that point, it is indeed true that the *force* $\vec{F} = q\vec{E}$ on the particle, and hence the particle's acceleration, are tangent to the field line. But we learned in Chapter 3 that when a particle moves on a curved path, its acceleration *cannot* be tangent to the path. So in general, the trajectory of a charged particle is *not* the same as a field line. ▌

Test Your Understanding of Section 21.6 Suppose the electric field lines in a region of space are straight lines. If a charged particle is released from rest in that region, will the trajectory of the particle be along a field line? ▌

21.7 Electric Dipoles

An **electric dipole** is a pair of point charges with equal magnitude and opposite sign (a positive charge q and a negative charge $-q$) separated by a distance d. We introduced electric dipoles in Example 21.8 (Section 21.5); the concept is worth exploring further because many physical systems, from molecules to TV antennas, can be described as electric dipoles. We will also use this concept extensively in our discussion of dielectrics in Chapter 24.

21.29 (a) Electric field lines produced by two equal point charges. The pattern is formed by grass seeds floating on a liquid above two charged wires. Compare this pattern with Fig. 21.28c. (b) The electric field causes polarization of the grass seeds, which in turn causes the seeds to align with the field.

(a)

(b)

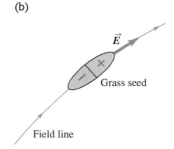

Grass seed

Field line

21.30 (a) A water molecule is an example of an electric dipole. (b) Each test tube contains a solution of a different substance in water. The large electric dipole moment of water makes it an excellent solvent.

(a) A water molecule, showing positive charge as red and negative charge as blue

The electric dipole moment $\vec{p}$ is directed from the negative end to the positive end of the molecule.

(b) Various substances dissolved in water

21.31 The net force on this electric dipole is zero, but there is a torque directed into the page that tends to rotate the dipole clockwise.

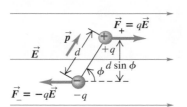

Figure 21.30 a shows a molecule of water (H_2O), which in many ways behaves like an electric dipole. The water molecule as a whole is electrically neutral, but the chemical bonds within the molecule cause a displacement of charge; the result is a net negative charge on the oxygen end of the molecule and a net positive charge on the hydrogen end, forming an electric dipole. The effect is equivalent to shifting one electron only about 4×10^{-11} m (about the radius of a hydrogen atom), but the consequences of this shift are profound. Water is an excellent solvent for ionic substances such as table salt (sodium chloride, NaCl) precisely because the water molecule is an electric dipole (Fig. 21.30b). When dissolved in water, salt dissociates into a positive sodium ion (Na^+) and a negative chlorine ion (Cl^-), which tend to be attracted to the negative and positive ends, respectively, of water molecules; this holds the ions in solution. If water molecules were not electric dipoles, water would be a poor solvent, and almost all of the chemistry that occurs in aqueous solutions would be impossible. This includes all of the biochemical reactions that occur in all of the life on earth. In a very real sense, your existence as a living being depends on electric dipoles!

We examine two questions about electric dipoles. First, what forces and torques does an electric dipole experience when placed in an external electric field (that is, a field set up by charges outside the dipole)? Second, what electric field does an electric dipole itself produce?

Force and Torque on an Electric Dipole

To start with the first question, let's place an electric dipole in a *uniform* external electric field $\vec{E}$, as shown in Fig. 21.31. The forces $\vec{F}_+$ and $\vec{F}_-$ on the two charges both have magnitude qE, but their directions are opposite, and they add to zero. *The net force on an electric dipole in a uniform external electric field is zero.*

However, the two forces don't act along the same line, so their *torques* don't add to zero. We calculate torques with respect to the center of the dipole. Let the angle between the electric field $\vec{E}$ and the dipole axis be ϕ; then the lever arm for both $\vec{F}_+$ and $\vec{F}_-$ is $(d/2)\sin\phi$. The torque of $\vec{F}_+$ and the torque of $\vec{F}_-$ both have the same magnitude of $(qE)(d/2)\sin\phi$, and both torques tend to rotate the dipole clockwise (that is, $\vec{\tau}$ is directed into the page in Fig. 21.31). Hence the magnitude of the net torque is twice the magnitude of either individual torque:

$$\tau = (qE)(d\sin\phi) \qquad (21.13)$$

where $d\sin\phi$ is the perpendicular distance between the lines of action of the two forces.

The product of the charge q and the separation d is the magnitude of a quantity called the **electric dipole moment,** denoted by p:

$$p = qd \qquad \text{(magnitude of electric dipole moment)} \qquad (21.14)$$

The units of p are charge times distance (C·m). For example, the magnitude of the electric dipole moment of a water molecule is $p = 6.13 \times 10^{-30}$ C·m.

CAUTION **The symbol p has multiple meanings** Be careful not to confuse dipole moment with momentum or pressure. There aren't as many letters in the alphabet as there are physical quantities, so some letters are used several times. The context usually makes it clear what we mean, but be careful. ▌

We further define the electric dipole moment to be a *vector* quantity $\vec{p}$. The magnitude of $\vec{p}$ is given by Eq. (21.14), and its direction is along the dipole axis from the negative charge to the positive charge as shown in Fig. 21.31.

In terms of p, Eq. (21.13) for the magnitude τ of the torque exerted by the field becomes

$$\tau = pE \sin\phi \qquad \text{(magnitude of the torque on an electric dipole)} \qquad (21.15)$$

Since the angle ϕ in Fig. 21.31 is the angle between the directions of the vectors $\vec{p}$ and $\vec{E}$, this is reminiscent of the expression for the magnitude of the *vector product* discussed in Section 1.10. (You may want to review that discussion.) Hence we can write the torque on the dipole in vector form as

$$\vec{\tau} = \vec{p} \times \vec{E} \qquad \text{(torque on an electric dipole, in vector form)} \qquad (21.16)$$

You can use the right-hand rule for the vector product to verify that in the situation shown in Fig. 21.31, $\vec{\tau}$ is directed into the page. The torque is greatest when $\vec{p}$ and $\vec{E}$ are perpendicular and is zero when they are parallel or antiparallel. The torque always tends to turn $\vec{p}$ to line it up with $\vec{E}$. The position $\phi = 0$, with $\vec{p}$ parallel to $\vec{E}$, is a position of stable equilibrium, and the position $\phi = \pi$, with $\vec{p}$ and $\vec{E}$ antiparallel, is a position of unstable equilibrium. The polarization of a grass seed in the apparatus of Fig. 21.29b gives it an electric dipole moment; the torque exerted by $\vec{E}$ then causes the seed to align with $\vec{E}$ and hence with the field lines.

Potential Energy of an Electric Dipole

When a dipole changes direction in an electric field, the electric-field torque does *work* on it, with a corresponding change in potential energy. The work dW done by a torque τ during an infinitesimal displacement $d\phi$ is given by Eq. (10.19): $dW = \tau\, d\phi$. Because the torque is in the direction of decreasing ϕ, we must write the torque as $\tau = -pE \sin\phi$, and

$$dW = \tau\, d\phi = -pE \sin\phi\, d\phi$$

In a finite displacement from ϕ_1 to ϕ_2 the total work done on the dipole is

$$W = \int_{\phi_1}^{\phi_2} (-pE\sin\phi)\, d\phi$$
$$= pE\cos\phi_2 - pE\cos\phi_1$$

The work is the negative of the change of potential energy, just as in Chapter 7: $W = U_1 - U_2$. So a suitable definition of potential energy U for this system is

$$U(\phi) = -pE\cos\phi \qquad (21.17)$$

In this expression we recognize the *scalar product* $\vec{p}\cdot\vec{E} = pE\cos\phi$, so we can also write

$$U = -\vec{p}\cdot\vec{E} \qquad \text{(potential energy for a dipole in an electric field)} \qquad (21.18)$$

The potential energy has its minimum (most negative) value $U = -pE$ at the stable equilibrium position, where $\phi = 0$ and $\vec{p}$ is parallel to $\vec{E}$. The potential energy is maximum when $\phi = \pi$ and $\vec{p}$ is antiparallel to $\vec{E}$; then $U = +pE$. At $\phi = \pi/2$, where $\vec{p}$ is perpendicular to $\vec{E}$, U is zero. We could define U differently so that it is zero at some other orientation of $\vec{p}$, but our definition is simplest.

Equation (21.18) gives us another way to look at the effect shown in Fig. 21.29. The electric field $\vec{E}$ gives each grass seed an electric dipole moment, and the grass seed then aligns itself with $\vec{E}$ to minimize the potential energy.

MasteringPHYSICS

PhET: Microwaves

Example 21.13 **Force and torque on an electric dipole**

Figure 21.32a shows an electric dipole in a uniform electric field of magnitude 5.0×10^5 N/C that is directed parallel to the plane of the figure. The charges are $\pm 1.6 \times 10^{-19}$ C; both lie in the plane and are separated by 0.125 nm $= 0.125 \times 10^{-9}$ m. Find (a) the net force exerted by the field on the dipole; (b) the magnitude and

Continued

21.32 (a) An electric dipole. (b) Directions of the electric dipole moment, electric field, and torque ($\vec{\tau}$ points out of the page).

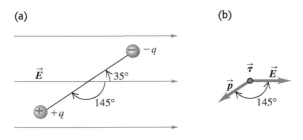

(a)

(b)

direction of the electric dipole moment; (c) the magnitude and direction of the torque; (d) the potential energy of the system in the position shown.

SOLUTION

IDENTIFY and SET UP: This problem uses the ideas of this section about an electric dipole placed in an electric field. We use the relationship $\vec{F} = q\vec{E}$ for each point charge to find the force on the dipole as a whole. Equation (21.14) gives the dipole moment, Eq. (21.16) gives the torque on the dipole, and Eq. (21.18) gives the potential energy of the system.

EXECUTE: (a) The field is uniform, so the forces on the two charges are equal and opposite. Hence the total force on the dipole is zero.

(b) The magnitude p of the electric dipole moment $\vec{p}$ is

$$p = qd = (1.6 \times 10^{-19}\ \text{C})(0.125 \times 10^{-9}\ \text{m})$$
$$= 2.0 \times 10^{-29}\ \text{C} \cdot \text{m}$$

The direction of $\vec{p}$ is from the negative to the positive charge, 145° clockwise from the electric-field direction (Fig. 21.32b).

(c) The magnitude of the torque is

$$\tau = pE\sin\phi = (2.0 \times 10^{-29}\ \text{C})(5.0 \times 10^5\ \text{N/C})(\sin 145°)$$
$$= 5.7 \times 10^{-24}\ \text{N} \cdot \text{m}$$

From the right-hand rule for vector products (see Section 1.10), the direction of the torque $\vec{\tau} = \vec{p} \times \vec{E}$ is out of the page. This corresponds to a counterclockwise torque that tends to align $\vec{p}$ with $\vec{E}$.

(d) The potential energy

$$U = -pE\cos\phi$$
$$= -(2.0 \times 10^{-29}\ \text{C} \cdot \text{m})(5.0 \times 10^5\ \text{N/C})(\cos 145°)$$
$$= 8.2 \times 10^{-24}\ \text{J}$$

EVALUATE: The charge magnitude, the distance between the charges, the dipole moment, and the potential energy are all very small, but are all typical of molecules.

In this discussion we have assumed that $\vec{E}$ is uniform, so there is no net force on the dipole. If $\vec{E}$ is not uniform, the forces at the ends may not cancel completely, and the net force may not be zero. Thus a body with zero net charge but an electric dipole moment can experience a net force in a nonuniform electric field. As we mentioned in Section 21.1, an uncharged body can be polarized by an electric field, giving rise to a separation of charge and an electric dipole moment. This is how uncharged bodies can experience electrostatic forces (see Fig. 21.8).

Field of an Electric Dipole

Now let's think of an electric dipole as a *source* of electric field. What does the field look like? The general shape of things is shown by the field map of Fig. 21.28b. At each point in the pattern the total $\vec{E}$ field is the vector sum of the fields from the two individual charges, as in Example 21.8 (Section 21.5). Try drawing diagrams showing this vector sum for several points.

To get quantitative information about the field of an electric dipole, we have to do some calculating, as illustrated in the next example. Notice the use of the principle of superposition of electric fields to add up the contributions to the field of the individual charges. Also notice that we need to use approximation techniques even for the relatively simple case of a field due to two charges. Field calculations often become very complicated, and computer analysis is typically used to determine the field due to an arbitrary charge distribution.

Example 21.14 **Field of an electric dipole, revisited**

An electric dipole is centered at the origin, with $\vec{p}$ in the direction of the +y-axis (Fig. 21.33). Derive an approximate expression for the electric field at a point P on the y-axis for which y is much larger than d. To do this, use the binomial expansion $(1 + x)^n \cong 1 + nx + n(n - 1)x^2/2 + \cdots$ (valid for the case $|x| < 1$).

SOLUTION

IDENTIFY and SET UP: We use the principle of superposition: The total electric field is the vector sum of the field produced by the positive charge and the field produced by the negative charge. At the field point P shown in Fig. 21.33, the field $\vec{E}_+$ of the positive charge has a positive (upward) y-component and the field $\vec{E}_-$ of

21.33 Finding the electric field of an electric dipole at a point on its axis.

the negative charge has a negative (downward) y-component. We add these components to find the total field and then apply the approximation that y is much greater than d.

EXECUTE: The total y-component E_y of electric field from the two charges is

$$E_y = \frac{q}{4\pi\epsilon_0}\left[\frac{1}{(y-d/2)^2} - \frac{1}{(y+d/2)^2}\right]$$

$$= \frac{q}{4\pi\epsilon_0 y^2}\left[\left(1 - \frac{d}{2y}\right)^{-2} - \left(1 + \frac{d}{2y}\right)^{-2}\right]$$

We used this same approach in Example 21.8 (Section 21.5). Now the approximation: When we are far from the dipole compared to its size, so $y \gg d$, we have $d/2y \ll 1$. With $n = -2$ and with $d/2y$ replacing x in the binomial expansion, we keep only the first two terms (the terms we discard are much smaller). We then have

$$\left(1 - \frac{d}{2y}\right)^{-2} \cong 1 + \frac{d}{y} \quad \text{and} \quad \left(1 + \frac{d}{2y}\right)^{-2} \cong 1 - \frac{d}{y}$$

Hence E_y is given approximately by

$$E_y \cong \frac{q}{4\pi\epsilon_0 y^2}\left[1 + \frac{d}{y} - \left(1 - \frac{d}{y}\right)\right] = \frac{qd}{2\pi\epsilon_0 y^3} = \frac{p}{2\pi\epsilon_0 y^3}$$

EVALUATE: An alternative route to this result is to put the fractions in the first expression for E_y over a common denominator, add, and then approximate the denominator $(y - d/2)^2(y + d/2)^2$ as y^4. We leave the details to you (see Exercise 21.60).

For points P off the coordinate axes, the expressions are more complicated, but at *all* points far away from the dipole (in any direction) the field drops off as $1/r^3$. We can compare this with the $1/r^2$ behavior of a point charge, the $1/r$ behavior of a long line charge, and the independence of r for a large sheet of charge. There are charge distributions for which the field drops off even more quickly. At large distances, the field of an *electric quadrupole*, which consists of two equal dipoles with opposite orientation, separated by a small distance, drops off as $1/r^4$.

Test Your Understanding of Section 21.7   An electric dipole is placed in a region of uniform electric field $\vec{E}$, with the electric dipole moment $\vec{p}$, pointing in the direction opposite to $\vec{E}$. Is the dipole (i) in stable equilibrium, (ii) in unstable equilibrium, or (iii) neither? (*Hint:* You many want to review Section 7.5.)

Electric charge, conductors, and insulators: The fundamental quantity in electrostatics is electric charge. There are two kinds of charge, positive and negative. Charges of the same sign repel each other; charges of opposite sign attract. Charge is conserved; the total charge in an isolated system is constant.

All ordinary matter is made of protons, neutrons, and electrons. The positive protons and electrically neutral neutrons in the nucleus of an atom are bound together by the nuclear force; the negative electrons surround the nucleus at distances much greater than the nuclear size. Electric interactions are chiefly responsible for the structure of atoms, molecules, and solids.

Conductors are materials in which charge moves easily; in insulators, charge does not move easily. Most metals are good conductors; most nonmetals are insulators.

Coulomb's law: For charges q_1 and q_2 separated by a distance r, the magnitude of the electric force on either charge is proportional to the product $q_1 q_2$ and inversely proportional to r^2. The force on each charge is along the line joining the two charges—repulsive if q_1 and q_2 have the same sign, attractive if they have opposite signs. In SI units the unit of electric charge is the coulomb, abbreviated C. (See Examples 21.1 and 21.2.)

When two or more charges each exert a force on a charge, the total force on that charge is the vector sum of the forces exerted by the individual charges. (See Examples 21.3 and 21.4.)

$$F = \frac{1}{4\pi\epsilon_0}\frac{|q_1 q_2|}{r^2} \qquad (21.2)$$

$$\frac{1}{4\pi\epsilon_0} = 8.988 \times 10^9 \ \text{N} \cdot \text{m}^2/\text{C}^2$$

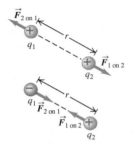

Electric field: Electric field $\vec{E}$, a vector quantity, is the force per unit charge exerted on a test charge at any point. The electric field produced by a point charge is directed radially away from or toward the charge. (See Examples 21.5–21.7.)

$$\vec{E} = \frac{\vec{F}_0}{q_0} \qquad (21.3)$$

$$\vec{E} = \frac{1}{4\pi\epsilon_0}\frac{q}{r^2}\hat{r} \qquad (21.7)$$

Superposition of electric fields: The electric field $\vec{E}$ of any combination of charges is the vector sum of the fields caused by the individual charges. To calculate the electric field caused by a continuous distribution of charge, divide the distribution into small elements, calculate the field caused by each element, and then carry out the vector sum, usually by integrating. Charge distributions are described by linear charge density λ, surface charge density σ, and volume charge density ρ. (See Examples 21.8–21.12.)

Electric field lines: Field lines provide a graphical representation of electric fields. At any point on a field line, the tangent to the line is in the direction of $\vec{E}$ at that point. The number of lines per unit area (perpendicular to their direction) is proportional to the magnitude of $\vec{E}$ at the point.

Electric dipoles: An electric dipole is a pair of electric charges of equal magnitude q but opposite sign, separated by a distance d. The electric dipole moment $\vec{p}$ has magnitude $p = qd$. The direction of $\vec{p}$ is from negative toward positive charge. An electric dipole in an electric field $\vec{E}$ experiences a torque $\vec{\tau}$ equal to the vector product of $\vec{p}$ and $\vec{E}$. The magnitude of the torque depends on the angle ϕ between $\vec{p}$ and $\vec{E}$. The potential energy U for an electric dipole in an electric field also depends on the relative orientation of $\vec{p}$ and $\vec{E}$. (See Examples 21.13 and 21.14.)

$$\tau = pE \sin \phi \qquad (21.15)$$

$$\vec{\tau} = \vec{p} \times \vec{E} \qquad (21.16)$$

$$U = -\vec{p} \cdot \vec{E} \qquad (21.18)$$

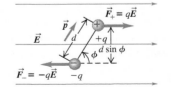

BRIDGING PROBLEM   Calculating Electric Field: Half a Ring of Charge

Positive charge Q is uniformly distributed around a semicircle of radius a as shown in Fig. 21.34. Find the magnitude and direction of the resulting electric field at point P, the center of curvature of the semicircle.

SOLUTION GUIDE

See MasteringPhysics® study area for a Video Tutor solution.

IDENTIFY and SET UP

1. The target variables are the components of the electric field at P.
2. Divide the semicircle into infinitesimal segments, each of which is a short circular arc of radius a and angle $d\theta$. What is the length of such a segment? How much charge is on a segment?

21.34

3. Consider an infinitesimal segment located at an angular position θ on the semicircle, measured from the lower right corner of the semicircle at $x = a$, $y = 0$. (Thus $\theta = \pi/2$ at $x = 0$, $y = a$ and $\theta = \pi$ at $x = -a$, $y = 0$.) What are the x- and y-components of the electric field at P (dE_x and dE_y) produced by just this segment?

EXECUTE

4. Integrate your expressions for dE_x and dE_y from $\theta = 0$ to $\theta = \pi$. The results will be the x-component and y-component of the electric field at P.
5. Use your results from step 4 to find the magnitude and direction of the field at P.

EVALUATE

6. Does your result for the electric-field magnitude have the correct units?
7. Explain how you could have found the x-component of the electric field using a symmetry argument.
8. What would be the electric field at P if the semicircle were extended to a full circle centered at P?

Problems

For instructor-assigned homework, go to www.masteringphysics.com

•, ••, •••: Problems of increasing difficulty. **CP**: Cumulative problems incorporating material from earlier chapters. **CALC**: Problems requiring calculus. **BIO**: Biosciences problems.

DISCUSSION QUESTIONS

Q21.1 If you peel two strips of transparent tape off the same roll and immediately let them hang near each other, they will repel each other. If you then stick the sticky side of one to the shiny side of the other and rip them apart, they will attract each other. Give a plausible explanation, involving transfer of electrons between the strips of tape, for this sequence of events.

Q21.2 Two metal spheres are hanging from nylon threads. When you bring the spheres close to each other, they tend to attract. Based on this information alone, discuss all the possible ways that the spheres could be charged. Is it possible that after the spheres touch, they will cling together? Explain.

Q21.3 The electric force between two charged particles becomes weaker with increasing distance. Suppose instead that the electric force were *independent* of distance. In this case, would a charged comb still cause a neutral insulator to become polarized as in Fig. 21.8? Why or why not? Would the neutral insulator still be attracted to the comb? Again, why or why not?

Q21.4 Your clothing tends to cling together after going through the dryer. Why? Would you expect more or less clinging if all your clothing were made of the same material (say, cotton) than if you dried different kinds of clothing together? Again, why? (You may want to experiment with your next load of laundry.)

Q21.5 An uncharged metal sphere hangs from a nylon thread. When a positively charged glass rod is brought close to the metal

sphere, the sphere is drawn toward the rod. But if the sphere touches the rod, it suddenly flies away from the rod. Explain why the sphere is first attracted and then repelled.

Q21.6 The free electrons in a metal are gravitationally attracted toward the earth. Why, then, don't they all settle to the bottom of the conductor, like sediment settling to the bottom of a river?

Q21.7 • Figure Q21.7 shows some of the electric field lines due to three point charges arranged along the vertical axis. All three charges have the same magnitude. (a) What are the signs of the three charges? Explain your reasoning. (b) At what point(s) is the magnitude of the electric field the smallest? Explain your reasoning. Explain how the fields produced by each individual point charge combine to give a small net field at this point or points.

Figure **Q21.7**

Q21.8 Good electrical conductors, such as metals, are typically good conductors of heat; electrical insulators, such as wood, are typically poor conductors of heat. Explain why there should be a relationship between electrical conduction and heat conduction in these materials.

Q21.9 • Suppose the charge shown in Fig. 21.28a is fixed in position. A small, positively charged particle is then placed at some point in the figure and released. Will the trajectory of the particle follow an electric field line? Why or why not? Suppose instead that the particle is placed at some point in Fig. 21.28b and released (the positive and negative charges shown in the figure are fixed in position). Will its trajectory follow an electric field line? Again, why or why not? Explain any differences between your answers for the two different situations.

Q21.10 Two identical metal objects are mounted on insulating stands. Describe how you could place charges of opposite sign but exactly equal magnitude on the two objects.

Q21.11 You can use plastic food wrap to cover a container by stretching the material across the top and pressing the overhanging material against the sides. What makes it stick? (*Hint:* The answer involves the electric force.) Does the food wrap stick to itself with equal tenacity? Why or why not? Does it work with metallic containers? Again, why or why not?

Q21.12 If you walk across a nylon rug and then touch a large metal object such as a doorknob, you may get a spark and a shock. Why does this tend to happen more on dry days than on humid days? (*Hint:* See Fig. 21.30.) Why are you less likely to get a shock if you touch a *small* metal object, such as a paper clip?

Q21.13 You have a negatively charged object. How can you use it to place a net negative charge on an insulated metal sphere? To place a net positive charge on the sphere?

Q21.14 When two point charges of equal mass and charge are released on a frictionless table, each has an initial acceleration a_0. If instead you keep one fixed and release the other one, what will be its initial acceleration: a_0, $2a_0$, or $a_0/2$? Explain.

Q21.15 A point charge of mass m and charge Q and another point charge of mass m but charge $2Q$ are released on a frictionless table. If the charge Q has an initial acceleration a_0, what will be the acceleration of $2Q$: a_0, $2a_0$, $4a_0$, $a_0/2$, or $a_0/4$? Explain.

Q21.16 A proton is placed in a uniform electric field and then released. Then an electron is placed at this same point and released. Do these two particles experience the same force? The same acceleration? Do they move in the same direction when released?

Q21.17 In Example 21.1 (Section 21.3) we saw that the electric force between two α particles is of the order of 10^{35} times as strong as the gravitational force. So why do we readily feel the gravity of the earth but no electrical force from it?

Q21.18 What similarities do electrical forces have with gravitational forces? What are the most significant differences?

Q21.19 Two irregular objects A and B carry charges of opposite sign. Figure Q21.19 shows the electric field lines near each of these objects. (a) Which object is positive, A or B? How do you know? (b) Where is the electric field stronger, close to A or close to B? How do you know?

Figure **Q21.19**

Q21.20 Atomic nuclei are made of protons and neutrons. This shows that there must be another kind of interaction in addition to gravitational and electric forces. Explain.

Q21.21 Sufficiently strong electric fields can cause atoms to become positively ionized—that is, to lose one or more electrons. Explain how this can happen. What determines how strong the field must be to make this happen?

Q21.22 The electric fields at point P due to the positive charges q_1 and q_2 are shown in Fig. Q21.22. Does the fact that they cross each other violate the statement in Section 21.6 that electric field lines never cross? Explain.

Q21.23 The air temperature and the velocity of the air have different values at different places in the earth's atmosphere. Is the air velocity a vector field? Why or why not? Is the air temperature a vector field? Again, why or why not?

Figure **Q21.22**

$\vec{E}_2$ $\vec{E}_1$

P

q_1 q_2

EXERCISES

Section 21.3 Coulomb's Law

21.1 •• Excess electrons are placed on a small lead sphere with mass 8.00 g so that its net charge is -3.20×10^{-9} C. (a) Find the number of excess electrons on the sphere. (b) How many excess electrons are there per lead atom? The atomic number of lead is 82, and its atomic mass is 207 g/mol.

21.2 • Lightning occurs when there is a flow of electric charge (principally electrons) between the ground and a thundercloud. The maximum rate of charge flow in a lightning bolt is about 20,000 C/s; this lasts for 100 μs or less. How much charge flows between the ground and the cloud in this time? How many electrons flow during this time?

21.3 •• BIO Estimate how many electrons there are in your body. Make any assumptions you feel are necessary, but clearly state what they are. (*Hint:* Most of the atoms in your body have equal numbers of electrons, protons, and neutrons.) What is the combined charge of all these electrons?

21.4 • **Particles in a Gold Ring.** You have a pure (24-karat) gold ring with mass 17.7 g. Gold has an atomic mass of 197 g/mol and an atomic number of 79. (a) How many protons are in the ring, and what is their total positive charge? (b) If the ring carries no net charge, how many electrons are in it?

21.5 • BIO **Signal Propagation in Neurons.** *Neurons* are components of the nervous system of the body that transmit signals as electrical impulses travel along their length. These impulses propagate when charge suddenly rushes into and then out of a part of the neuron called an *axon*. Measurements have shown that, during the inflow part of this cycle, approximately 5.6×10^{11} Na$^+$ (sodium ions) per meter, each with charge $+e$, enter the axon. How many coulombs of charge enter a 1.5-cm length of the axon during this process?

21.6 • Two small spheres spaced 20.0 cm apart have equal charge. How many excess electrons must be present on each sphere if the magnitude of the force of repulsion between them is 4.57×10^{-21} N?

21.7 •• An average human weighs about 650 N. If two such generic humans each carried 1.0 coulomb of excess charge, one positive and one negative, how far apart would they have to be for the electric attraction between them to equal their 650-N weight?

21.8 •• Two small aluminum spheres, each having mass 0.0250 kg, are separated by 80.0 cm. (a) How many electrons does each sphere contain? (The atomic mass of aluminum is 26.982 g/mol, and its atomic number is 13.) (b) How many electrons would have to be removed from one sphere and added to the other to cause an attractive force between the spheres of magnitude 1.00×10^4 N (roughly 1 ton)? Assume that the spheres may be treated as point charges. (c) What fraction of all the electrons in each sphere does this represent?

21.9 •• Two small plastic spheres are given positive electrical charges. When they are 15.0 cm apart, the repulsive force between them has magnitude 0.220 N. What is the charge on each sphere (a) if the two charges are equal and (b) if one sphere has four times the charge of the other?

21.10 •• **What If We Were Not Neutral?** A 75-kg person holds out his arms so that his hands are 1.7 m apart. Typically, a person's hand makes up about 1.0% of his or her body weight. For round numbers, we shall assume that all the weight of each hand is due to the calcium in the bones, and we shall treat the hands as point charges. One mole of Ca contains 40.18 g, and each atom has 20 protons and 20 electrons. Suppose that only 1.0% of the positive charges in each hand were unbalanced by negative charge. (a) How many Ca atoms does each hand contain? (b) How many coulombs of unbalanced charge does each hand contain? (c) What force would the person's arms have to exert on his hands to prevent them from flying off? Does it seem likely that his arms are capable of exerting such a force?

21.11 •• Two very small 8.55-g spheres, 15.0 cm apart from center to center, are charged by adding equal numbers of electrons to each of them. Disregarding all other forces, how many electrons would you have to add to each sphere so that the two spheres will accelerate at $25.0g$ when released? Which way will they accelerate?

21.12 •• **Just How Strong Is the Electric Force?** Suppose you had two small boxes, each containing 1.0 g of protons. (a) If one were placed on the moon by an astronaut and the other were left on the earth, and if they were connected by a very light (and very long!) string, what would be the tension in the string? Express your answer in newtons and in pounds. Do you need to take into account the gravitational forces of the earth and moon on the protons? Why? (b) What gravitational force would each box of protons exert on the other box?

21.13 • In an experiment in space, one proton is held fixed and another proton is released from rest a distance of 2.50 mm away. (a) What is the initial acceleration of the proton after it is released? (b) Sketch qualitative (no numbers!) acceleration–time and velocity–time graphs of the released proton's motion.

21.14 • A negative charge of -0.550 μC exerts an upward 0.200-N force on an unknown charge 0.300 m directly below it. (a) What is the unknown charge (magnitude and sign)? (b) What are the magnitude and direction of the force that the unknown charge exerts on the -0.550-μC charge?

21.15 •• Three point charges are arranged on a line. Charge $q_3 = +5.00$ nC and is at the origin. Charge $q_2 = -3.00$ nC and is at $x = +4.00$ cm. Charge q_1 is at $x = +2.00$ cm. What is q_1 (magnitude and sign) if the net force on q_3 is zero?

21.16 •• In Example 21.4, suppose the point charge on the y-axis at $y = -0.30$ m has negative charge -2.0 μC, and the other charges remain the same. Find the magnitude and direction of the net force on Q. How does your answer differ from that in Example 21.4? Explain the differences.

21.17 •• In Example 21.3, calculate the net force on charge q_1.

21.18 •• In Example 21.4, what is the net force (magnitude and direction) on charge q_1 exerted by the other two charges?

21.19 •• Three point charges are arranged along the x-axis. Charge $q_1 = +3.00$ μC is at the origin, and charge $q_2 = -5.00$ μC is at $x = 0.200$ m. Charge $q_3 = -8.00$ μC. Where is q_3 located if the net force on q_1 is 7.00 N in the $-x$-direction?

21.20 •• Repeat Exercise 21.19 for $q_3 = +8.00$ μC.

21.21 •• Two point charges are located on the y-axis as follows: charge $q_1 = -1.50$ nC at $y = -0.600$ m, and charge $q_2 = +3.20$ nC at the origin ($y = 0$). What is the total force (magnitude and direction) exerted by these two charges on a third charge $q_3 = +5.00$ nC located at $y = -0.400$ m?

21.22 •• Two point charges are placed on the x-axis as follows: Charge $q_1 = +4.00$ nC is located at $x = 0.200$ m, and charge $q_2 = +5.00$ nC is at $x = -0.300$ m. What are the magnitude and direction of the total force exerted by these two charges on a negative point charge $q_3 = -6.00$ nC that is placed at the origin?

21.23 •• **BIO** **Base Pairing in DNA, I.** The two sides of the DNA double helix are connected by pairs of bases (adenine, thymine, cytosine, and guanine). Because of the geometric shape of these molecules, adenine bonds with thymine and cytosine bonds with guanine. Figure E21.23 shows the thymine–adenine bond. Each charge shown is $\pm e$, and the H—N distance is 0.110 nm. (a) Calculate the *net* force that thymine exerts on adenine. Is it attractive or repulsive? To keep the calculations fairly simple, yet reasonable, consider only the forces due to the O—H—N and the N—H—N combinations, assuming that these two combinations are parallel to each other. Remember, however, that in the O—H—N set, the O^- exerts a force on both the H^+ and the N^-, and likewise along the N—H—N set. (b) Calculate the force on the electron in the hydrogen atom, which is 0.0529 nm from the proton. Then compare the strength of the bonding force of the electron in hydrogen with the bonding force of the adenine–thymine molecules.

Figure **E21.23**

21.24 •• **BIO** **Base Pairing in DNA, II.** Refer to Exercise 21.23. Figure E21.24 shows the bonding of the cytosine and guanine molecules. The O—H and H—N distances are each 0.110 nm. In this case, assume that the bonding is due only to the forces along the O—H—O, N—H—N, and O—H—N combinations, and assume also that these three combinations are parallel to each other. Calculate the *net* force that cytosine exerts on guanine due to the preceding three combinations. Is this force attractive or repulsive?

Figure **E21.24**

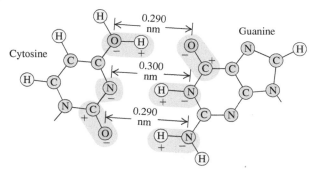

Section 21.4 Electric Field and Electric Forces

21.25 • **CP** A proton is placed in a uniform electric field of 2.75×10^3 N/C. Calculate: (a) the magnitude of the electric force felt by the proton; (b) the proton's acceleration; (c) the proton's speed after 1.00 μs in the field, assuming it starts from rest.

21.26 • A particle has charge -3.00 nC. (a) Find the magnitude and direction of the electric field due to this particle at a point 0.250 m directly above it. (b) At what distance from this particle does its electric field have a magnitude of 12.0 N/C?

21.27 • **CP** A proton is traveling horizontally to the right at 4.50×10^6 m/s. (a) Find the magnitude and direction of the weakest electric field that can bring the proton uniformly to rest over a distance of 3.20 cm. (b) How much time does it take the proton to stop after entering the field? (c) What minimum field (magnitude and direction) would be needed to stop an electron under the conditions of part (a)?

21.28 • **CP** An electron is released from rest in a uniform electric field. The electron accelerates vertically upward, traveling 4.50 m in the first 3.00 μs after it is released. (a) What are the magnitude and direction of the electric field? (b) Are we justified in ignoring the effects of gravity? Justify your answer quantitatively.

21.29 •• (a) What must the charge (sign and magnitude) of a 1.45-g particle be for it to remain stationary when placed in a downward-directed electric field of magnitude 650 N/C? (b) What is the magnitude of an electric field in which the electric force on a proton is equal in magnitude to its weight?

21.30 •• A point charge is placed at each corner of a square with side length a. The charges all have the same magnitude q. Two of the charges are positive and two are negative, as shown in Fig. E21.30. What is the direction of the net electric field at the center of the square due to the four charges, and what is its magnitude in terms of q and a?

Figure **E21.30**

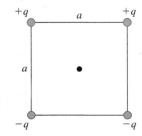

21.31 • Two point charges are separated by 25.0 cm (Fig. E21.31). Find the net electric field these charges produce at (a) point A and (b) point B. (c) What would be the magnitude and direction of the electric force this combination of charges would produce on a proton at A?

Figure **E21.31**

21.32 •• **Electric Field of the Earth.** The earth has a net electric charge that causes a field at points near its surface equal to 150 N/C and directed in toward the center of the earth. (a) What magnitude and sign of charge would a 60-kg human have to acquire to overcome his or her weight by the force exerted by the earth's electric field? (b) What would be the force of repulsion between two people each with the charge calculated in part (a) and separated by a distance of 100 m? Is use of the earth's electric field a feasible means of flight? Why or why not?

21.33 •• **CP** An electron is projected with an initial speed $v_0 = 1.60 \times 10^6$ m/s into the uniform field between the parallel plates in Fig. E21.33. Assume that the field between the plates is uniform and directed vertically downward, and that the field outside the plates is zero. The electron enters the field at a point

Figure **E21.33**

midway between the plates. (a) If the electron just misses the upper plate as it emerges from the field, find the magnitude of the electric field. (b) Suppose that in Fig. E21.33 the electron is replaced by a proton with the same initial speed v_0. Would the proton hit one of the plates? If the proton would not hit one of the plates, what would be the magnitude and direction of its vertical displacement as it exits the region between the plates? (c) Compare the paths traveled by the electron and the proton and explain the differences. (d) Discuss whether it is reasonable to ignore the effects of gravity for each particle.

21.34 •• Point charge $q_1 = -5.00$ nC is at the origin and point charge $q_2 = +3.00$ nC is on the x-axis at $x = 3.00$ cm. Point P is on the y-axis at $y = 4.00$ cm. (a) Calculate the electric fields $\vec{E}_1$ and $\vec{E}_2$ at point P due to the charges q_1 and q_2. Express your results in terms of unit vectors (see Example 21.6). (b) Use the results of part (a) to obtain the resultant field at P, expressed in unit vector form.

21.35 •• **CP** In Exercise 21.33, what is the speed of the electron as it emerges from the field?

21.36 • (a) Calculate the magnitude and direction (relative to the $+x$-axis) of the electric field in Example 21.6. (b) A -2.5-nC point charge is placed at point P in Fig. 21.19. Find the magnitude and direction of (i) the force that the -8.0-nC charge at the origin exerts on this charge and (ii) the force that this charge exerts on the -8.0-nC charge at the origin.

21.37 •• If two electrons are each 1.50×10^{-10} m from a proton, as shown in Fig. E21.37, find the magnitude and direction of the net electric force they will exert on the proton.

Figure **E21.37**

21.38 •• **CP** A uniform electric field exists in the region between two oppositely charged plane parallel plates. A proton is released from rest at the surface of the positively charged plate and strikes the surface of the opposite plate, 1.60 cm distant from the first, in a time interval of 1.50×10^{-6} s. (a) Find the magnitude of the electric field. (b) Find the speed of the proton when it strikes the negatively charged plate.

21.39 • A point charge is at the origin. With this point charge as the source point, what is the unit vector $\hat{r}$ in the direction of (a) the field point at $x = 0$, $y = -1.35$ m; (b) the field point at $x = 12.0$ cm, $y = 12.0$ cm; (c) the field point at $x = -1.10$ m, $y = 2.60$ m? Express your results in terms of the unit vectors $\hat{i}$ and $\hat{j}$.

21.40 •• A $+8.75$-μC point charge is glued down on a horizontal frictionless table. It is tied to a -6.50-μC point charge by a light, nonconducting 2.50-cm wire. A uniform electric field of magnitude 1.85×10^8 N/C is directed parallel to the wire, as shown in Fig. E21.40. (a) Find the tension in the wire. (b) What would the tension be if both charges were negative?

Figure **E21.40**

21.41 •• (a) An electron is moving east in a uniform electric field of 1.50 N/C directed to the west. At point A, the velocity of the electron is 4.50×10^5 m/s toward the east. What is the speed of the electron when it reaches point B, 0.375 m east of point A? (b) A proton is moving in the uniform electric field of part (a). At point A, the velocity of the proton is 1.90×10^4 m/s, east. What is the speed of the proton at point B?

Section 21.5 Electric-Field Calculations

21.42 • Two point charges Q and $+q$ (where q is positive) produce the net electric field shown at point P in Fig. E21.42. The field points parallel to the line connecting the two charges. (a) What can you conclude about the sign and magnitude of Q? Explain your reasoning. (b) If the lower charge were negative instead, would it be possible for the field to have the direction shown in the figure? Explain your reasoning.

Figure **E21.42**

21.43 •• Two positive point charges q are placed on the x-axis, one at $x = a$ and one at $x = -a$. (a) Find the magnitude and direction of the electric field at $x = 0$. (b) Derive an expression for the electric field at points on the x-axis. Use your result to graph the x-component of the electric field as a function of x, for values of x between $-4a$ and $+4a$.

21.44 • The two charges q_1 and q_2 shown in Fig. E21.44 have equal magnitudes. What is the direction of the net electric field due to these two charges at points A (midway between the charges), B, and C if (a) both charges are negative, (b) both charges are positive, (c) q_1 is positive and q_2 is negative.

Figure **E21.44**

21.45 • A $+2.00$-nC point charge is at the origin, and a second -5.00-nC point charge is on the x-axis at $x = 0.800$ m. (a) Find the electric field (magnitude and direction) at each of the following points on the x-axis: (i) $x = 0.200$ m; (ii) $x = 1.20$ m; (iii) $x = -0.200$ m. (b) Find the net electric force that the two charges would exert on an electron placed at each point in part (a).

21.46 •• Repeat Exercise 21.44, but now let $q_1 = -4.00$ nC.

21.47 • Three negative point charges lie along a line as shown in Fig. E21.47. Find the magnitude and direction of the electric field this combination of charges produces at point P, which lies 6.00 cm from the -2.00-μC charge measured perpendicular to the line connecting the three charges.

Figure **E21.47**

21.48 •• BIO **Electric Field of Axons.** A nerve signal is transmitted through a neuron when an excess of Na^+ ions suddenly enters the axon, a long cylindrical part of the neuron. Axons are approximately 10.0 μm in diameter, and measurements show that about 5.6×10^{11} Na^+ ions per meter (each of charge $+e$) enter during this process. Although the axon is a long cylinder, the charge does not all enter everywhere at the same time. A plausible model would be a series of point charges moving along the axon. Let us look at a 0.10-mm length of the axon and model it as a point charge. (a) If the charge that enters each meter of the axon gets distributed uniformly along it, how many coulombs of charge enter a 0.10-mm length of the axon? (b) What electric field (magnitude and direction) does the sudden influx of charge produce at the surface of the body if the axon is 5.00 cm below the skin? (c) Certain sharks can respond to electric fields as weak as 1.0 μN/C.

How far from this segment of axon could a shark be and still detect its electric field?

21.49 • In a rectangular coordinate system a positive point charge $q = 6.00 \times 10^{-9}$ C is placed at the point $x = +0.150$ m, $y = 0$, and an identical point charge is placed at $x = -0.150$ m, $y = 0$. Find the x- and y-components, the magnitude, and the direction of the electric field at the following points: (a) the origin; (b) $x = 0.300$ m, $y = 0$; (c) $x = 0.150$ m, $y = -0.400$ m; (d) $x = 0$, $y = 0.200$ m.

21.50 •• A point charge $q_1 = -4.00$ nC is at the point $x = 0.600$ m, $y = 0.800$ m, and a second point charge $q_2 = +6.00$ nC is at the point $x = 0.600$ m, $y = 0$. Calculate the magnitude and direction of the net electric field at the origin due to these two point charges.

21.51 •• Repeat Exercise 21.49 for the case where the point charge at $x = +0.150$ m, $y = 0$ is positive and the other is negative, each with magnitude 6.00×10^{-9} C.

21.52 •• A very long, straight wire has charge per unit length 1.50×10^{-10} C/m. At what distance from the wire is the electric-field magnitude equal to 2.50 N/C?

21.53 • A ring-shaped conductor with radius $a = 2.50$ cm has a total positive charge $Q = +0.125$ nC uniformly distributed around it, as shown in Fig. 21.23. The center of the ring is at the origin of coordinates O. (a) What is the electric field (magnitude and direction) at point P, which is on the x-axis at $x = 40.0$ cm? (b) A point charge $q = -2.50$ μC is placed at the point P described in part (a). What are the magnitude and direction of the force exerted by the charge q on the ring?

21.54 •• A straight, nonconducting plastic wire 8.50 cm long carries a charge density of $+175$ nC/m distributed uniformly along its length. It is lying on a horizontal tabletop. (a) Find the magnitude and direction of the electric field this wire produces at a point 6.00 cm directly above its midpoint. (b) If the wire is now bent into a circle lying flat on the table, find the magnitude and direction of the electric field it produces at a point 6.00 cm directly above its center.

21.55 •• A charge of -6.50 nC is spread uniformly over the surface of one face of a nonconducting disk of radius 1.25 cm. (a) Find the magnitude and direction of the electric field this disk produces at a point P on the axis of the disk a distance of 2.00 cm from its center. (b) Suppose that the charge were all pushed away from the center and distributed uniformly on the outer rim of the disk. Find the magnitude and direction of the electric field at point P. (c) If the charge is all brought to the center of the disk, find the magnitude and direction of the electric field at point P. (d) Why is the field in part (a) stronger than the field in part (b)? Why is the field in part (c) the strongest of the three fields?

Section 21.7 Electric Dipoles

21.56 • The ammonia molecule (NH_3) has a dipole moment of 5.0×10^{-30} C·m. Ammonia molecules in the gas phase are placed in a uniform electric field $\vec{E}$ with magnitude 1.6×10^6 N/C. (a) What is the change in electric potential energy when the dipole moment of a molecule changes its orientation with respect to $\vec{E}$ from parallel to perpendicular? (b) At what absolute temperature T is the average translational kinetic energy $\frac{3}{2}kT$ of a molecule equal to the change in potential energy calculated in part (a)? (*Note:* Above this temperature, thermal agitation prevents the dipoles from aligning with the electric field.)

21.57 • Point charges $q_1 = -4.5$ nC and $q_2 = +4.5$ nC are separated by 3.1 mm, forming an electric dipole. (a) Find the electric dipole moment (magnitude and direction). (b) The charges are in a uniform electric field whose direction makes an angle of 36.9° with the line connecting the charges. What is the magnitude of this field if the torque exerted on the dipole has magnitude 7.2×10^{-9} N·m?

21.58 • The dipole moment of the water molecule (H_2O) is 6.17×10^{-30} C·m. Consider a water molecule located at the origin whose dipole moment $\vec{p}$ points in the +x-direction. A chlorine ion (Cl^-), of charge -1.60×10^{-19} C, is located at $x = 3.00 \times 10^{-9}$ m. Find the magnitude and direction of the electric force that the water molecule exerts on the chlorine ion. Is this force attractive or repulsive? Assume that x is much larger than the separation d between the charges in the dipole, so that the approximate expression for the electric field along the dipole axis derived in Example 21.14 can be used.

21.59 • **Torque on a Dipole.** An electric dipole with dipole moment $\vec{p}$ is in a uniform electric field $\vec{E}$. (a) Find the orientations of the dipole for which the torque on the dipole is zero. (b) Which of the orientations in part (a) is stable, and which is unstable? (*Hint:* Consider a small displacement away from the equilibrium position and see what happens.) (c) Show that for the stable orientation in part (b), the dipole's own electric field tends to oppose the external field.

21.60 •• Consider the electric dipole of Example 21.14. (a) Derive an expression for the magnitude of the electric field produced by the dipole at a point on the x-axis in Fig. 21.33. What is the direction of this electric field? (b) How does the electric field at points on the x-axis depend on x when x is very large?

21.61 • Three charges are at the corners of an isosceles triangle as shown in Fig. E21.61. The ± 5.00-μC charges form a dipole. (a) Find the force (magnitude and direction) the -10.00-μC charge exerts on the dipole. (b) For an axis perpendicular to the line connecting the ± 5.00-μC charges at the midpoint of this line, find the torque (magnitude and direction) exerted on the dipole by the -10.00-μC charge.

Figure **E21.61**

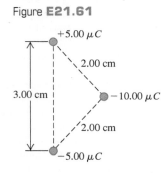

21.62 • A dipole consisting of charges $\pm e$, 220 nm apart, is placed between two very large (essentially infinite) sheets carrying equal but opposite charge densities of 125 $\mu C/m^2$. (a) What is the maximum potential energy this dipole can have due to the sheets, and how should it be oriented relative to the sheets to attain this value? (b) What is the maximum torque the sheets can exert on the dipole, and how should it be oriented relative to the sheets to attain this value? (c) What net force do the two sheets exert on the dipole?

PROBLEMS

21.63 ••• Four identical charges Q are placed at the corners of a square of side L. (a) In a free-body diagram, show all of the forces that act on one of the charges. (b) Find the magnitude and direction of the total force exerted on one charge by the other three charges.

21.64 ••• Two charges, one of 2.50 μC and the other of -3.50 μC, are placed on the x-axis, one at the origin and the other at $x = 0.600$ m, as shown in Fig. P21.64. Find the position on the x-axis where the net force on a small charge $+q$ would be zero.

Figure **P21.64**

21.65 •• Three point charges are arranged along the x-axis. Charge $q_1 = -4.50$ nC is located at $x = 0.200$ m, and charge $q_2 = +2.50$ nC is at $x = -0.300$ m. A positive point charge q_3 is located at the origin. (a) What must the value of q_3 be for the net force on this point charge to have magnitude 4.00 μN? (b) What is the direction of the net force on q_3? (c) Where along the x-axis can q_3 be placed and the net force on it be zero, other than the trivial answers of $x = +\infty$ and $x = -\infty$?

21.66 •• A charge $q_1 = +5.00$ nC is placed at the origin of an xy-coordinate system, and a charge $q_2 = -2.00$ nC is placed on the positive x-axis at $x = 4.00$ cm. (a) If a third charge $q_3 = +6.00$ nC is now placed at the point $x = 4.00$ cm, $y = 3.00$ cm, find the x- and y-components of the total force exerted on this charge by the other two. (b) Find the magnitude and direction of this force.

21.67 •• **CP** Two positive point charges Q are held fixed on the x-axis at $x = a$ and $x = -a$. A third positive point charge q, with mass m, is placed on the x-axis away from the origin at a coordinate x such that $|x| \ll a$. The charge q, which is free to move along the x-axis, is then released. (a) Find the frequency of oscillation of the charge q. (*Hint:* Review the definition of simple harmonic motion in Section 14.2. Use the binomial expansion $(1 + z)^n = 1 + nz + n(n - 1)z^2/2 + \cdots$, valid for the case $|z| < 1$.) (b) Suppose instead that the charge q were placed on the y-axis at a coordinate y such that $|y| \ll a$, and then released. If this charge is free to move anywhere in the xy-plane, what will happen to it? Explain your answer.

21.68 •• **CP** Two identical spheres with mass m are hung from silk threads of length L, as shown in Fig. P21.68. Each sphere has the same charge, so $q_1 = q_2 = q$. The radius of each sphere is very small compared to the distance between the spheres, so they may be treated as point charges. Show that if the angle θ is small, the equilibrium separation d between the spheres is $d = (q^2L/2\pi\epsilon_0 mg)^{1/3}$. (*Hint:* If θ is small, then $\tan \theta \cong \sin \theta$.)

Figure **P21.68**

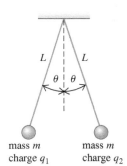

mass m
charge q_1

mass m
charge q_2

21.69 ••• **CP** Two small spheres with mass $m = 15.0$ g are hung by silk threads of length $L = 1.20$ m from a common point (Fig. P21.68). When the spheres are given equal quantities of negative charge, so that $q_1 = q_2 = q$, each thread hangs at $\theta = 25.0°$ from the vertical. (a) Draw a diagram showing the forces on each sphere. Treat the spheres as point charges. (b) Find the magnitude of q. (c) Both threads are now shortened to length $L = 0.600$ m, while the charges q_1 and q_2 remain unchanged. What new angle will each thread make with the vertical? (*Hint:* This part of the problem can be solved numerically by using trial values for θ and adjusting the values of θ until a self-consistent answer is obtained.)

21.70 •• **CP** Two identical spheres are each attached to silk threads of length $L = 0.500$ m and hung from a common point (Fig. P21.68). Each sphere has mass $m = 8.00$ g. The radius of each sphere is very small compared to the distance between the spheres, so they may be treated as point charges. One sphere is given positive charge q_1, and the other a different positive charge q_2; this causes the spheres to separate so that when the spheres are in equilibrium, each thread makes an angle $\theta = 20.0°$ with the vertical. (a) Draw a free-body diagram for each sphere when in equilibrium, and label all the forces that act on each sphere. (b) Determine the magnitude of the electrostatic force that acts on each sphere, and determine the tension in each thread. (c) Based on the information you have been given, what can you say about the magnitudes of q_1 and q_2? Explain your answers. (d) A small wire is now connected between the spheres, allowing charge to be transferred from one sphere to the other until the two spheres have equal charges; the wire is then removed. Each thread now makes an angle of $30.0°$ with the vertical. Determine the original charges. (*Hint:* The total charge on the pair of spheres is conserved.)

21.71 •• Sodium chloride (NaCl, ordinary table salt) is made up of positive sodium ions (Na^+) and negative chloride ions (Cl^-). (a) If a point charge with the same charge and mass as all the Na^+ ions in 0.100 mol of NaCl is 2.00 cm from a point charge with the same charge and mass as all the Cl^- ions, what is the magnitude of the attractive force between these two point charges? (b) If the positive point charge in part (a) is held in place and the negative point charge is released from rest, what is its initial acceleration? (See Appendix D for atomic masses.) (c) Does it seem reasonable that the ions in NaCl could be separated in this way? Why or why not? (In fact, when sodium chloride dissolves in water, it breaks up into Na^+ and Cl^- ions. However, in this situation there are additional electric forces exerted by the water molecules on the ions.)

21.72 •• A -5.00-nC point charge is on the x-axis at $x = 1.20$ m. A second point charge Q is on the x-axis at -0.600 m. What must be the sign and magnitude of Q for the resultant electric field at the origin to be (a) 45.0 N/C in the $+x$-direction, (b) 45.0 N/C in the $-x$-direction?

21.73 •• **CP** A small 12.3-g plastic ball is tied to a very light 28.6-cm string that is attached to the vertical wall of a room (Fig. P21.73). A uniform horizontal electric field exists in this room. When the ball has been given an excess charge of -1.11 μC, you observe that it remains suspended, with the string making an angle of $17.4°$ with the wall. Find the magnitude and direction of the electric field in the room.

Figure **P21.73**

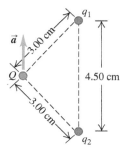

21.74 •• **CP** At $t = 0$ a very small object with mass 0.400 mg and charge $+9.00$ μC is traveling at 125 m/s in the $-x$-direction. The charge is moving in a uniform electric field that is in the $+y$-direction and that has magnitude $E = 895$ N/C. The gravitational force on the particle can be neglected. How far is the particle from the origin at $t = 7.00$ ms?

21.75 •• Two particles having charges $q_1 = 0.500$ nC and $q_2 = 8.00$ nC are separated by a distance of 1.20 m. At what point along the line connecting the two charges is the total electric field due to the two charges equal to zero?

21.76 ••• Two point charges q_1 and q_2 are held in place 4.50 cm apart. Another point charge $Q = -1.75$ μC of mass 5.00 g is initially located 3.00 cm from each of these charges (Fig. P21.76) and released from rest. You observe that the initial acceleration of Q is 324 m/s^2 upward, parallel to the line connecting the two point charges. Find q_1 and q_2.

Figure **P21.76**

21.77 • Three identical point charges q are placed at each of three corners of a square of side L. Find the magnitude and direction of the net force on a point charge $-3q$ placed (a) at the center of the square and (b) at the vacant corner of the square. In each case, draw a free-body diagram showing the forces exerted on the $-3q$ charge by each of the other three charges.

21.78 ••• Three point charges are placed on the y-axis: a charge q at $y = a$, a charge $-2q$ at the origin, and a charge q at $y = -a$. Such an arrangement is called an electric quadrupole. (a) Find the magnitude and direction of the electric field at points on the positive x-axis. (b) Use the binomial expansion to find an approximate expression for the electric field valid for $x \gg a$. Contrast this behavior to that of the electric field of a point charge and that of the electric field of a dipole.

21.79 •• **CP** **Strength of the Electric Force.** Imagine two 1.0-g bags of protons, one at the earth's north pole and the other at the south pole. (a) How many protons are in each bag? (b) Calculate the gravitational attraction and the electrical repulsion that each bag exerts on the other. (c) Are the forces in part (b) large enough for you to feel if you were holding one of the bags?

21.80 • **Electric Force Within the Nucleus.** Typical dimensions of atomic nuclei are of the order of 10^{-15} m (1 fm). (a) If two protons in a nucleus are 2.0 fm apart, find the magnitude of the electric force each one exerts on the other. Express the answer in newtons and in pounds. Would this force be large enough for a person to feel? (b) Since the protons repel each other so strongly, why don't they shoot out of the nucleus?

21.81 •• **If Atoms Were Not Neutral . . .** Because the charges on the electron and proton have the same absolute value, atoms are electrically neutral. Suppose this were not precisely true, and the absolute value of the charge of the electron were less than the charge of the proton by 0.00100%. (a) Estimate what the net charge of this textbook would be under these circumstances. Make any assumptions you feel are justified, but state clearly what they are. (*Hint:* Most of the atoms in this textbook have equal numbers of electrons, protons, and neutrons.) (b) What would be the magnitude of the electric force between two textbooks placed 5.0 m apart? Would this force be attractive or repulsive? Estimate what the acceleration of each book would be if the books were 5.0 m apart and there were no non-electric forces on them. (c) Discuss how the fact that ordinary matter is stable shows that the absolute values of the charges on the electron and proton must be identical to a *very* high level of accuracy.

21.82 ••• **CP** Two tiny spheres of mass 6.80 mg carry charges of equal magnitude,

Figure **P21.82**

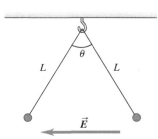

72.0 nC, but opposite sign. They are tied to the same ceiling hook by light strings of length 0.530 m. When a horizontal uniform electric field E that is directed to the left is turned on, the spheres hang at rest with the angle θ between the strings equal to 50.0° (Fig. P21.82). (a) Which ball (the one on the right or the one on the left) has positive charge? (b) What is the magnitude E of the field?

21.83 •• **CP** Consider a model of a hydrogen atom in which an electron is in a circular orbit of radius $r = 5.29 \times 10^{-11}$ m around a stationary proton. What is the speed of the electron in its orbit?

21.84 •• **CP** A small sphere with mass 9.00 μg and charge -4.30 μC is moving in a circular orbit around a stationary sphere that has charge $+7.50$ μC. If the speed of the small sphere is 5.90×10^3 m/s, what is the radius of its orbit? Treat the spheres as point charges and ignore gravity.

21.85 •• Two small copper spheres each have radius 1.00 mm. (a) How many atoms does each sphere contain? (b) Assume that each copper atom contains 29 protons and 29 electrons. We know that electrons and protons have charges of exactly the same magnitude, but let's explore the effect of small differences (see also Problem 21.81). If the charge of a proton is $+e$ and the magnitude of the charge of an electron is 0.100% smaller, what is the net charge of each sphere and what force would one sphere exert on the other if they were separated by 1.00 m?

21.86 ••• **CP Operation of an Inkjet Printer.** In an inkjet printer, letters are built up by squirting drops of ink at the paper from a rapidly moving nozzle. The ink drops, which have a mass of 1.4×10^{-8} g each, leave the nozzle and travel toward the paper at 20 m/s, passing through a charging unit that gives each drop a positive charge q by removing some electrons from it. The drops then pass between parallel deflecting plates 2.0 cm long where there is a uniform vertical electric field with magnitude 8.0×10^4 N/C. If a drop is to be deflected 0.30 mm by the time it reaches the end of the deflection plates, what magnitude of charge must be given to the drop?

21.87 •• **CP** A proton is projected into a uniform electric field that points vertically upward and has magnitude E. The initial velocity of the proton has a magnitude v_0 and is directed at an angle α below the horizontal. (a) Find the maximum distance h_{max} that the proton descends vertically below its initial elevation. You can ignore gravitational forces. (b) After what horizontal distance d does the proton return to its original elevation? (c) Sketch the trajectory of the proton. (d) Find the numerical values of h_{max} and d if $E = 500$ N/C, $v_0 = 4.00 \times 10^5$ m/s, and $\alpha = 30.0°$.

21.88 • A negative point charge $q_1 = -4.00$ nC is on the x-axis at $x = 0.60$ m. A second point charge q_2 is on the x-axis at $x = -1.20$ m. What must the sign and magnitude of q_2 be for the net electric field at the origin to be (a) 50.0 N/C in the $+x$-direction and (b) 50.0 N/C in the $-x$-direction?

21.89 •• **CALC** Positive charge Q is distributed uniformly along the x-axis from $x = 0$ to $x = a$. A positive point charge q is located on the positive x-axis at $x = a + r$, a distance r to the right of the end of Q (Fig. P21.89). (a) Calculate the x- and y-components of the electric field produced by the charge distribution Q at points on the positive x-axis where $x > a$. (b) Calculate the force (magnitude and direction) that the charge distribution Q exerts on q. (c) Show that if $r \gg a$, the magnitude of the force in part (b) is approximately $Qq/4\pi\epsilon_0 r^2$. Explain why this result is obtained.

Figure **P21.89**

21.90 •• **CALC** Positive charge Q is distributed uniformly along the positive y-axis between $y = 0$ and $y = a$. A negative point charge $-q$ lies on the positive x-axis, a distance x from the origin (Fig. P21.90). (a) Calculate the x- and y-components of the electric field produced by the charge distribution Q at points on the positive x-axis. (b) Calculate the x- and y-components of the force that the charge distribution Q exerts on q. (c) Show that if $x \gg a$, $F_x \cong -Qq/4\pi\epsilon_0 x^2$ and $F_y \cong +Qqa/8\pi\epsilon_0 x^3$. Explain why this result is obtained.

Figure **P21.90**

21.91 •• A charged line like that shown in Fig. 21.24 extends from $y = 2.50$ cm to $y = -2.50$ cm. The total charge distributed uniformly along the line is -7.00 nC. (a) Find the electric field (magnitude and direction) on the x-axis at $x = 10.0$ cm. (b) Is the magnitude of the electric field you calculated in part (a) larger or smaller than the electric field 10.0 cm from a point charge that has the same total charge as this finite line of charge? In terms of the approximation used to derive $E = Q/4\pi\epsilon_0 x^2$ for a point charge from Eq. (21.9), explain why this is so. (c) At what distance x does the result for the finite line of charge differ by 1.0% from that for the point charge?

21.92 • **CP A Parallel Universe.** Imagine a parallel universe in which the electric force has the same properties as in our universe but there is no gravity. In this parallel universe, the sun carries charge Q, the earth carries charge $-Q$, and the electric attraction between them keeps the earth in orbit. The earth in the parallel universe has the same mass, the same orbital radius, and the same orbital period as in our universe. Calculate the value of Q. (Consult Appendix F as needed.)

21.93 ••• A uniformly charged disk like the disk in Fig. 21.25 has radius 2.50 cm and carries a total charge of 7.0×10^{-12} C. (a) Find the electric field (magnitude and direction) on the x-axis at $x = 20.0$ cm. (b) Show that for $x \gg R$, Eq. (21.11) becomes $E = Q/4\pi\epsilon_0 x^2$, where Q is the total charge on the disk. (c) Is the magnitude of the electric field you calculated in part (a) larger or smaller than the electric field 20.0 cm from a point charge that has the same total charge as this disk? In terms of the approximation used in part (b) to derive $E = Q/4\pi\epsilon_0 x^2$ for a point charge from Eq. (21.11), explain why this is so. (d) What is the percent difference between the electric fields produced by the finite disk and by a point charge with the same charge at $x = 20.0$ cm and at $x = 10.0$ cm?

21.94 •• **BIO Electrophoresis.** Electrophoresis is a process used by biologists to separate different biological molecules (such as proteins) from each other according to their ratio of charge to size. The materials to be separated are in a viscous solution that produces a drag force F_D proportional to the size and speed of the molecule. We can express this relationship as $F_D = KRv$, where R is the radius of the molecule (modeled as being spherical), v is its speed, and K is a constant that depends on the viscosity of the

Figure **P21.94**

solution. The solution is placed in an external electric field E so that the electric force on a particle of charge q is $F = qE$. (a) Show that when the electric field is adjusted so that the two forces (electric and viscous drag) just balance, the ratio of q to R is Kv/E. (b) Show that if we leave the electric field on for a time T, the distance x that the molecule moves during that time is $x = (ET/k)(q/R)$. (c) Suppose you have a sample containing three different biological molecules for which the molecular ratio q/R for material 2 is twice that of material 1 and the ratio for material 3 is three times that of material 1. Show that the distances migrated by these molecules after the same amount of time are $x_2 = 2x_1$ and $x_3 = 3x_1$. In other words, material 2 travels twice as far as material 1, and material 3 travels three times as far as material 1. Therefore, we have separated these molecules according to their ratio of charge to size. In practice, this process can be carried out in a special gel or paper, along which the biological molecules migrate. (Fig. P21.94). The process can be rather slow, requiring several hours for separations of just a centimeter or so.

21.95 • **CALC** Positive charge $+Q$ is distributed uniformly along the $+x$-axis from $x = 0$ to $x = a$. Negative charge $-Q$ is distributed uniformly along the $-x$-axis from $x = 0$ to $x = -a$. (a) A positive point charge q lies on the positive y-axis, a distance y from the origin. Find the force (magnitude and direction) that the positive and negative charge distributions together exert on q. Show that this force is proportional to y^{-3} for $y \gg a$. (b) Suppose instead that the positive point charge q lies on the positive x-axis, a distance $x > a$ from the origin. Find the force (magnitude and direction) that the charge distribution exerts on q. Show that this force is proportional to x^{-3} for $x \gg a$.

21.96 •• **CP** A small sphere with mass m carries a positive charge q and is attached to one end of a silk fiber of length L. The other end of the fiber is attached to a large vertical insulating sheet that has a positive surface charge density σ. Show that when the sphere is in equilibrium, the fiber makes an angle equal to arctan $(q\sigma/2mg\epsilon_0)$ with the vertical sheet.

21.97 •• **CALC** Negative charge $-Q$ is distributed uniformly around a quarter-circle of radius a that lies in the first quadrant, with the center of curvature at the origin. Find the x- and y-components of the net electric field at the origin.

21.98 •• **CALC** A semicircle of radius a is in the first and second quadrants, with the center of curvature at the origin. Positive charge $+Q$ is distributed uniformly around the left half of the semicircle, and negative charge $-Q$ is distributed uniformly around the right half of the semicircle (Fig. P21.98). What are the magnitude and direction of the net electric field at the origin produced by this distribution of charge?

Figure **P21.98**

21.99 •• Two 1.20-m nonconducting wires meet at a right angle. One segment carries $+2.50$ μC of charge distributed uniformly along its length, and the other carries -2.50 μC distributed uniformly along it, as shown in Fig. P21.99.

Figure **P21.99**

(a) Find the magnitude and direction of the electric field these wires produce at point P, which is 60.0 cm from each wire. (b) If an electron is released at P, what are the magnitude and direction of the net force that these wires exert on it?

21.100 • Two very large parallel sheets are 5.00 cm apart. Sheet A carries a uniform surface charge density of -9.50μC/m^2, and sheet B, which is to the right of A, carries a uniform charge density of -11.6 μC/m^2. Assume the sheets are large enough to be treated as infinite. Find the magnitude and direction of the net electric field these sheets produce at a point (a) 4.00 cm to the right of sheet A; (b) 4.00 cm to the left of sheet A; (c) 4.00 cm to the right of sheet B.

21.101 • Repeat Problem 21.100 for the case where sheet B is positive.

21.102 • Two very large horizontal sheets are 4.25 cm apart and carry equal but opposite uniform surface charge densities of magnitude σ. You want to use these sheets to hold stationary in the region between them an oil droplet of mass 324 μg that carries an excess of five electrons. Assuming that the drop is in vacuum, (a) which way should the electric field between the plates point, and (b) what should σ be?

21.103 •• An infinite sheet with positive charge per unit area σ lies in the xy-plane. A second infinite sheet with negative charge per unit area $-\sigma$ lies in the yz-plane. Find the net electric field at all points that do not lie in either of these planes. Express your answer in terms of the unit vectors $\hat{\imath}, \hat{\jmath}$, and $\hat{k}$.

21.104 •• **CP** A thin disk with a circular hole at its center, called an *annulus,* has inner radius R_1 and outer radius R_2 (Fig. P21.104). The disk has a uniform positive surface charge density σ on its surface. (a) Determine the total electric charge on the annulus. (b) The annulus lies in the yz-plane, with its center at the origin. For an arbitrary point on the x-axis (the axis of the annulus), find the magnitude and direction of the electric field $\vec{E}$. Consider points both above and below the annulus in Fig. P21.104. (c) Show that at points on the x-axis that are sufficiently close to the origin, the magnitude of the electric field is approximately proportional to the distance between the center of the annulus and the point. How close is "sufficiently close"? (d) A point particle with mass m and negative charge $-q$ is free to move along the x-axis (but cannot move off the axis). The particle is originally placed at rest at $x = 0.01R_1$ and released. Find the frequency of oscillation of the particle. (*Hint:* Review Section 14.2. The annulus is held stationary.)

Figure **P21.104**

CHALLENGE PROBLEMS

21.105 ••• Three charges are placed as shown in Fig. P21.105. The magnitude of q_1 is 2.00 μC, but its sign and the value of the charge q_2 are not known. Charge q_3 is $+4.00$ μC, and the net force $\vec{F}$ on q_3 is entirely in the negative x-direction. (a) Considering the different possible signs of q_1, there are four possible force diagrams representing the forces $\vec{F}_1$ and $\vec{F}_2$ that q_1 and q_2 exert on q_3. Sketch these four possible force configurations.

Figure **P21.105**

(b) Using the sketches from part (a) and the direction of $\vec{F}$, deduce the signs of the charges q_1 and q_2. (c) Calculate the magnitude of q_2. (d) Determine F, the magnitude of the net force on q_3.

21.106 ••• Two charges are placed as shown in Fig. P21.106. The magnitude of q_1 is 3.00 μC, but its sign and the value of the charge q_2 are not known. The direction of the net electric field $\vec{E}$ at point P is entirely in the negative y-direction. (a) Considering the different possible signs of q_1 and q_2, there are four possible diagrams that could represent the electric fields $\vec{E}_1$ and $\vec{E}_2$ produced by q_1 and q_2. Sketch the four possible electric-field configurations. (b) Using the sketches from part (a) and the direction of $\vec{E}$, deduce the signs of q_1 and q_2. (c) Determine the magnitude of $\vec{E}$.

Figure **P21.106**

21.107 ••• **CALC** Two thin rods of length L lie along the x-axis, one between $x = a/2$ and $x = a/2 + L$ and the other between $x = -a/2$ and $x = -a/2 - L$. Each rod has positive charge Q distributed uniformly along its length. (a) Calculate the electric field produced by the second rod at points along the positive x-axis. (b) Show that the magnitude of the force that one rod exerts on the other is

$$F = \frac{Q^2}{4\pi\epsilon_0 L^2}\ln\left[\frac{(a+L)^2}{a(a+2L)}\right]$$

(c) Show that if $a \gg L$, the magnitude of this force reduces to $F = Q^2/4\pi\epsilon_0 a^2$. (*Hint:* Use the expansion $\ln(1+z) = z - z^2/2 + z^3/3 - \cdots$, valid for $|z| \ll 1$. Carry *all* expansions to at least order L^2/a^2.) Interpret this result.

Answers

Chapter Opening Question ?

Water molecules have a permanent electric dipole moment: One end of the molecule has a positive charge and the other end has a negative charge. These ends attract negative and positive ions, respectively, holding the ions apart in solution. Water is less effective as a solvent for materials whose molecules do not ionize (called *nonionic* substances), such as oils.

Test Your Understanding Questions

21.1 Answers: (a) the plastic rod weighs more, (b) the glass rod weighs less, (c) the fur weighs less, (d) the silk weighs more The plastic rod gets a negative charge by taking electrons from the fur, so the rod weighs a little more and the fur weighs a little less after the rubbing. By contrast, the glass rod gets a positive charge by giving electrons to the silk. Hence, after they are rubbed together, the glass rod weighs a little less and the silk weighs a little more. The weight change is *very* small: The number of electrons transferred is a small fraction of a mole, and a mole of electrons has a mass of only $(6.02 \times 10^{23}$ electrons$)(9.11 \times 10^{-31}$ kg/electron$) = 5.48 \times 10^{-7}$ kg $= 0.548$ milligram!

21.2 Answers: (a) (i), (b) (ii) Before the two spheres touch, the negatively charged sphere exerts a repulsive force on the electrons in the other sphere, causing zones of positive and negative induced charge (see Fig. 21.7b). The positive zone is closer to the negatively charged sphere than the negative zone, so there is a net force of attraction that pulls the spheres together, like the comb and insulator in Fig. 21.8b. Once the two metal spheres touch, some of the excess electrons on the negatively charged sphere will flow onto the other sphere (because metals are conductors). Then both spheres will have a net negative charge and will repel each other.

21.3 Answer: (iv) The force exerted by q_1 on Q is still as in Example 21.4. The magnitude of the force exerted by q_2 on Q is still equal to $F_{1\text{ on }Q}$, but the direction of the force is now *toward* q_2 at an angle α below the x-axis. Hence the x-components of the two forces cancel while the (negative) y-components add together, and the total electric force is in the negative y-direction.

21.4 Answers: (a) (ii), (b) (i) The electric field $\vec{E}$ produced by a positive point charge points directly away from the charge (see Fig. 21.18a) and has a magnitude that depends on the distance r from the charge to the field point. Hence a second, negative point charge $q < 0$ will feel a force $\vec{F} = q\vec{E}$ that points directly toward the positive charge and has a magnitude that depends on the distance r between the two charges. If the negative charge moves directly toward the positive charge, the direction of the force remains the same but the force magnitude increases as the distance r decreases. If the negative charge moves in a circle around the positive charge, the force magnitude stays the same (because the distance r is constant) but the force direction changes.

21.5 Answer: (iv) Think of a pair of segments of length dy, one at coordinate $y > 0$ and the other at coordinate $-y < 0$. The upper segment has a positive charge and produces an electric field $d\vec{E}$ at P that points away from the segment, so this $d\vec{E}$ has a positive x-component and a negative y-component, like the vector $d\vec{E}$ in Fig. 21.24. The lower segment has the same amount of negative charge. It produces a $d\vec{E}$ that has the same magnitude but points *toward* the lower segment, so it has a negative x-component and a negative y-component. By symmetry, the two x-components are equal but opposite, so they cancel. Thus the total electric field has only a negative y-component.

21.6 Answer: yes If the field lines are straight, $\vec{E}$ must point in the same direction throughout the region. Hence the force $\vec{F} = q\vec{E}$ on a particle of charge q is always in the same direction. A particle released from rest accelerates in a straight line in the direction of $\vec{F}$, and so its trajectory is a straight line along a field line.

21.7 Answer: (ii) Equations (21.17) and (21.18) tell us that the potential energy for a dipole in an electric field is $U = -\vec{p} \cdot \vec{E} = -pE\cos\phi$, where ϕ is the angle between the directions of $\vec{p}$ and $\vec{E}$. If $\vec{p}$ and $\vec{E}$ point in opposite directions, so that $\phi = 180°$, we have $\cos\phi = -1$ and $U = +pE$. This is the maximum value that U can have. From our discussion of energy diagrams in Section 7.5, it follows that this is a situation of unstable equilibrium.

Bridging Problem

Answer: $E = 2kQ/\pi a^2$ in the $-y$-direction

GAUSS'S LAW

? This child acquires an electric charge by touching the charged metal sphere. The charged hairs on the child's head repel and stand out. If the child stands *inside* a large, charged metal sphere, will her hair stand on end?

LEARNING GOALS

By studying this chapter, you will learn:

• How you can determine the amount of charge within a closed surface by examining the electric field on the surface.

• What is meant by electric flux, and how to calculate it.

• How Gauss's law relates the electric flux through a closed surface to the charge enclosed by the surface.

• How to use Gauss's law to calculate the electric field due to a symmetric charge distribution.

• Where the charge is located on a charged conductor.

O ften, there are both an easy way and a hard way to do a job; the easy way may involve nothing more than using the right tools. In physics, an important tool for simplifying problems is the *symmetry properties* of systems. Many physical systems have symmetry; for example, a cylindrical body doesn't look any different after you've rotated it around its axis, and a charged metal sphere looks just the same after you've turned it about any axis through its center.

Gauss's law is part of the key to using symmetry considerations to simplify electric-field calculations. For example, the field of a straight-line or plane-sheet charge distribution, which we derived in Section 21.5 using some fairly strenuous integrations, can be obtained in a few lines with the help of Gauss's law. But Gauss's law is more than just a way to make certain calculations easier. Indeed, it is a fundamental statement about the relationship between electric charges and electric fields. Among other things, Gauss's law can help us understand how electric charge distributes itself over conducting bodies.

Here's what Gauss's law is all about. Given any general distribution of charge, we surround it with an imaginary surface that encloses the charge. Then we look at the electric field at various points on this imaginary surface. Gauss's law is a relationship between the field at *all* the points on the surface and the total charge enclosed within the surface. This may sound like a rather indirect way of expressing things, but it turns out to be a tremendously useful relationship. Above and beyond its use as a calculational tool, Gauss's law can help us gain deeper insights into electric fields. We will make use of these insights repeatedly in the next several chapters as we pursue our study of electromagnetism.

22.1 Charge and Electric Flux

In Chapter 21 we asked the question, "Given a charge distribution, what is the electric field produced by that distribution at a point *P*?" We saw that the answer could be found by representing the distribution as an assembly of point charges,

The discussion of Gauss's law in this section is based on and inspired by the innovative ideas of Ruth W. Chabay and Bruce A. Sherwood in *Electric and Magnetic Interactions* (John Wiley & Sons, 1994).

ActivPhysics 11.7: Electric Flux

22.1 How can you measure the charge inside a box without opening it?

(a) A box containing an unknown amount of charge

(b) Using a test charge outside the box to probe the amount of charge inside the box

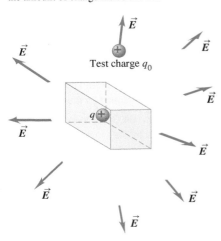

each of which produces an electric field $\vec{E}$ given by Eq. (21.7). The total field at P is then the vector sum of the fields due to all the point charges.

But there is an alternative relationship between charge distributions and electric fields. To discover this relationship, let's stand the question of Chapter 21 on its head and ask, "If the electric field pattern is known in a given region, what can we determine about the charge distribution in that region?"

Here's an example. Consider the box shown in Fig. 22.1a, which may or may not contain electric charge. We'll imagine that the box is made of a material that has no effect on any electric fields; it's of the same breed as the massless rope and the frictionless incline. Better still, let the box represent an *imaginary* surface that may or may not enclose some charge. We'll refer to the box as a **closed surface** because it completely encloses a volume. How can you determine how much (if any) electric charge lies within the box?

Knowing that a charge distribution produces an electric field and that an electric field exerts a force on a test charge, you move a test charge q_0 around the vicinity of the box. By measuring the force $\vec{F}$ experienced by the test charge at different positions, you make a three-dimensional map of the electric field $\vec{E} = \vec{F}/q_0$ outside the box. In the case shown in Fig. 22.1b, the map turns out to be the same as that of the electric field produced by a positive point charge (Fig. 21.28a). From the details of the map, you can find the exact value of the point charge inside the box.

To determine the contents of the box, we actually need to measure $\vec{E}$ only on the *surface* of the box. In Fig. 22.2a there is a single *positive* point charge inside the box, and in Fig. 22.2b there are two such charges. The field patterns on the surfaces of the boxes are different in detail, but in each case the electric field points *out* of the box. Figures 22.2c and 22.2d show cases with one and two *negative* point charges, respectively, inside the box. Again, the details of $\vec{E}$ are different for the two cases, but the electric field points *into* each box.

Electric Flux and Enclosed Charge

In Section 21.4 we mentioned the analogy between electric-field vectors and the velocity vectors of a fluid in motion. This analogy can be helpful, even though an electric field does not actually "flow." Using this analogy, in Figs. 22.2a and 22.2b, in which the electric field vectors point out of the surface, we say that there is an *outward* **electric flux.** (The word "flux" comes from a Latin word meaning "flow.") In Figs. 22.2c and 22.2d the $\vec{E}$ vectors point into the surface, and the electric flux is *inward.*

Figure 22.2 suggests a simple relationship: Positive charge inside the box goes with an outward electric flux through the box's surface, and negative charge inside goes with an inward electric flux. What happens if there is *zero* charge

22.2 The electric field on the surface of boxes containing (a) a single positive point charge, (b) two positive point charges, (c) a single negative point charge, or (d) two negative point charges.

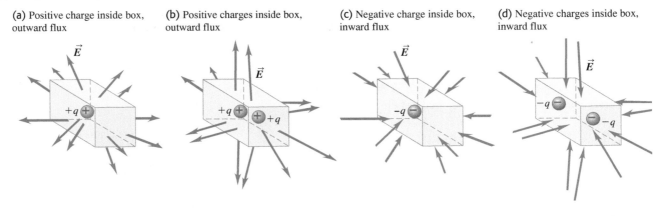

(a) Positive charge inside box, outward flux

(b) Positive charges inside box, outward flux

(c) Negative charge inside box, inward flux

(d) Negative charges inside box, inward flux

inside the box? In Fig. 22.3a the box is empty and $\vec{E} = 0$ everywhere, so there is no electric flux into or out of the box. In Fig. 22.3b, one positive and one negative point charge of equal magnitude are enclosed within the box, so the *net* charge inside the box is zero. There is an electric field, but it "flows into" the box on half of its surface and "flows out of" the box on the other half. Hence there is no *net* electric flux into or out of the box.

The box is again empty in Fig. 22.3c. However, there is charge present *outside* the box; the box has been placed with one end parallel to a uniformly charged infinite sheet, which produces a uniform electric field perpendicular to the sheet (as we learned in Example 21.11 of Section 21.5). On one end of the box, $\vec{E}$ points into the box; on the opposite end, $\vec{E}$ points out of the box; and on the sides, $\vec{E}$ is parallel to the surface and so points neither into nor out of the box. As in Fig. 22.3b, the inward electric flux on one part of the box exactly compensates for the outward electric flux on the other part. So in all of the cases shown in Fig. 22.3, there is no *net* electric flux through the surface of the box, and no *net* charge is enclosed in the box.

Figures 22.2 and 22.3 demonstrate a connection between the *sign* (positive, negative, or zero) of the *net* charge enclosed by a closed surface and the sense (outward, inward, or none) of the net electric flux through the surface. There is also a connection between the *magnitude* of the net charge inside the closed surface and the *strength* of the net "flow" of $\vec{E}$ over the surface. In both Figs. 22.4a and 22.4b there is a single point charge inside the box, but in Fig. 22.4b the magnitude of the charge is twice as great, and so $\vec{E}$ is everywhere twice as great in magnitude as in Fig. 22.4a. If we keep in mind the fluid-flow analogy, this means that the net outward electric flux is also twice as great in Fig. 22.4b as in Fig. 22.4a. This suggests that the net electric flux through the surface of the box is *directly proportional* to the magnitude of the net charge enclosed by the box.

This conclusion is independent of the size of the box. In Fig. 22.4c the point charge $+q$ is enclosed by a box with twice the linear dimensions of the box in Fig. 22.4a. The magnitude of the electric field of a point charge decreases with distance according to $1/r^2$, so the average magnitude of $\vec{E}$ on each face of the large box in Fig. 22.4c is just $\frac{1}{4}$ of the average magnitude on the corresponding face in Fig. 22.4a. But each face of the large box has exactly four times the area of the corresponding face of the small box. Hence the outward electric flux is the *same* for the two boxes if we *define* electric flux as follows: For each face of the box, take the product of the average perpendicular component of $\vec{E}$ and the area of that face; then add up the results from all faces of the box. With this definition the net electric flux due to a single point charge inside the box is independent of the size of the box and depends only on the net charge inside the box.

22.3 Three cases in which there is zero *net* charge inside a box and no net electric flux through the surface of the box. (a) An empty box with $\vec{E} = 0$. (b) A box containing one positive and one equal-magnitude negative point charge. (c) An empty box immersed in a uniform electric field.

(a) No charge inside box, zero flux

(b) Zero *net* charge inside box, inward flux cancels outward flux.

(c) No charge inside box, inward flux cancels outward flux.

22.4 (a) A box enclosing a positive point charge $+q$. (b) Doubling the charge causes the magnitude of $\vec{E}$ to double, and it doubles the electric flux through the surface. (c) If the charge stays the same but the dimensions of the box are doubled, the flux stays the same. The magnitude of $\vec{E}$ on the surface decreases by a factor of $\frac{1}{4}$, but the area through which $\vec{E}$ "flows" increases by a factor of 4.

(a) A box containing a charge

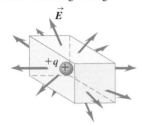

(b) Doubling the enclosed charge doubles the flux.

(c) Doubling the box dimensions *does not change* the flux.

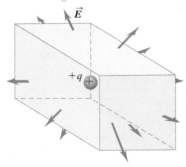

To summarize, for the special cases of a closed surface in the shape of a rectangular box and charge distributions made up of point charges or infinite charged sheets, we have found:

1. Whether there is a net outward or inward electric flux through a closed surface depends on the sign of the enclosed charge.
2. Charges *outside* the surface do not give a net electric flux through the surface.
3. The net electric flux is directly proportional to the net amount of charge enclosed within the surface but is otherwise independent of the size of the closed surface.

These observations are a qualitative statement of *Gauss's law.*

Do these observations hold true for other kinds of charge distributions and for closed surfaces of arbitrary shape? The answer to these questions will prove to be yes. But to explain why this is so, we need a precise mathematical statement of what we mean by electric flux. We develop this in the next section.

Test Your Understanding of Section 22.1   If all of the dimensions of the box in Fig. 22.2a are increased by a factor of 3, what effect will this change have on the electric flux through the box? (i) The flux will be $3^2 = 9$ times greater; (ii) the flux will be 3 times greater; (iii) the flux will be unchanged; (iv) the flux will be $\frac{1}{3}$ as great; (v) the flux will be $\left(\frac{1}{3}\right)^2 = \frac{1}{9}$ as great; (vi) not enough information is given to decide. ❚

22.2 Calculating Electric Flux

In the preceding section we introduced the concept of *electric flux*. We used this to give a rough qualitative statement of Gauss's law: The net electric flux through a closed surface is directly proportional to the net charge inside that surface. To be able to make full use of this law, we need to know how to *calculate* electric flux. To do this, let's again make use of the analogy between an electric field $\vec{E}$ and the field of velocity vectors $\vec{v}$ in a flowing fluid. (Again, keep in mind that this is only an analogy; an electric field is *not* a flow.)

Flux: Fluid-Flow Analogy

Figure 22.5 shows a fluid flowing steadily from left to right. Let's examine the volume flow rate dV/dt (in, say, cubic meters per second) through the wire rectangle with area A. When the area is perpendicular to the flow velocity $\vec{v}$ (Fig. 22.5a) and the flow velocity is the same at all points in the fluid, the volume flow rate dV/dt is the area A multiplied by the flow speed v:

$$\frac{dV}{dt} = vA$$

When the rectangle is tilted at an angle ϕ (Fig. 22.5b) so that its face is not perpendicular to $\vec{v}$, the area that counts is the silhouette area that we see when we look in the direction of $\vec{v}$. This area, which is outlined in red and labeled $A_\perp$ in Fig. 22.5b, is the *projection* of the area A onto a surface perpendicular to $\vec{v}$. Two sides of the projected rectangle have the same length as the original one, but the other two are foreshortened by a factor of $\cos\phi$, so the projected area $A_\perp$ is equal to $A\cos\phi$. Then the volume flow rate through A is

$$\frac{dV}{dt} = vA\cos\phi$$

If $\phi = 90°$, $dV/dt = 0$; the wire rectangle is edge-on to the flow, and no fluid passes through the rectangle.

Also, $v \cos \phi$ is the component of the vector $\vec{v}$ perpendicular to the plane of the area A. Calling this component $v_\perp$, we can rewrite the volume flow rate as

$$\frac{dV}{dt} = v_\perp A$$

We can express the volume flow rate more compactly by using the concept of *vector area $\vec{A}$*, a vector quantity with magnitude A and a direction perpendicular to the plane of the area we are describing. The vector area $\vec{A}$ describes both the size of an area and its orientation in space. In terms of $\vec{A}$, we can write the volume flow rate of fluid through the rectangle in Fig. 22.5b as a scalar (dot) product:

$$\frac{dV}{dt} = \vec{v} \cdot \vec{A}$$

Flux of a Uniform Electric Field

Using the analogy between electric field and fluid flow, we now define electric flux in the same way as we have just defined the volume flow rate of a fluid; we simply replace the fluid velocity $\vec{v}$ by the electric field $\vec{E}$. The symbol that we use for electric flux is Φ_E (the capital Greek letter phi; the subscript E is a reminder that this is *electric* flux). Consider first a flat area A perpendicular to a uniform electric field $\vec{E}$ (Fig. 22.6a). We define the electric flux through this area to be the product of the field magnitude E and the area A:

$$\Phi_E = EA$$

Roughly speaking, we can picture Φ_E in terms of the field lines passing through A. Increasing the area means that more lines of $\vec{E}$ pass through the area, increasing the flux; a stronger field means more closely spaced lines of $\vec{E}$ and therefore more lines per unit area, so again the flux increases.

If the area A is flat but not perpendicular to the field $\vec{E}$, then fewer field lines pass through it. In this case the area that counts is the silhouette area that we see when looking in the direction of $\vec{E}$. This is the area $A_\perp$ in Fig. 22.6b and is equal to $A \cos \phi$ (compare to Fig. 22.5b). We generalize our definition of electric flux for a uniform electric field to

$$\Phi_E = EA \cos \phi \qquad \text{(electric flux for uniform } \vec{E}\text{, flat surface)} \qquad (22.1)$$

Since $E \cos \phi$ is the component of $\vec{E}$ perpendicular to the area, we can rewrite Eq. (22.1) as

$$\Phi_E = E_\perp A \qquad \text{(electric flux for uniform } \vec{E}\text{, flat surface)} \qquad (22.2)$$

In terms of the vector area $\vec{A}$ perpendicular to the area, we can write the electric flux as the scalar product of $\vec{E}$ and $\vec{A}$:

$$\Phi_E = \vec{E} \cdot \vec{A} \qquad \text{(electric flux for uniform } \vec{E}\text{, flat surface)} \qquad (22.3)$$

Equations (22.1), (22.2), and (22.3) express the electric flux for a *flat* surface and a *uniform* electric field in different but equivalent ways. The SI unit for electric flux is $1\ \mathrm{N \cdot m^2 / C}$. Note that if the area is edge-on to the field, $\vec{E}$ and $\vec{A}$ are perpendicular and the flux is zero (Fig. 22.6c).

We can represent the direction of a vector area $\vec{A}$ by using a *unit vector $\hat{n}$* perpendicular to the area; $\hat{n}$ stands for "normal." Then

$$\vec{A} = A\hat{n} \qquad (22.4)$$

A surface has two sides, so there are two possible directions for $\hat{n}$ and $\vec{A}$. We must always specify which direction we choose. In Section 22.1 we related the charge inside a *closed* surface to the electric flux through the surface. With a closed surface we will always choose the direction of $\hat{n}$ to be *outward*, and we

22.5 The volume flow rate of fluid through the wire rectangle (a) is vA when the area of the rectangle is perpendicular to $\vec{v}$ and (b) is $vA \cos \phi$ when the rectangle is tilted at an angle ϕ.

(a) A wire rectangle in a fluid

(b) The wire rectangle tilted by an angle ϕ

Application Flux Through a Basking Shark's Mouth

Unlike aggressive carnivorous sharks such as great whites, a basking shark feeds passively on plankton in the water that passes through the shark's gills as it swims. To survive on these tiny organisms requires a huge flux of water through a basking shark's immense mouth, which can be up to a meter across. The water flux—the product of the shark's speed through the water and the area of its mouth—can be up to $0.5\ \mathrm{m^3/s}$ (500 liters per second, or almost 5×10^5 gallons per hour). In a similar way, the flux of electric field through a surface depends on the magnitude of the field and the area of the surface (as well as the relative orientation of the field and surface).

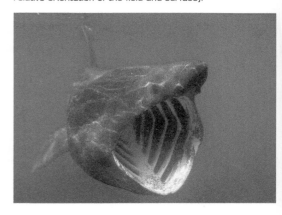

22.6 A flat surface in a uniform electric field. The electric flux Φ_E through the surface equals the scalar product of the electric field $\vec{E}$ and the area vector $\vec{A}$.

(a) Surface is face-on to electric field:
- $\vec{E}$ and $\vec{A}$ are parallel (the angle between $\vec{E}$ and $\vec{A}$ is $\phi = 0$).
- The flux $\Phi_E = \vec{E} \cdot \vec{A} = EA$.

(b) Surface is tilted from a face-on orientation by an angle ϕ:
- The angle between $\vec{E}$ and $\vec{A}$ is ϕ.
- The flux $\Phi_E = \vec{E} \cdot \vec{A} = EA \cos\phi$.

(c) Surface is edge-on to electric field:
- $\vec{E}$ and $\vec{A}$ are perpendicular (the angle between $\vec{E}$ and $\vec{A}$ is $\phi = 90°$).
- The flux $\Phi_E = \vec{E} \cdot \vec{A} = EA \cos 90° = 0$.

will speak of the flux *out of* a closed surface. Thus what we called "outward electric flux" in Section 22.1 corresponds to a *positive* value of Φ_E, and what we called "inward electric flux" corresponds to a *negative* value of Φ_E.

Flux of a Nonuniform Electric Field

What happens if the electric field $\vec{E}$ isn't uniform but varies from point to point over the area A? Or what if A is part of a curved surface? Then we divide A into many small elements dA, each of which has a unit vector $\hat{n}$ perpendicular to it and a vector area $d\vec{A} = \hat{n}\, dA$. We calculate the electric flux through each element and integrate the results to obtain the total flux:

$$\Phi_E = \int E \cos\phi\, dA = \int E_\perp\, dA = \int \vec{E} \cdot d\vec{A} \quad \begin{array}{l}\text{(general definition} \\ \text{of electric flux)}\end{array} \quad (22.5)$$

We call this integral the **surface integral** of the component $E_\perp$ over the area, or the surface integral of $\vec{E} \cdot d\vec{A}$. In specific problems, one form of the integral is sometimes more convenient than another. Example 22.3 at the end of this section illustrates the use of Eq. (22.5).

In Eq. (22.5) the electric flux $\int E_\perp\, dA$ is equal to the *average* value of the perpendicular component of the electric field, multiplied by the area of the surface. This is the same definition of electric flux that we were led to in Section 22.1, now expressed more mathematically. In the next section we will see the connection between the total electric flux through *any* closed surface, no matter what its shape, and the amount of charge enclosed within that surface.

Example 22.1 **Electric flux through a disk**

A disk of radius 0.10 m is oriented with its normal unit vector $\hat{n}$ at 30° to a uniform electric field $\vec{E}$ of magnitude 2.0×10^3 N/C (Fig. 22.7). (Since this isn't a closed surface, it has no "inside" or "outside." That's why we have to specify the direction of $\hat{n}$ in the figure.) (a) What is the electric flux through the disk? (b) What is the flux through the disk if it is turned so that $\hat{n}$ is perpendicular to $\vec{E}$? (c) What is the flux through the disk if $\hat{n}$ is parallel to $\vec{E}$?

22.7 The electric flux Φ_E through a disk depends on the angle between its normal $\hat{n}$ and the electric field $\vec{E}$.

SOLUTION

IDENTIFY and SET UP: This problem is about a flat surface in a uniform electric field, so we can apply the ideas of this section. We calculate the electric flux using Eq. (22.1).

EXECUTE: (a) The area is $A = \pi(0.10 \text{ m})^2 = 0.0314 \text{ m}^2$ and the angle between $\vec{E}$ and $\vec{A} = A\hat{n}$ is $\phi = 30°$, so from Eq. (22.1),

$$\Phi_E = EA\cos\phi = (2.0 \times 10^3 \text{ N/C})(0.0314 \text{ m}^2)(\cos 30°)$$
$$= 54 \text{ N} \cdot \text{m}^2/\text{C}$$

(b) The normal to the disk is now perpendicular to $\vec{E}$, so $\phi = 90°$, $\cos\phi = 0$, and $\Phi_E = 0$.

(c) The normal to the disk is parallel to $\vec{E}$, so $\phi = 0$ and $\cos\phi = 1$:

$$\Phi_E = EA\cos\phi = (2.0 \times 10^3 \text{ N/C})(0.0314 \text{ m}^2)(1)$$
$$= 63 \text{ N} \cdot \text{m}^2/\text{C}$$

EVALUATE: As a check on our results, note that our answer to part (b) is smaller than that to part (a), which is in turn smaller than that to part (c). Is all this as it should be?

Example 22.2   Electric flux through a cube

An imaginary cubical surface of side L is in a region of uniform electric field $\vec{E}$. Find the electric flux through each face of the cube and the total flux through the cube when (a) it is oriented with two of its faces perpendicular to $\vec{E}$ (Fig. 22.8a) and (b) the cube is turned by an angle θ about a vertical axis (Fig. 22.8b).

SOLUTION

IDENTIFY and SET UP: Since $\vec{E}$ is uniform and each of the six faces of the cube is flat, we find the flux Φ_{Ei} through each face using Eqs. (22.3) and (22.4). The total flux through the cube is the sum of the six individual fluxes.

EXECUTE: (a) Figure 22.8a shows the unit vectors $\hat{n}_1$ through $\hat{n}_6$ for each face; each unit vector points *outward* from the cube's closed surface. The angle between $\vec{E}$ and $\hat{n}_1$ is 180°, the angle between $\vec{E}$

and $\hat{n}_2$ is 0°, and the angle between $\vec{E}$ and each of the other four unit vectors is 90°. Each face of the cube has area L^2, so the fluxes through the faces are

$$\Phi_{E1} = \vec{E} \cdot \hat{n}_1 A = EL^2\cos 180° = -EL^2$$
$$\Phi_{E2} = \vec{E} \cdot \hat{n}_2 A = EL^2\cos 0° = +EL^2$$
$$\Phi_{E3} = \Phi_{E4} = \Phi_{E5} = \Phi_{E6} = EL^2\cos 90° = 0$$

The flux is negative on face 1, where $\vec{E}$ is directed into the cube, and positive on face 2, where $\vec{E}$ is directed out of the cube. The total flux through the cube is

$$\Phi_E = \Phi_{E1} + \Phi_{E2} + \Phi_{E3} + \Phi_{E4} + \Phi_{E5} + \Phi_{E6}$$
$$= -EL^2 + EL^2 + 0 + 0 + 0 + 0 = 0$$

(b) The field $\vec{E}$ is directed into faces 1 and 3, so the fluxes through them are negative; $\vec{E}$ is directed out of faces 2 and 4, so the fluxes through them are positive. We find

$$\Phi_{E1} = \vec{E} \cdot \hat{n}_1 A = EL^2\cos(180° - \theta) = -EL^2\cos\theta$$
$$\Phi_{E2} = \vec{E} \cdot \hat{n}_2 A = +EL^2\cos\theta$$
$$\Phi_{E3} = \vec{E} \cdot \hat{n}_3 A = EL^2\cos(90° + \theta) = -EL^2\sin\theta$$
$$\Phi_{E4} = \vec{E} \cdot \hat{n}_4 A = EL^2\cos(90° - \theta) = +EL^2\sin\theta$$
$$\Phi_{E5} = \Phi_{E6} = EL^2\cos 90° = 0$$

The total flux $\Phi_E = \Phi_{E1} + \Phi_{E2} + \Phi_{E3} + \Phi_{E4} + \Phi_{E5} + \Phi_{E6}$ through the surface of the cube is again zero.

EVALUATE: We came to the same conclusion in our discussion of Fig. 22.3c: There is zero net flux of a uniform electric field through a closed surface that contains no electric charge.

22.8 Electric flux of a uniform field $\vec{E}$ through a cubical box of side L in two orientations.

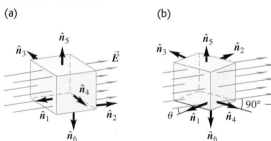

(a)   (b)

Example 22.3   Electric flux through a sphere

A point charge $q = +3.0 \ \mu\text{C}$ is surrounded by an imaginary sphere of radius $r = 0.20$ m centered on the charge (Fig. 22.9). Find the resulting electric flux through the sphere.

SOLUTION

IDENTIFY and SET UP: The surface is not flat and the electric field is not uniform, so to calculate the electric flux (our target variable)

we must use the general definition, Eq. (22.5). We use Eq. (22.5) to calculate the electric flux (our target variable). Because the sphere is centered on the point charge, at any point on the spherical surface, $\vec{E}$ is directed out of the sphere perpendicular to the surface. The positive direction for both $\hat{n}$ and $E_\perp$ is outward, so $E_\perp = E$ and the flux through a surface element dA is $\vec{E} \cdot d\vec{A} = E \, dA$. This greatly simplifies the integral in Eq. (22.5).

Continued

22.9 Electric flux through a sphere centered on a point charge.

EXECUTE: We must evaluate the integral of Eq. (22.5), $\Phi_E = \int E\,dA$. At any point on the sphere of radius r the electric field has the same magnitude $E = q/4\pi\epsilon_0 r^2$. Hence E can be taken outside the integral, which becomes $\Phi_E = E\int dA = EA$, where A is the

area of the spherical surface: $A = 4\pi r^2$. Hence the total flux through the sphere is

$$\Phi_E = EA = \frac{q}{4\pi\epsilon_0 r^2}4\pi r^2 = \frac{q}{\epsilon_0}$$

$$= \frac{3.0 \times 10^{-6}\,\text{C}}{8.85 \times 10^{-12}\,\text{C}^2/\text{N}\cdot\text{m}^2} = 3.4 \times 10^5\,\text{N}\cdot\text{m}^2/\text{C}$$

EVALUATE: The radius r of the sphere cancels out of the result for Φ_E. We would have obtained the same flux with a sphere of radius 2.0 m or 200 m. We came to essentially the same conclusion in our discussion of Fig. 22.4 in Section 22.1, where we considered rectangular closed surfaces of two different sizes enclosing a point charge. There we found that the flux of $\vec{E}$ was independent of the size of the surface; the same result holds true for a spherical surface. Indeed, the flux through *any* surface enclosing a single point charge is independent of the shape or size of the surface, as we'll soon see.

Test Your Understanding of Section 22.2 Rank the following surfaces in order from most positive to most negative electric flux. (i) a flat rectangular surface with vector area $\vec{A} = (6.0\,\text{m}^2)\hat{\imath}$ in a uniform electric field $\vec{E} = (4.0\,\text{N/C})\hat{\jmath}$; (ii) a flat circular surface with vector area $\vec{A} = (3.0\,\text{m}^2)\hat{\jmath}$ in a uniform electric field $\vec{E} = (4.0\,\text{N/C})\hat{\imath} + (2.0\,\text{N/C})\hat{\jmath}$; (iii) a flat square surface with vector area $\vec{A} = (3.0\,\text{m}^2)\hat{\imath} + (7.0\,\text{m}^2)\hat{\jmath}$ in a uniform electric field $\vec{E} = (4.0\,\text{N/C})\hat{\imath} - (2.0\,\text{N/C})\hat{\jmath}$; (iv) a flat oval surface with vector area $\vec{A} = (3.0\,\text{m}^2)\hat{\imath} - (7.0\,\text{m}^2)\hat{\jmath}$ in a uniform electric field $\vec{E} = (4.0\,\text{N/C})\hat{\imath} - (2.0\,\text{N/C})\hat{\jmath}$.

22.3 Gauss's Law

22.10 Carl Friedrich Gauss helped develop several branches of mathematics, including differential geometry, real analysis, and number theory. The "bell curve" of statistics is one of his inventions. Gauss also made state-of-the-art investigations of the earth's magnetism and calculated the orbit of the first asteroid to be discovered.

Gauss's law is an alternative to Coulomb's law. While completely equivalent to Coulomb's law, Gauss's law provides a different way to express the relationship between electric charge and electric field. It was formulated by Carl Friedrich Gauss (1777–1855), one of the greatest mathematicians of all time (Fig. 22.10).

Point Charge Inside a Spherical Surface

Gauss's law states that the total electric flux through any closed surface (a surface enclosing a definite volume) is proportional to the total (net) electric charge inside the surface. In Section 22.1 we observed this relationship qualitatively for certain special cases; now we'll develop it more rigorously. We'll start with the field of a single positive point charge q. The field lines radiate out equally in all directions. We place this charge at the center of an imaginary spherical surface with radius R. The magnitude E of the electric field at every point on the surface is given by

$$E = \frac{1}{4\pi\epsilon_0}\frac{q}{R^2}$$

At each point on the surface, $\vec{E}$ is perpendicular to the surface, and its magnitude is the same at every point, just as in Example 22.3 (Section 22.2). The total electric flux is the product of the field magnitude E and the total area $A = 4\pi R^2$ of the sphere:

$$\Phi_E = EA = \frac{1}{4\pi\epsilon_0}\frac{q}{R^2}(4\pi R^2) = \frac{q}{\epsilon_0} \qquad (22.6)$$

The flux is independent of the radius R of the sphere. It depends only on the charge q enclosed by the sphere.

We can also interpret this result in terms of field lines. Figure 22.11 shows two spheres with radii R and $2R$ centered on the point charge q. Every field line that passes through the smaller sphere also passes through the larger sphere, so the total flux through each sphere is the same.

What is true of the entire sphere is also true of any portion of its surface. In Fig. 22.11 an area dA is outlined on the sphere of radius R and then projected onto the sphere of radius $2R$ by drawing lines from the center through points on the boundary of dA. The area projected on the larger sphere is clearly $4\,dA$. But since the electric field due to a point charge is inversely proportional to r^2, the field magnitude is $\frac{1}{4}$ as great on the sphere of radius $2R$ as on the sphere of radius R. Hence the electric flux is the same for both areas and is independent of the radius of the sphere.

Point Charge Inside a Nonspherical Surface

This projection technique shows us how to extend this discussion to nonspherical surfaces. Instead of a second sphere, let us surround the sphere of radius R by a surface of irregular shape, as in Fig. 22.12a. Consider a small element of area dA on the irregular surface; we note that this area is *larger* than the corresponding element on a spherical surface at the same distance from q. If a normal to dA makes an angle ϕ with a radial line from q, two sides of the area projected onto the spherical surface are foreshortened by a factor $\cos\phi$ (Fig. 22.12b). The other two sides are unchanged. Thus the electric flux through the spherical surface element is equal to the flux $E\,dA\cos\phi$ through the corresponding irregular surface element.

We can divide the entire irregular surface into elements dA, compute the electric flux $E\,dA\cos\phi$ for each, and sum the results by integrating, as in Eq. (22.5). Each of the area elements projects onto a corresponding spherical surface element. Thus the *total* electric flux through the irregular surface, given by any of the forms of Eq. (22.5), must be the same as the total flux through a sphere, which Eq. (22.6) shows is equal to q/ϵ_0. Thus, for the irregular surface,

$$\Phi_E = \oint \vec{E} \cdot d\vec{A} = \frac{q}{\epsilon_0} \tag{22.7}$$

Equation (22.7) holds for a surface of *any* shape or size, provided only that it is a *closed* surface enclosing the charge q. The circle on the integral sign reminds us that the integral is always taken over a *closed* surface.

The area elements $d\vec{A}$ and the corresponding unit vectors $\hat{n}$ always point *out of* the volume enclosed by the surface. The electric flux is then positive in areas

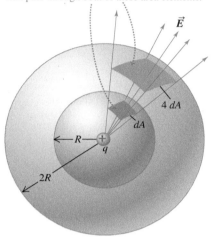

22.11 Projection of an element of area dA of a sphere of radius R onto a concentric sphere of radius $2R$. The projection multiplies each linear dimension by 2, so the area element on the larger sphere is $4\,dA$.

The same number of field lines and the same flux pass through both of these area elements.

(a) The outward normal to the surface makes an angle ϕ with the direction of $\vec{E}$.

$E_\perp$ ϕ $\vec{E}$

dA

r

R q

(b)

$E_\perp$ ϕ $\vec{E}$

dA

ϕ

$dA \cos\phi$

q

The projection of the area element dA onto the spherical surface is $dA \cos\phi$.

22.12 Calculating the electric flux through a nonspherical surface.

where the electric field points out of the surface and negative where it points inward. Also, $E_\perp$ is positive at points where $\vec{E}$ points out of the surface and negative at points where $\vec{E}$ points into the surface.

If the point charge in Fig. 22.12 is negative, the $\vec{E}$ field is directed radially *inward;* the angle ϕ is then greater than 90°, its cosine is negative, and the integral in Eq. (22.7) is negative. But since q is also negative, Eq. (22.7) still holds.

For a closed surface enclosing *no* charge,

$$\Phi_E = \oint \vec{E} \cdot d\vec{A} = 0$$

22.13 A point charge *outside* a closed surface that encloses no charge. If an electric field line from the external charge enters the surface at one point, it must leave at another.

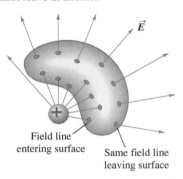

Field line entering surface Same field line leaving surface

This is the mathematical statement that when a region contains no charge, any field lines caused by charges *outside* the region that enter on one side must leave again on the other side. (In Section 22.1 we came to the same conclusion by considering the special case of a rectangular box in a uniform field.) Figure 22.13 illustrates this point. *Electric field lines can begin or end inside a region of space only when there is charge in that region.*

General Form of Gauss's Law

Now comes the final step in obtaining the general form of Gauss's law. Suppose the surface encloses not just one point charge q but several charges q_1, q_2, $q_3, \ldots$. The total (resultant) electric field $\vec{E}$ at any point is the vector sum of the $\vec{E}$ fields of the individual charges. Let Q_{encl} be the *total* charge enclosed by the surface: $Q_{encl} = q_1 + q_2 + q_3 + \cdots$. Also let $\vec{E}$ be the *total* field at the position of the surface area element $d\vec{A}$, and let $E_\perp$ be its component perpendicular to the plane of that element (that is, parallel to $d\vec{A}$). Then we can write an equation like Eq. (22.7) for each charge and its corresponding field and add the results. When we do, we obtain the general statement of Gauss's law:

$$\Phi_E = \oint \vec{E} \cdot d\vec{A} = \frac{Q_{encl}}{\epsilon_0} \qquad \text{(Gauss's law)} \qquad (22.8)$$

The total electric flux through a closed surface is equal to the total (net) electric charge inside the surface, divided by ϵ_0.

CAUTION **Gaussian surfaces are imaginary** Remember that the closed surface in Gauss's law is *imaginary;* there need not be any material object at the position of the surface. We often refer to a closed surface used in Gauss's law as a **Gaussian surface.**

Using the definition of Q_{encl} and the various ways to express electric flux given in Eq. (22.5), we can express Gauss's law in the following equivalent forms:

$$\Phi_E = \oint E \cos \phi \, dA = \oint E_\perp \, dA = \oint \vec{E} \cdot d\vec{A} = \frac{Q_{encl}}{\epsilon_0} \quad \begin{array}{l}\text{(various forms} \\ \text{of Gauss's law)}\end{array} \qquad (22.9)$$

As in Eq. (22.5), the various forms of the integral all express the same thing, the total electric flux through the Gaussian surface, in different terms. One form is sometimes more convenient than another.

As an example, Fig. 22.14a shows a spherical Gaussian surface of radius r around a positive point charge $+q$. The electric field points out of the Gaussian surface, so at every point on the surface $\vec{E}$ is in the same direction as $d\vec{A}$, $\phi = 0$, and $E_\perp$ is equal to the field magnitude $E = q/4\pi\epsilon_0 r^2$. Since E is the same at all points

(a) Gaussian surface around positive charge: positive (outward) flux

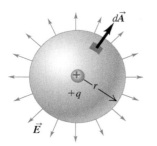

(b) Gaussian surface around negative charge: negative (inward) flux

22.14 Spherical Gaussian surfaces around **(a)** a positive point charge and **(b)** a negative point charge.

on the surface, we can take it outside the integral in Eq. (22.9). Then the remaining integral is $\int dA = A = 4\pi r^2$, the area of the sphere. Hence Eq. (22.9) becomes

$$\Phi_E = \oint E_\perp \, dA = \oint \left(\frac{q}{4\pi\epsilon_0 r^2}\right) dA = \frac{q}{4\pi\epsilon_0 r^2} \oint dA = \frac{q}{4\pi\epsilon_0 r^2} 4\pi r^2 = \frac{q}{\epsilon_0}$$

The enclosed charge Q_{encl} is just the charge $+q$, so this agrees with Gauss's law. If the Gaussian surface encloses a *negative* point charge as in Fig. 22.14b, then $\vec{E}$ points *into* the surface at each point in the direction opposite $d\vec{A}$. Then $\phi = 180°$ and $E_\perp$ is equal to the negative of the field magnitude: $E_\perp = -E = -|-q|/4\pi\epsilon_0 r^2 = -q/4\pi\epsilon_0 r^2$. Equation (22.9) then becomes

$$\Phi_E = \oint E_\perp \, dA = \oint \left(\frac{-q}{4\pi\epsilon_0 r^2}\right) dA = \frac{-q}{4\pi\epsilon_0 r^2} \oint dA = \frac{-q}{4\pi\epsilon_0 r^2} 4\pi r^2 = \frac{-q}{\epsilon_0}$$

This again agrees with Gauss's law because the enclosed charge in Fig. 22.14b is $Q_{encl} = -q$.

In Eqs. (22.8) and (22.9), Q_{encl} is always the algebraic sum of all the positive and negative charges enclosed by the Gaussian surface, and $\vec{E}$ is the *total* field at each point on the surface. Also note that in general, this field is caused partly by charges inside the surface and partly by charges outside. But as Fig. 22.13 shows, the outside charges do *not* contribute to the total (net) flux through the surface. So Eqs. (22.8) and (22.9) are correct even when there are charges outside the surface that contribute to the electric field at the surface. When $Q_{encl} = 0$, the total flux through the Gaussian surface must be zero, even though some areas may have positive flux and others may have negative flux (see Fig. 22.3b).

Gauss's law is the definitive answer to the question we posed at the beginning of Section 22.1: "If the electric field pattern is known in a given region, what can we determine about the charge distribution in that region?" It provides a relationship between the electric field on a closed surface and the charge distribution within that surface. But in some cases we can use Gauss's law to answer the reverse question: "If the charge distribution is known, what can we determine about the electric field that the charge distribution produces?" Gauss's law may seem like an unappealing way to address this question, since it may look as though evaluating the integral in Eq. (22.8) is a hopeless task. Sometimes it is, but other times it is surprisingly easy. Here's an example in which *no* integration is involved at all; we'll work out several more examples in the next section.

Conceptual Example 22.4 **Electric flux and enclosed charge**

Figure 22.15 shows the field produced by two point charges $+q$ and $-q$ (an electric dipole). Find the electric flux through each of the closed surfaces A, B, C, and D.

SOLUTION

Gauss's law, Eq. (22.8), says that the total electric flux through a closed surface is equal to the total enclosed charge divided by ϵ_0. In

Continued

Fig. 22.15, surface *A* (shown in red) encloses the positive charge, so $Q_{encl} = +q$; surface *B* (in blue) encloses the negative charge, so $Q_{encl} = -q$; surface *C* (in purple) encloses *both* charges, so $Q_{encl} = +q + (-q) = 0$; and surface *D* (in yellow) encloses no charges, so $Q_{encl} = 0$. Hence, without having to do any integration, we have $\Phi_{EA} = +q/\epsilon_0$, $\Phi_{EB} = -q/\epsilon_0$, and $\Phi_{EC} = \Phi_{ED} = 0$. These results depend only on the charges enclosed within each Gaussian surface, not on the precise shapes of the surfaces.

We can draw similar conclusions by examining the electric field lines. All the field lines that cross surface *A* are directed out of the surface, so the flux through *A* must be positive. Similarly, the flux through *B* must be negative since all of the field lines that cross that surface point inward. For both surface *C* and surface *D*, there are as many field lines pointing into the surface as there are field lines pointing outward, so the flux through each of these surfaces is zero.

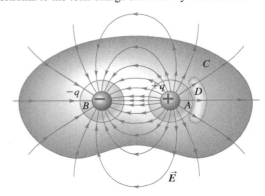

22.15 The net number of field lines leaving a closed surface is proportional to the total charge enclosed by that surface.

22.16 Five Gaussian surfaces and six point charges.

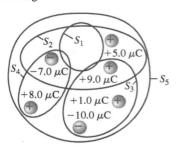

Test Your Understanding of Section 22.3 Figure 22.16 shows six point charges that all lie in the same plane. Five Gaussian surfaces—S_1, S_2, S_3, S_4, and S_5—each enclose part of this plane, and Fig. 22.16 shows the intersection of each surface with the plane. Rank these five surfaces in order of the electric flux through them, from most positive to most negative.

22.4 Applications of Gauss's Law

Gauss's law is valid for *any* distribution of charges and for *any* closed surface. Gauss's law can be used in two ways. If we know the charge distribution, and if it has enough symmetry to let us evaluate the integral in Gauss's law, we can find the field. Or if we know the field, we can use Gauss's law to find the charge distribution, such as charges on conducting surfaces.

In this section we present examples of both kinds of applications. As you study them, watch for the role played by the symmetry properties of each system. We will use Gauss's law to calculate the electric fields caused by several simple charge distributions; the results are collected in a table in the chapter summary.

In practical problems we often encounter situations in which we want to know the electric field caused by a charge distribution on a conductor. These calculations are aided by the following remarkable fact: *When excess charge is placed on a solid conductor and is at rest, it resides entirely on the surface, not in the interior of the material.* (By *excess* we mean charges other than the ions and free electrons that make up the neutral conductor.) Here's the proof. We know from Section 21.4 that in an electrostatic situation (with all charges at rest) the electric field $\vec{E}$ at every point in the interior of a conducting material is zero. If $\vec{E}$ were *not* zero, the excess charges would move. Suppose we construct a Gaussian surface inside the conductor, such as surface *A* in Fig. 22.17. Because $\vec{E} = 0$ everywhere on this surface, Gauss's law requires that the net charge inside the surface is zero. Now imagine shrinking the surface like a collapsing balloon until it encloses a region so small that we may consider it as a point *P*; then the charge at that point must be zero. We can do this anywhere inside the conductor, so *there can be no excess charge at any point within a solid conductor; any excess charge must reside on the conductor's surface.* (This result is for a *solid* conductor. In the next section we'll discuss what can happen if the conductor has cavities in its interior.) We will make use of this fact frequently in the examples that follow.

22.17 Under electrostatic conditions (charges not in motion), any excess charge on a solid conductor resides entirely on the conductor's surface.

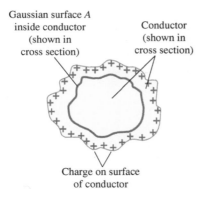

Gaussian surface *A* inside conductor (shown in cross section)

Conductor (shown in cross section)

Charge on surface of conductor

Problem-Solving Strategy 22.1   Gauss's Law

IDENTIFY *the relevant concepts:* Gauss's law is most useful when the charge distribution has spherical, cylindrical, or planar symmetry. In these cases the symmetry determines the direction of $\vec{E}$. Then Gauss's law yields the magnitude of $\vec{E}$ if we are given the charge distribution, and vice versa. In either case, begin the analysis by asking the question: What is the symmetry?

SET UP *the problem* using the following steps:
1. List the known and unknown quantities and identify the target variable.
2. Select the appropriate closed, imaginary Gaussian surface. For spherical symmetry, use a concentric spherical surface. For cylindrical symmetry, use a coaxial cylindrical surface with flat ends perpendicular to the axis of symmetry (like a soup can). For planar symmetry, use a cylindrical surface (like a tuna can) with its flat ends parallel to the plane.

EXECUTE *the solution* as follows:
1. Determine the appropriate size and placement of your Gaussian surface. To evaluate the field magnitude at a particular point, the surface must include that point. It may help to place one end of a can-shaped surface within a conductor, where $\vec{E}$ and therefore Φ are zero, or to place its ends equidistant from a charged plane.
2. Evaluate the integral $\oint E_\perp \, dA$ in Eq. (22.9). In this equation $E_\perp$ is the perpendicular component of the *total* electric field at each point on the Gaussian surface. A well-chosen Gaussian surface should make integration trivial or unnecessary. If the surface comprises several separate surfaces, such as the sides and ends

of a cylinder, the integral $\oint E_\perp \, dA$ over the entire closed surface is the sum of the integrals $\int E_\perp \, dA$ over the separate surfaces. Consider points 3–6 as you work.

3. If $\vec{E}$ is *perpendicular* (normal) at every point to a surface with area A, if it points *outward* from the interior of the surface, and if it has the same *magnitude* at every point on the surface, then $E_\perp = E = $ constant, and $\int E_\perp \, dA$ over that surface is equal to EA. (If $\vec{E}$ is inward, then $E_\perp = -E$ and $\int E_\perp \, dA = -EA$.) This should be the case for part or all of your Gaussian surface. If $\vec{E}$ is tangent to a surface at every point, then $E_\perp = 0$ and the integral over that surface is zero. This may be the case for parts of a cylindrical Gaussian surface. If $\vec{E} = 0$ at every point on a surface, the integral is zero.
4. Even when there is *no* charge within a Gaussian surface, the field at any given point on the surface is not necessarily zero. In that case, however, the total electric flux through the surface is always zero.
5. The flux integral $\oint E_\perp \, dA$ can be approximated as the difference between the numbers of electric lines of force leaving and entering the Gaussian surface. In this sense the flux gives the sign of the enclosed charge, but is only proportional to it; zero flux corresponds to zero enclosed charge.
6. Once you have evaluated $\oint E_\perp \, dA$, use Eq. (22.9) to solve for your target variable.

EVALUATE *your answer:* If your result is a *function* that describes how the magnitude of the electric field varies with position, ensure that it makes sense.

Example 22.5   Field of a charged conducting sphere

We place a total positive charge q on a solid conducting sphere with radius R (Fig. 22.18). Find $\vec{E}$ at any point inside or outside the sphere.

22.18 Calculating the electric field of a conducting sphere with positive charge q. Outside the sphere, the field is the same as if all of the charge were concentrated at the center of the sphere.

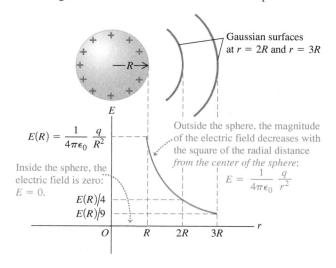

$$E(R) = \frac{1}{4\pi\epsilon_0} \frac{q}{R^2}$$

Inside the sphere, the electric field is zero: $E = 0$.

Outside the sphere, the magnitude of the electric field decreases with the square of the radial distance *from the center of the sphere:*
$$E = \frac{1}{4\pi\epsilon_0} \frac{q}{r^2}$$

$E(R)/4$
$E(R)/9$

SOLUTION

IDENTIFY and SET UP: As we discussed earlier in this section, all of the charge must be on the surface of the sphere. The charge is free to move on the conductor, and there is no preferred position on the surface; the charge is therefore distributed *uniformly* over the surface, and the system is spherically symmetric. To exploit this symmetry, we take as our Gaussian surface a sphere of radius r centered on the conductor. We can calculate the field inside or outside the conductor by taking $r < R$ or $r > R$, respectively. In either case, the point at which we want to calculate $\vec{E}$ lies on the Gaussian surface.

EXECUTE: The spherical symmetry means that the direction of the electric field must be radial; that's because there is no preferred direction parallel to the surface, so $\vec{E}$ can have no component parallel to the surface. There is also no preferred orientation of the sphere, so the field magnitude E can depend only on the distance r from the center and must have the same value at all points on the Gaussian surface.

For $r > R$ the entire conductor is within the Gaussian surface, so the enclosed charge is q. The area of the Gaussian surface is $4\pi r^2$, and $\vec{E}$ is uniform over the surface and perpendicular to it at each point. The flux integral $\oint E_\perp \, dA$ is then just $E(4\pi r^2)$, and Eq. (22.8) gives

Continued

$$E(4\pi r^2) = \frac{q}{\epsilon_0} \quad \text{and}$$

$$E = \frac{1}{4\pi\epsilon_0}\frac{q}{r^2} \quad \text{(outside a charged conducting sphere)}$$

This expression is the same as that for a point charge; outside the charged sphere, its field is the same as though the entire charge were concentrated at its center. Just outside the surface of the sphere, where $r = R$,

$$E = \frac{1}{4\pi\epsilon_0}\frac{q}{R^2} \quad \text{(at the surface of a charged conducting sphere)}$$

CAUTION **Flux can be positive or negative** Remember that we have chosen the charge q to be *positive*. If the charge is negative, the electric field is radially *inward* instead of radially outward, and the electric flux through the Gaussian surface is negative. The electric-field magnitudes outside and at the surface of the sphere are given by the same expressions as above, except that q denotes the *magnitude* (absolute value) of the charge.

For $r < R$ we again have $E(4\pi r^2) = Q_{encl}/\epsilon_0$. But now our Gaussian surface (which lies entirely within the conductor)

encloses *no* charge, so $Q_{encl} = 0$. The electric field inside the conductor is therefore zero.

EVALUATE: We already knew that $\vec{E} = 0$ inside a solid conductor (whether spherical or not) when the charges are at rest. Figure 22.18 shows E as a function of the distance r from the center of the sphere. Note that in the limit as $R \rightarrow 0$, the sphere becomes a point charge; there is then only an "outside," and the field is everywhere given by $E = q/4\pi\epsilon_0 r^2$. Thus we have deduced Coulomb's law from Gauss's law. (In Section 22.3 we deduced Gauss's law from Coulomb's law; the two laws are equivalent.)

We can also use this method for a conducting spherical *shell* (a spherical conductor with a concentric spherical hole inside) if there is no charge inside the hole. We use a spherical Gaussian surface with radius r less than the radius of the hole. If there *were* a field inside the hole, it would have to be radial and spherically symmetric as before, so $E = Q_{encl}/4\pi\epsilon_0 r^2$. But now there is no enclosed charge, so $Q_{encl} = 0$ and $E = 0$ inside the hole.

Can you use this same technique to find the electric field in the region between a charged sphere and a concentric hollow conducting sphere that surrounds it?

Example 22.6 | Field of a uniform line charge

Electric charge is distributed uniformly along an infinitely long, thin wire. The charge per unit length is λ (assumed positive). Find the electric field using Gauss's law.

SOLUTION

IDENTIFY and SET UP: We found in Example 21.10 (Section 21.5) that the field $\vec{E}$ of a uniformly charged, infinite wire is radially outward if λ is positive and radially inward if λ is negative, and that the field magnitude E depends only on the radial distance from the wire. This suggests that we use a *cylindrical* Gaussian surface, of radius r and arbitrary length l, coaxial with the wire and with its ends perpendicular to the wire (Fig. 22.19).

EXECUTE: The flux through the flat ends of our Gaussian surface is zero because the radial electric field is parallel to these ends, and so $\vec{E} \cdot \hat{n} = 0$. On the cylindrical part of our surface we have $\vec{E} \cdot \hat{n} = E_\perp = E$ everywhere. (If λ were negative, we would have

22.19 A coaxial cylindrical Gaussian surface is used to find the electric field outside an infinitely long, charged wire.

$\vec{E} \cdot \hat{n} = E_\perp = -E$ everywhere.) The area of the cylindrical surface is $2\pi r l$, so the flux through it—and hence the total flux Φ_E through the Gaussian surface—is $EA = 2\pi r l E$. The total enclosed charge is $Q_{encl} = \lambda l$, and so from Gauss's law, Eq. (22.8),

$$\Phi_E = 2\pi r l E = \frac{\lambda l}{\epsilon_0} \quad \text{and}$$

$$E = \frac{1}{2\pi\epsilon_0}\frac{\lambda}{r} \quad \text{(field of an infinite line of charge)}$$

We found this same result in Example 21.10 with *much* more effort.

If λ is *negative*, $\vec{E}$ is directed radially inward, and in the above expression for E we must interpret λ as the absolute value of the charge per unit length.

EVALUATE: We saw in Example 21.10 that the *entire* charge on the wire contributes to the field at any point, and yet we consider only that part of the charge $Q_{encl} = \lambda l$ within the Gaussian surface when we apply Gauss's law. There's nothing inconsistent here; it takes the entire charge to give the field the properties that allow us to calculate Φ_E so easily, and Gauss's law always applies to the enclosed charge only. If the wire is short, the symmetry of the infinite wire is lost, and E is not uniform over a coaxial, cylindrical Gaussian surface. Gauss's law then *cannot* be used to find Φ_E; we must solve the problem the hard way, as in Example 21.10.

We can use the Gaussian surface in Fig. 22.19 to show that the field outside a long, uniformly charged cylinder is the same as though all the charge were concentrated on a line along its axis (see Problem 22.42). We can also calculate the electric field in the space between a charged cylinder and a coaxial hollow conducting cylinder surrounding it (see Problem 22.39).

Example 22.7 **Field of an infinite plane sheet of charge**

Use Gauss's law to find the electric field caused by a thin, flat, infinite sheet with a uniform positive surface charge density σ.

SOLUTION

IDENTIFY and SET UP: In Example 21.11 (Section 21.5) we found that the field $\vec{E}$ of a uniformly charged infinite sheet is normal to the sheet, and that its magnitude is independent of the distance from the sheet. To take advantage of these symmetry properties, we use a cylindrical Gaussian surface with ends of area A and with its axis perpendicular to the sheet of charge (Fig. 22.20).

22.20 A cylindrical Gaussian surface is used to find the field of an infinite plane sheet of charge.

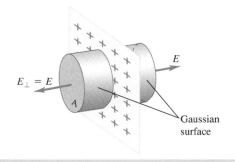

EXECUTE: The flux through the cylindrical part of our Gaussian surface is zero because $\vec{E} \cdot \hat{n} = 0$ everywhere. The flux through each flat end of the surface is $+EA$ because $\vec{E} \cdot \hat{n} = E_{\perp} = E$ everywhere, so the total flux through both ends—and hence the total flux Φ_E through the Gaussian surface—is $+2EA$. The total enclosed charge is $Q_{encl} = \sigma A$, and so from Gauss's law,

$$2EA = \frac{\sigma A}{\epsilon_0} \quad \text{and}$$

$$E = \frac{\sigma}{2\epsilon_0} \quad \text{(field of an infinite sheet of charge)}$$

In Example 21.11 we found this same result using a much more complex calculation.

If σ is negative, $\vec{E}$ is directed *toward* the sheet, the flux through the Gaussian surface in Fig. 22.20 is negative, and σ in the expression $E = \sigma/2\epsilon_0$ denotes the magnitude (absolute value) of the charge density.

EVALUATE: Again we see that, given favorable symmetry, we can deduce electric fields using Gauss's law much more easily than using Coulomb's law.

Example 22.8 **Field between oppositely charged parallel conducting plates**

Two large plane parallel conducting plates are given charges of equal magnitude and opposite sign; the surface charge densities are $+\sigma$ and $-\sigma$. Find the electric field in the region between the plates.

SOLUTION

IDENTIFY and SET UP: Figure 22.21a shows the field. Because opposite charges attract, most of the charge accumulates at the opposing faces of the plates. A small amount of charge resides on the *outer* surfaces of the plates, and there is some spreading or "fringing" of

the field at the edges. But if the plates are very large in comparison to the distance between them, the amount of charge on the outer surfaces is negligibly small, and the fringing can be neglected except near the edges. In this case we can assume that the field is uniform in the interior region between the plates, as in Fig. 22.21b, and that the charges are distributed uniformly over the opposing surfaces. To exploit this symmetry, we can use the shaded Gaussian surfaces S_1, S_2, S_3, and S_4. These surfaces are cylinders with flat ends of area A; one end of each surface lies *within* a plate.

22.21 Electric field between oppositely charged parallel plates.

(a) Realistic drawing

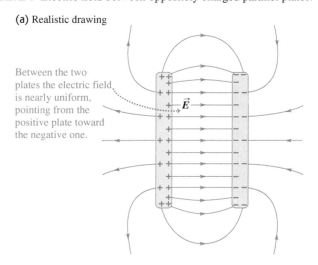

Between the two plates the electric field is nearly uniform, pointing from the positive plate toward the negative one.

(b) Idealized model

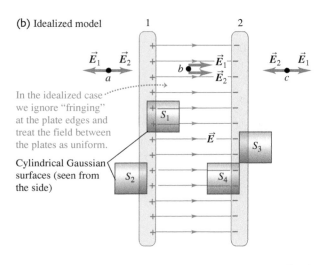

In the idealized case we ignore "fringing" at the plate edges and treat the field between the plates as uniform.

Cylindrical Gaussian surfaces (seen from the side)

Continued

EXECUTE: The left-hand end of surface S_1 is within the positive plate 1. Since the field is zero within the volume of any solid conductor under electrostatic conditions, there is no electric flux through this end. The electric field between the plates is perpendicular to the right-hand end, so on that end, $E_\perp$ is equal to E and the flux is EA; this is positive, since $\vec{E}$ is directed out of the Gaussian surface. There is no flux through the side walls of the cylinder, since these walls are parallel to $\vec{E}$. So the total flux integral in Gauss's law is EA. The net charge enclosed by the cylinder is σA, so Eq. (22.8) yields $EA = \sigma A/\epsilon_0$; we then have

$$E = \frac{\sigma}{\epsilon_0} \quad \text{(field between oppositely charged conducting plates)}$$

The field is uniform and perpendicular to the plates, and its magnitude is independent of the distance from either plate. The Gaussian surface S_4 yields the same result. Surfaces S_2 and S_3 yield $E = 0$ to the left of plate 1 and to the right of plate 2, respectively. We leave these calculations to you (see Exercise 22.29).

EVALUATE: We obtained the same results in Example 21.11 by using the principle of superposition of electric fields. The fields due to the two sheets of charge (one on each plate) are $\vec{E}_1$ and $\vec{E}_2$; from Example 22.7, both of these have magnitude $\sigma/2\epsilon_0$. The total electric field at any point is the vector sum $\vec{E} = \vec{E}_1 + \vec{E}_2$. At points a and c in Fig. 22.21b, $\vec{E}_1$ and $\vec{E}_2$ point in opposite directions, and their sum is zero. At point b, $\vec{E}_1$ and $\vec{E}_2$ are in the same direction; their sum has magnitude $E = \sigma/\epsilon_0$, just as we found above using Gauss's law.

Example 22.9 Field of a uniformly charged sphere

Positive electric charge Q is distributed uniformly *throughout the volume* of an *insulating* sphere with radius R. Find the magnitude of the electric field at a point P a distance r from the center of the sphere.

SOLUTION

IDENTIFY and SET UP: As in Example 22.5, the system is spherically symmetric. Hence we can use the conclusions of that example about the direction and magnitude of $\vec{E}$. To make use of the spherical symmetry, we choose as our Gaussian surface a sphere with radius r, concentric with the charge distribution.

EXECUTE: From symmetry, the direction of $\vec{E}$ is radial at every point on the Gaussian surface, so $E_\perp = E$ and the field magnitude E is the same at every point on the surface. Hence the total electric flux through the Gaussian surface is the product of E and the total area of the surface $A = 4\pi r^2$—that is, $\Phi_E = 4\pi r^2 E$.

The amount of charge enclosed within the Gaussian surface depends on r. To find E *inside* the sphere, we choose $r < R$. The volume charge density ρ is the charge Q divided by the volume of the entire charged sphere of radius R:

$$\rho = \frac{Q}{4\pi R^3/3}$$

The volume V_{encl} enclosed by the Gaussian surface is $\frac{4}{3}\pi r^3$, so the total charge Q_{encl} enclosed by that surface is

$$Q_{\text{encl}} = \rho V_{\text{encl}} = \left(\frac{Q}{4\pi R^3/3}\right)\left(\tfrac{4}{3}\pi r^3\right) = Q\frac{r^3}{R^3}$$

Then Gauss's law, Eq. (22.8), becomes

$$4\pi r^2 E = \frac{Q}{\epsilon_0}\frac{r^3}{R^3} \quad \text{or}$$

$$E = \frac{1}{4\pi\epsilon_0}\frac{Qr}{R^3} \quad \begin{array}{l}\text{(field inside a uniformly}\\\text{charged sphere)}\end{array}$$

The field magnitude is proportional to the distance r of the field point from the center of the sphere (see the graph of E versus r in Fig. 22.22).

To find E *outside* the sphere, we take $r > R$. This surface encloses the entire charged sphere, so $Q_{\text{encl}} = Q$, and Gauss's law gives

$$4\pi r^2 E = \frac{Q}{\epsilon_0} \quad \text{or}$$

$$E = \frac{1}{4\pi\epsilon_0}\frac{Q}{r^2} \quad \begin{array}{l}\text{(field outside a uniformly}\\\text{charged sphere)}\end{array}$$

22.22 The magnitude of the electric field of a uniformly charged insulating sphere. Compare this with the field for a conducting sphere (see Fig. 22.18).

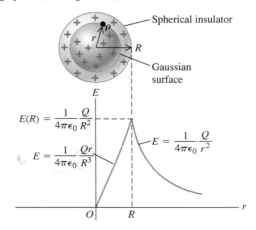

The field outside *any* spherically symmetric charged body varies as $1/r^2$, as though the entire charge were concentrated at the center. This is graphed in Fig. 22.22.

If the charge is *negative*, $\vec{E}$ is radially *inward* and in the expressions for E we interpret Q as the absolute value of the charge.

EVALUATE: Notice that if we set $r = R$ in either expression for E, we get the same result $E = Q/4\pi\epsilon_0 R^2$ for the magnitude of the field at the surface of the sphere. This is because the magnitude E is a *continuous* function of r. By contrast, for the charged conducting sphere of Example 22.5 the electric-field magnitude is *discontinuous* at $r = R$ (it jumps from $E = 0$ just inside the sphere to $E = Q/4\pi\epsilon_0 R^2$ just outside the sphere). In general, the electric field $\vec{E}$ is discontinuous in magnitude, direction, or both wherever there is a *sheet* of charge, such as at the surface of a charged conducting sphere (Example 22.5), at the surface of an infinite charged sheet (Example 22.7), or at the surface of a charged conducting plate (Example 22.8).

The approach used here can be applied to *any* spherically symmetric distribution of charge, even if it is not radially uniform, as it was here. Such charge distributions occur within many atoms and atomic nuclei, so Gauss's law is useful in atomic and nuclear physics.

Example 22.10 **Charge on a hollow sphere**

A thin-walled, hollow sphere of radius 0.250 m has an unknown charge distributed uniformly over its surface. At a distance of 0.300 m from the center of the sphere, the electric field points radially inward and has magnitude 1.80×10^2 N/C. How much charge is on the sphere?

SOLUTION

IDENTIFY and SET UP: The charge distribution is spherically symmetric. As in Examples 22.5 and 22.9, it follows that the electric field is radial everywhere and its magnitude is a function only of the radial distance r from the center of the sphere. We use a spherical Gaussian surface that is concentric with the charge distribution and has radius $r = 0.300$ m. Our target variable is $Q_{encl} = q$.

EXECUTE: The charge distribution is the same as if the charge were on the surface of a 0.250-m-radius conducting sphere. Hence we can borrow the results of Example 22.5. We note that the electric

field here is directed toward the sphere, so that q must be *negative*. Furthermore, the electric field is directed into the Gaussian surface, so that $E_{\perp} = -E$ and $\Phi_E = \oint E_{\perp}\, dA = -E(4\pi r^2)$.

By Gauss's law, the flux is equal to the charge q on the sphere (all of which is enclosed by the Gaussian surface) divided by ϵ_0. Solving for q, we find

$$q = -E(4\pi\epsilon_0 r^2) = -(1.80 \times 10^2 \text{ N/C})(4\pi)$$
$$\times (8.854 \times 10^{-12} \text{ C}^2/\text{N}\cdot\text{m}^2)(0.300 \text{ m})^2$$
$$= -1.80 \times 10^{-9} \text{ C} = -1.80 \text{ nC}$$

EVALUATE: To determine the charge, we had to know the electric field at *all* points on the Gaussian surface so that we could calculate the flux integral. This was possible here because the charge distribution is highly symmetric. If the charge distribution is irregular or lacks symmetry, Gauss's law is not very useful for calculating the charge distribution from the field, or vice versa.

Test Your Understanding of Section 22.4 You place a known amount of charge Q on the irregularly shaped conductor shown in Fig. 22.17. If you know the size and shape of the conductor, can you use Gauss's law to calculate the electric field at an arbitrary position outside the conductor?

Application Charge Distribution Inside a Nerve Cell

The interior of a human nerve cell contains both positive potassium ions (K^+) and negatively charged protein molecules (Pr^-). Potassium ions can flow out of the cell through the cell membrane, but the much larger protein molecules cannot. The result is that the interior of the cell has a net negative charge. (The fluid outside the cell has a positive charge that balances this.) The fluid within the cell is a good conductor, so the Pr^- molecules distribute themselves on the outer surface of the fluid—that is, on the inner surface of the cell membrane, which is an insulator. This is true no matter what the shape of the cell.

22.5 Charges on Conductors

We have learned that in an electrostatic situation (in which there is no net motion of charge) the electric field at every point within a conductor is zero and that any excess charge on a solid conductor is located entirely on its surface (Fig. 22.23a). But what if there is a *cavity* inside the conductor (Fig. 22.23b)? If there is no charge within the cavity, we can use a Gaussian surface such as A (which lies completely within the material of the conductor) to show that the *net* charge on the *surface of the cavity* must be zero, because $\vec{E} = 0$ everywhere on the Gaussian surface. In fact, we can prove in this situation that there can't be any charge *anywhere* on the cavity surface. We will postpone detailed proof of this statement until Chapter 23.

Suppose we place a small body with a charge q inside a cavity within a conductor (Fig. 22.23c). The conductor is uncharged and is insulated from the charge q. Again $\vec{E} = 0$ everywhere on surface A, so according to Gauss's law the *total* charge inside this surface must be zero. Therefore there must be a charge $-q$ distributed on the surface of the cavity, drawn there by the charge q inside the cavity. The *total* charge on the conductor must remain zero, so a charge $+q$ must appear

22.23 Finding the electric field within a charged conductor.

(a) Solid conductor with charge q_C

The charge q_C resides entirely on the surface of the conductor. The situation is electrostatic, so $\vec{E} = 0$ within the conductor.

(b) The same conductor with an internal cavity

Because $\vec{E} = 0$ at all points within the conductor, the electric field at all points on the Gaussian surface must be zero.

(c) An isolated charge q placed in the cavity

For $\vec{E}$ to be zero at all points on the Gaussian surface, the surface of the cavity must have a total charge $-q$.

either on its outer surface or inside the material. But we showed that in an electrostatic situation there can't be any excess charge within the material of a conductor. So we conclude that the charge $+q$ must appear on the outer surface. By the same reasoning, if the conductor originally had a charge q_C, then the total charge on the outer surface must be $q_C + q$ after the charge q is inserted into the cavity.

Conceptual Example 22.11 **A conductor with a cavity**

A solid conductor with a cavity carries a total charge of $+7$ nC. Within the cavity, insulated from the conductor, is a point charge of -5 nC. How much charge is on each surface (inner and outer) of the conductor?

22.24 Our sketch for this problem. There is zero electric field inside the bulk conductor and hence zero flux through the Gaussian surface shown, so the charge on the cavity wall must be the opposite of the point charge.

SOLUTION

Figure 22.24 shows the situation. If the charge in the cavity is $q = -5$ nC, the charge on the inner cavity surface must be $-q = -(-5$ nC$) = +5$ nC. The conductor carries a *total* charge of $+7$ nC, none of which is in the interior of the material. If $+5$ nC is on the inner surface of the cavity, then there must be $(+7$ nC$) - (+5$ nC$) = +2$ nC on the outer surface of the conductor.

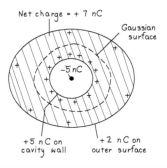

Net charge = + 7 nC
Gaussian surface
−5 nC
+5 nC on cavity wall
+2 nC on outer surface

Testing Gauss's Law Experimentally

We can now consider a historic experiment, shown in Fig. 22.25. We mount a conducting container on an insulating stand. The container is initially uncharged. Then we hang a charged metal ball from an insulating thread (Fig. 22.25a), lower it into the container, and put the lid on (Fig. 22.25b). Charges are induced on the walls of the container, as shown. But now we let the ball *touch* the inner wall (Fig. 22.25c). The surface of the ball becomes part of the cavity surface. The situation is now the same as Fig. 22.23b; if Gauss's law is correct, the net charge on the cavity surface must be zero. Thus the ball must lose all its charge. Finally, we pull the ball out; we find that it has indeed lost all its charge.

This experiment was performed in the 19th century by the English scientist Michael Faraday, using a metal icepail with a lid, and it is called **Faraday's icepail experiment.** The result confirms the validity of Gauss's law and therefore of

22.25 (a) A charged conducting ball suspended by an insulating thread outside a conducting container on an insulating stand. (b) The ball is lowered into the container, and the lid is put on. (c) The ball is touched to the inner surface of the container.

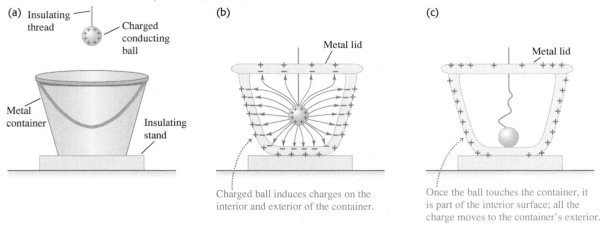

(a) Insulating thread — Charged conducting ball
Metal container   Insulating stand

(b) Metal lid
Charged ball induces charges on the interior and exterior of the container.

(c) Metal lid
Once the ball touches the container, it is part of the interior surface; all the charge moves to the container's exterior.

22.26 Cutaway view of the essential parts of a Van de Graaff electrostatic generator. The electron sink at the bottom draws electrons from the belt, giving it a positive charge; at the top the belt attracts electrons away from the conducting shell, giving the shell a positive charge.

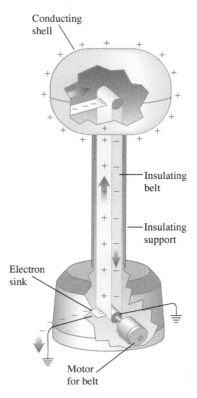

Coulomb's law. Faraday's result was significant because Coulomb's experimental method, using a torsion balance and dividing of charges, was not very precise; it is very difficult to confirm the $1/r^2$ dependence of the electrostatic force by direct force measurements. By contrast, experiments like Faraday's test the validity of Gauss's law, and therefore of Coulomb's law, with much greater precision. Modern versions of this experiment have shown that the exponent 2 in the $1/r^2$ of Coulomb's law does not differ from precisely 2 by more than 10^{-16}. So there is no reason to believe it is anything other than exactly 2.

The same principle behind Faraday's icepail experiment is used in a *Van de Graaff electrostatic generator* (Fig. 22.26). A charged belt continuously carries charge to the inside of a conducting shell. By Gauss's law, there can never be any charge on the inner surface of this shell, so the charge is immediately carried away to the outside surface of the shell. As a result, the charge on the shell and the electric field around it can become very large very rapidly. The Van de Graaff generator is used as an accelerator of charged particles and for physics demonstrations.

This principle also forms the basis for *electrostatic shielding*. Suppose we have a very sensitive electronic instrument that we want to protect from stray electric fields that might cause erroneous measurements. We surround the instrument with a conducting box, or we line the walls, floor, and ceiling of the room with a conducting material such as sheet copper. The external electric field redistributes the free electrons in the conductor, leaving a net positive charge on the outer surface in some regions and a net negative charge in others (Fig. 22.27). This charge distribution causes an additional electric field such that the *total* field at every point inside the box is zero, as Gauss's law says it must be. The charge distribution on the box also alters the shapes of the field lines near the box, as the figure shows. Such a setup is often called a *Faraday cage*. The same physics tells

22.27 (a) A conducting box (a Faraday cage) immersed in a uniform electric field. The field of the induced charges on the box combines with the uniform field to give zero total field inside the box. (b) This person is inside a Faraday cage, and so is protected from the powerful electric discharge.

(a)

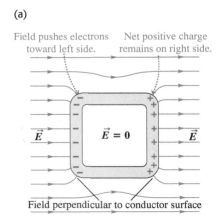

Field pushes electrons toward left side. Net positive charge remains on right side.

$\vec{E}$ $\vec{E} = 0$ $\vec{E}$

Field perpendicular to conductor surface

(b)

you that one of the safest places to be in a lightning storm is inside an automobile; if the car is struck by lightning, the charge tends to remain on the metal skin of the vehicle, and little or no electric field is produced inside the passenger compartment.

Field at the Surface of a Conductor

Finally, we note that there is a direct relationship between the $\vec{E}$ field at a point just outside any conductor and the surface charge density σ at that point. In general, σ varies from point to point on the surface. We will show in Chapter 23 that at any such point, the direction of $\vec{E}$ is always *perpendicular* to the surface. (You can see this effect in Fig. 22.27a.)

To find a relationship between σ at any point on the surface and the perpendicular component of the electric field at that point, we construct a Gaussian surface in the form of a small cylinder (Fig. 22.28). One end face, with area A, lies within the conductor and the other lies just outside. The electric field is zero at all points within the conductor. Outside the conductor the component of $\vec{E}$ perpendicular to the side walls of the cylinder is zero, and over the end face the perpendicular component is equal to $E_{\perp}$. (If σ is positive, the electric field points out of the conductor and $E_{\perp}$ is positive; if σ is negative, the field points inward and $E_{\perp}$ is negative.) Hence the total flux through the surface is $E_{\perp}A$. The charge enclosed within the Gaussian surface is σA, so from Gauss's law,

22.28 The field just outside a charged conductor is perpendicular to the surface, and its perpendicular component $E_{\perp}$ is equal to σ/ϵ_0.

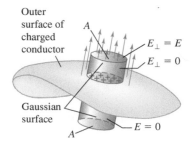

Outer surface of charged conductor

A

$E_{\perp} = E$

$E_{\perp} = 0$

Gaussian surface

A

$E = 0$

$$E_{\perp}A = \frac{\sigma A}{\epsilon_0} \quad \text{and} \quad E_{\perp} = \frac{\sigma}{\epsilon_0} \qquad \begin{array}{l}\text{(field at the surface} \\ \text{of a conductor)}\end{array} \qquad (22.10)$$

We can check this with the results we have obtained for spherical, cylindrical, and plane surfaces.

We showed in Example 22.8 that the field magnitude between two infinite flat oppositely charged conducting plates also equals σ/ϵ_0. In this case the field magnitude E is the same at *all* distances from the plates, but in all other cases E decreases with increasing distance from the surface.

Conceptual Example 22.12   **Field at the surface of a conducting sphere**

Verify Eq. (22.10) for a conducting sphere with radius R and total charge q.

SOLUTION

In Example 22.5 (Section 22.4) we showed that the electric field just outside the surface is

$$E = \frac{1}{4\pi\epsilon_0}\frac{q}{R^2}$$

The surface charge density is uniform and equal to q divided by the surface area of the sphere:

$$\sigma = \frac{q}{4\pi R^2}$$

Comparing these two expressions, we see that $E = \sigma/\epsilon_0$, which verifies Eq. (22.10).

Example 22.13   **Electric field of the earth**

The earth (a conductor) has a net electric charge. The resulting electric field near the surface has an average value of about 150 N/C, directed toward the center of the earth. (a) What is the corresponding surface charge density? (b) What is the *total* surface charge of the earth?

SOLUTION

IDENTIFY and SET UP: We are given the electric-field magnitude at the surface of the conducting earth. We can calculate the surface charge density σ using Eq. (22.10). The total charge Q on the earth's surface is then the product of σ and the earth's surface area.

EXECUTE: (a) The direction of the field means that σ is negative (corresponding to $\vec{E}$ being directed *into* the surface, so $E_\perp$ is negative). From Eq. (22.10),

$$\sigma = \epsilon_0 E_\perp = (8.85 \times 10^{-12} \text{ C}^2/\text{N} \cdot \text{m}^2)(-150 \text{ N/C})$$
$$= -1.33 \times 10^{-9} \text{ C/m}^2 = -1.33 \text{ nC/m}^2$$

(b) The earth's surface area is $4\pi R_E^2$, where $R_E = 6.38 \times 10^6$ m is the radius of the earth (see Appendix F). The total charge Q is the product $4\pi R_E^2\sigma$, or

$$Q = 4\pi(6.38 \times 10^6 \text{ m})^2(-1.33 \times 10^{-9} \text{ C/m}^2)$$
$$= -6.8 \times 10^5 \text{ C} = -680 \text{ kC}$$

EVALUATE: You can check our result in part (b) using the result of Example 22.5. Solving for Q, we find

$$Q = 4\pi\epsilon_0 R^2 E_\perp$$
$$= \frac{1}{9.0 \times 10^9 \text{ N} \cdot \text{m}^2/\text{C}^2}(6.38 \times 10^6 \text{ m})^2 (-150 \text{ N/C})$$
$$= -6.8 \times 10^5 \text{ C}$$

One electron has a charge of -1.60×10^{-19} C. Hence this much excess negative electric charge corresponds to there being $(-6.8 \times 10^5 \text{ C})/(-1.60 \times 10^{-19} \text{ C}) = 4.2 \times 10^{24}$ excess electrons on the earth, or about 7 moles of excess electrons. This is compensated by an equal *deficiency* of electrons in the earth's upper atmosphere, so the combination of the earth and its atmosphere is electrically neutral.

Test Your Understanding of Section 22.5   A hollow conducting sphere has no net charge. There is a positive point charge q at the center of the spherical cavity within the sphere. You connect a conducting wire from the outside of the sphere to ground. Will you measure an electric field outside the sphere?

Electric flux: Electric flux is a measure of the "flow" of electric field through a surface. It is equal to the product of an area element and the perpendicular component of $\vec{E}$, integrated over a surface. (See Examples 22.1–22.3.)

$$\Phi_E = \int E\cos\phi\, dA$$

$$= \int E_\perp\, dA = \int \vec{E} \cdot d\vec{A} \quad (22.5)$$

Gauss's law: Gauss's law states that the total electric flux through a closed surface, which can be written as the surface integral of the component of $\vec{E}$ normal to the surface, equals a constant times the total charge Q_{encl} enclosed by the surface. Gauss's law is logically equivalent to Coulomb's law, but its use greatly simplifies problems with a high degree of symmetry. (See Examples 22.4–22.10.)

When excess charge is placed on a conductor and is at rest, it resides entirely on the surface, and $\vec{E} = 0$ everywhere in the material of the conductor. (See Examples 22.11–22.13.)

$$\Phi_E = \oint E\cos\phi\, dA$$

$$= \oint E_\perp\, dA = \oint \vec{E} \cdot d\vec{A}$$

$$= \frac{Q_{encl}}{\epsilon_0} \quad (22.8), (22.9)$$

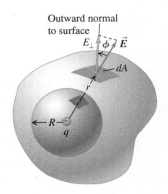

Electric field of various symmetric charge distributions: The following table lists electric fields caused by several symmetric charge distributions. In the table, q, Q, λ, and σ refer to the *magnitudes* of the quantities.

Charge Distribution	Point in Electric Field	Electric Field Magnitude
Single point charge q	Distance r from q	$E = \dfrac{1}{4\pi\epsilon_0}\dfrac{q}{r^2}$
Charge q on surface of conducting sphere with radius R	Outside sphere, $r > R$	$E = \dfrac{1}{4\pi\epsilon_0}\dfrac{q}{r^2}$
	Inside sphere, $r < R$	$E = 0$
Infinite wire, charge per unit length λ	Distance r from wire	$E = \dfrac{1}{2\pi\epsilon_0}\dfrac{\lambda}{r}$
Infinite conducting cylinder with radius R, charge per unit length λ	Outside cylinder, $r > R$	$E = \dfrac{1}{2\pi\epsilon_0}\dfrac{\lambda}{r}$
	Inside cylinder, $r < R$	$E = 0$
Solid insulating sphere with radius R, charge Q distributed uniformly throughout volume	Outside sphere, $r > R$	$E = \dfrac{1}{4\pi\epsilon_0}\dfrac{Q}{r^2}$
	Inside sphere, $r < R$	$E = \dfrac{1}{4\pi\epsilon_0}\dfrac{Qr}{R^3}$
Infinite sheet of charge with uniform charge per unit area σ	Any point	$E = \dfrac{\sigma}{2\epsilon_0}$
Two oppositely charged conducting plates with surface charge densities $+\sigma$ and $-\sigma$	Any point between plates	$E = \dfrac{\sigma}{\epsilon_0}$
Charged conductor	Just outside the conductor	$E = \dfrac{\sigma}{\epsilon_0}$

BRIDGING PROBLEM   Electric Field Inside a Hydrogen Atom

A hydrogen atom is made up of a proton of charge $+Q = 1.60 \times 10^{-19}$ C and an electron of charge $-Q = -1.60 \times 10^{-19}$ C. The proton may be regarded as a point charge at $r = 0$, the center of the atom. The motion of the electron causes its charge to be "smeared out" into a spherical distribution around the proton, so that the electron is equivalent to a charge per unit volume of $\rho(r) = -(Q/\pi a_0^3)e^{-2r/a_0}$, where $a_0 = 5.29 \times 10^{-11}$ m is called the *Bohr radius*. (a) Find the total amount of the hydrogen atom's charge that is enclosed within a sphere with radius r centered on the proton. (b) Find the electric field (magnitude and direction) caused by the charge of the hydrogen atom as a function of r. (c) Make a graph as a function of r of the ratio of the electric-field magnitude E to the magnitude of the field due to the proton alone.

SOLUTION GUIDE

See MasteringPhysics® study area for a Video Tutor solution.

IDENTIFY and SET UP

1. The charge distribution in this problem is spherically symmetric, just as in Example 22.9, so you can solve it using Gauss's law.
2. The charge within a sphere of radius r includes the proton charge $+Q$ plus the portion of the electron charge distribution that lies within the sphere. The difference from Example 22.9 is that the electron charge distribution is *not* uniform, so the charge enclosed within a sphere of radius r is *not* simply the charge density multiplied by the volume $4\pi r^3/3$ of the sphere. Instead, you'll have to do an integral.

3. Consider a thin spherical shell centered on the proton, with radius r' and infinitesimal thickness dr'. Since the shell is so thin, every point within the shell is at essentially the same radius from the proton. Hence the amount of electron charge within this shell *is* equal to the electron charge density $\rho(r')$ at this radius multiplied by the volume dV of the shell. What is dV in terms of r'?
4. The total electron charge within a radius r equals the integral of $\rho(r')dV$ from $r' = 0$ to $r' = r$. Set up this integral (but don't solve it yet), and use it to write an expression for the total charge (including the proton) within a sphere of radius r.

EXECUTE

5. Integrate your expression from step 4 to find the charge within radius r. *Hint:* Integrate by substitution: Change the integration variable from r' to $x = 2r'/a_0$. You can calculate the integral $\int x^2e^{-x}\, dx$ using integration by parts, or you can look it up in a table of integrals or on the World Wide Web.
6. Use Gauss's law and your results from step 5 to find the electric field at a distance r from the proton.
7. Find the ratio referred to in part (c) and graph it versus r. (You'll actually find it simplest to graph this function versus the quantity r/a_0.)

EVALUATE

8. How do your results for the enclosed charge and the electric-field magnitude behave in the limit $r \to 0$? In the limit $r \to \infty$? Explain your results.

Problems

For instructor-assigned homework, go to www.masteringphysics.com

•, ••, •••: Problems of increasing difficulty. **CP:** Cumulative problems incorporating material from earlier chapters. **CALC:** Problems requiring calculus. **BIO:** Biosciences problems.

DISCUSSION QUESTIONS

Q22.1 A rubber balloon has a single point charge in its interior. Does the electric flux through the balloon depend on whether or not it is fully inflated? Explain your reasoning.

Q22.2 Suppose that in Fig. 22.15 both charges were positive. What would be the fluxes through each of the four surfaces in the example?

Q22.3 In Fig. 22.15, suppose a third point charge were placed outside the purple Gaussian surface C. Would this affect the electric flux through any of the surfaces A, B, C, or D in the figure? Why or why not?

Q22.4 A certain region of space bounded by an imaginary closed surface contains no charge. Is the electric field always zero everywhere on the surface? If not, under what circumstances is it zero on the surface?

Q22.5 A spherical Gaussian surface encloses a point charge q. If the point charge is moved from the center of the sphere to a point away from the center, does the electric field at a point on the surface change? Does the total flux through the Gaussian surface change? Explain.

Q22.6 You find a sealed box on your doorstep. You suspect that the box contains several charged metal spheres packed in insulating material. How can you determine the total net charge inside the box without opening the box? Or isn't this possible?

Q22.7 A solid copper sphere has a net positive charge. The charge is distributed uniformly over the surface of the sphere, and the electric field inside the sphere is zero. Then a negative point charge outside the sphere is brought close to the surface of the sphere. Is all the net charge on the sphere still on its surface? If so, is this charge still distributed uniformly over the surface? If it is not uniform, how is it distributed? Is the electric field inside the sphere still zero? In each case justify your answers.

Q22.8 If the electric field of a point charge were proportional to $1/r^3$ instead of $1/r^2$, would Gauss's law still be valid? Explain your reasoning. (*Hint:* Consider a spherical Gaussian surface centered on a single point charge.)

Q22.9 In a conductor, one or more electrons from each atom are free to roam throughout the volume of the conductor. Does this contradict the statement that any excess charge on a solid conductor must reside on its surface? Why or why not?

Q22.10 You charge up the van de Graaff generator shown in Fig. 22.26, and then bring an identical but uncharged hollow conducting sphere near it, without letting the two spheres touch. Sketch the distribution of charges on the second sphere. What is the net flux through the second sphere? What is the electric field inside the second sphere?

Q22.11 A lightning rod is a rounded copper rod mounted on top of a building and welded to a heavy copper cable running down into the ground. Lightning rods are used to protect houses and barns from lightning; the lightning current runs through the copper rather than through the building. Why? Why should the end of the rod be rounded?

Q22.12 A solid conductor has a cavity in its interior. Would the presence of a point charge inside the cavity affect the electric field outside the conductor? Why or why not? Would the presence of a point charge outside the conductor affect the electric field inside the cavity? Again, why or why not?

Q22.13 Explain this statement: "In a static situation, the electric field at the surface of a conductor can have no component parallel to the surface because this would violate the condition that the charges on the surface are at rest." Would this same statement be valid for the electric field at the surface of an *insulator*? Explain your answer and the reason for any differences between the cases of a conductor and an insulator.

Q22.14 In a certain region of space, the electric field $\vec{E}$ is uniform. (a) Use Gauss's law to prove that this region of space must be electrically neutral; that is, the volume charge density ρ must be zero. (b) Is the converse true? That is, in a region of space where there is no charge, must $\vec{E}$ be uniform? Explain.

Q22.15 (a) In a certain region of space, the volume charge density ρ has a uniform positive value. Can $\vec{E}$ be uniform in this region? Explain. (b) Suppose that in this region of uniform positive ρ there is a "bubble" within which $\rho = 0$. Can $\vec{E}$ be uniform within this bubble? Explain.

EXERCISES

Section 22.2 Calculating Electric Flux

22.1 • A flat sheet of paper of area 0.250 m² is oriented so that the normal to the sheet is at an angle of 60° to a uniform electric field of magnitude 14 N/C. (a) Find the magnitude of the electric flux through the sheet. (b) Does the answer to part (a) depend on the shape of the sheet? Why or why not? (c) For what angle ϕ between the normal to the sheet and the electric field is the magnitude of the flux through the sheet (i) largest and (ii) smallest? Explain your answers.

22.2 •• A flat sheet is in the shape of a rectangle with sides of lengths 0.400 m and 0.600 m. The sheet is immersed in a uniform electric field of magnitude 75.0 N/C that is directed at 20° from the plane of the sheet (Fig. E22.2). Find the magnitude of the electric flux through the sheet.

Figure **E22.2**

22.3 • You measure an electric field of 1.25×10^6 N/C at a distance of 0.150 m from a point charge. There is no other source of electric field in the region other than this point charge. (a) What is the electric flux through the surface of a sphere that has this charge at its center and that has radius 0.150 m? (b) What is the magnitude of this charge?

22.4 • It was shown in Example 21.11 (Section 21.5) that the electric field due to an infinite line of charge is perpendicular to the line and has magnitude $E = \lambda/2\pi\epsilon_0 r$. Consider an imaginary cylinder with radius $r = 0.250$ m and length $l = 0.400$ m that has an infinite line of positive charge running along its axis. The charge per unit length on the line is $\lambda = 3.00 \ \mu\text{C/m}$. (a) What is the electric flux through the cylinder due to this infinite line of charge? (b) What is the flux through the cylinder if its radius is increased to $r = 0.500$ m? (c) What is the flux through the cylinder if its length is increased to $l = 0.800$ m?

22.5 •• A hemispherical surface with radius r in a region of uniform electric field $\vec{E}$ has its axis aligned parallel to the direction of the field. Calculate the flux through the surface.

22.6 • The cube in Fig. E22.6 has sides of length $L =$ 10.0 cm. The electric field is uniform, has magnitude $E = 4.00 \times 10^3$ N/C, and is parallel to the xy-plane at an angle of 53.1° measured from the $+x$-axis toward the $+y$-axis. (a) What is the electric flux through each of the six cube faces S_1, S_2, S_3, S_4, S_5, and S_6? (b) What is the total electric flux through all faces of the cube?

Figure **E22.6**

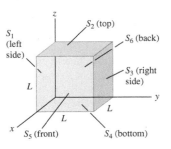

Section 22.3 Gauss's Law

22.7 • **BIO** As discussed in Section 22.5, human nerve cells have a net negative charge and the material in the interior of the cell is a good conductor. If a cell has a net charge of -8.65 pC, what are the magnitude and direction (inward or outward) of the net flux through the cell boundary?

22.8 • The three small spheres shown in Fig. E22.8 carry charges $q_1 = 4.00$ nC, $q_2 = -7.80$ nC, and $q_3 = 2.40$ nC. Find the net electric flux through each of the following closed surfaces shown in cross section in the figure: (a) S_1; (b) S_2; (c) S_3; (d) S_4; (e) S_5. (f) Do your answers to parts (a)–(e) depend on how the charge is distributed over each small sphere? Why or why not?

Figure **E22.8**

Surface	What it encloses
S_1	q_1
S_2	q_2
S_3	q_1 and q_2
S_4	q_1 and q_3
S_5	q_1 and q_2 and q_3

22.9 •• A charged paint is spread in a very thin uniform layer over the surface of a plastic sphere of diameter 12.0 cm, giving it a charge of $-35.0 \ \mu\text{C}$. Find the electric field (a) just inside the paint layer; (b) just outside the paint layer; (c) 5.00 cm outside the surface of the paint layer.

22.10 • A point charge $q_1 = 4.00$ nC is located on the x-axis at $x = 2.00$ m, and a second point charge $q_2 = -6.00$ nC is on the y-axis at $y = 1.00$ m. What is the total electric flux due to these two point charges through a spherical surface centered at the origin and with radius (a) 0.500 m, (b) 1.50 m, (c) 2.50 m?

22.11 • A 6.20-μC point charge is at the center of a cube with sides of length 0.500 m. (a) What is the electric flux through one of the six faces of the cube? (b) How would your answer to part (a) change if the sides were 0.250 m long? Explain.

22.12 • **Electric Fields in an Atom.** The nuclei of large atoms, such as uranium, with 92 protons, can be modeled as spherically symmetric spheres of charge. The radius of the uranium nucleus is approximately 7.4×10^{-15} m. (a) What is the electric field this nucleus produces just outside its surface? (b) What magnitude of electric field does it produce at the distance of the electrons, which is about 1.0×10^{-10} m? (c) The electrons can be modeled as forming a uniform shell of negative charge. What net electric field do they produce at the location of the nucleus?

22.13 • A point charge of +5.00 μC is located on the x-axis at $x = 4.00$ m, next to a spherical surface of radius 3.00 m centered at the origin. (a) Calculate the magnitude of the electric field at $x = 3.00$ m. (b) Calculate the magnitude of the electric field at $x = -3.00$ m. (c) According to Gauss's law, the net flux through the sphere is zero because it contains no charge. Yet the field due to the external charge is much stronger on the near side of the sphere (i.e., at $x = 3.00$ m) than on the far side (at $x = -3.00$ m). How, then, can the flux into the sphere (on the near side) equal the flux out of it (on the far side)? Explain. A sketch will help.

Section 22.4 Applications of Gauss's Law and
Section 22.5 Charges on Conductors

22.14 •• A solid metal sphere with radius 0.450 m carries a net charge of 0.250 nC. Find the magnitude of the electric field (a) at a point 0.100 m outside the surface of the sphere and (b) at a point inside the sphere, 0.100 m below the surface.

22.15 •• Two very long uniform lines of charge are parallel and are separated by 0.300 m. Each line of charge has charge per unit length +5.20 μC/m. What magnitude of force does one line of charge exert on a 0.0500-m section of the other line of charge?

22.16 • Some planetary scientists have suggested that the planet Mars has an electric field somewhat similar to that of the earth, producing a net electric flux of 3.63×10^{16} N·m^2/C at the planet's surface, directed toward the center of the planet. Calculate: (a) the total electric charge on the planet; (b) the electric field at the planet's surface (refer to the astronomical data inside the back cover); (c) the charge density on Mars, assuming all the charge is uniformly distributed over the planet's surface.

22.17 •• How many excess electrons must be added to an isolated spherical conductor 32.0 cm in diameter to produce an electric field of 1150 N/C just outside the surface?

22.18 •• The electric field 0.400 m from a very long uniform line of charge is 840 N/C. How much charge is contained in a 2.00-cm section of the line?

22.19 •• A very long uniform line of charge has charge per unit length 4.80 μC/m and lies along the x-axis. A second long uniform line of charge has charge per unit length -2.40 μC/m and is parallel to the x-axis at $y = 0.400$ m. What is the net electric field (magnitude and direction) at the following points on the y-axis: (a) $y = 0.200$ m and (b) $y = 0.600$ m?

22.20 • (a) At a distance of 0.200 cm from the center of a charged conducting sphere with radius 0.100 cm, the electric field is 480 N/C. What is the electric field 0.600 cm from the center of the sphere? (b) At a distance of 0.200 cm from the axis of a very long charged conducting cylinder with radius 0.100 cm, the electric field is 480 N/C. What is the electric field 0.600 cm from the axis of the cylinder? (c) At a distance of 0.200 cm from a large uniform sheet of charge, the electric field is 480 N/C. What is the electric field 1.20 cm from the sheet?

22.21 •• A hollow, conducting sphere with an outer radius of 0.250 m and an inner radius of 0.200 m has a uniform surface charge density of $+6.37 \times 10^{-6}$ C/m^2. A charge of -0.500 μC is now introduced into the cavity inside the sphere. (a) What is the new charge density on the outside of the sphere? (b) Calculate the strength of the electric field just outside the sphere. (c) What is the electric flux through a spherical surface just inside the inner surface of the sphere?

22.22 •• A point charge of -2.00 μC is located in the center of a spherical cavity of radius 6.50 cm inside an insulating charged solid. The charge density in the solid is $\rho = 7.35 \times 10^{-4}$ C/m^3. Calculate the electric field inside the solid at a distance of 9.50 cm from the center of the cavity.

22.23 •• The electric field at a distance of 0.145 m from the surface of a solid insulating sphere with radius 0.355 m is 1750 N/C. (a) Assuming the sphere's charge is uniformly distributed, what is the charge density inside it? (b) Calculate the electric field inside the sphere at a distance of 0.200 m from the center.

22.24 •• CP A very small object with mass 8.20×10^{-9} kg and positive charge 6.50×10^{-9} C is projected directly toward a very large insulating sheet of positive charge that has uniform surface charge density 5.90×10^{-8} C/m^2. The object is initially 0.400 m from the sheet. What initial speed must the object have in order for its closest distance of approach to the sheet to be 0.100 m?

22.25 •• CP At time $t = 0$ a proton is a distance of 0.360 m from a very large insulating sheet of charge and is moving parallel to the sheet with speed 9.70×10^2 m/s. The sheet has uniform surface charge density 2.34×10^{-9} C/m^2. What is the speed of the proton at $t = 5.00 \times 10^{-8}$ s?

22.26 •• CP An electron is released from rest at a distance of 0.300 m from a large insulating sheet of charge that has uniform surface charge density $+2.90 \times 10^{-12}$ C/m^2. (a) How much work is done on the electron by the electric field of the sheet as the electron moves from its initial position to a point 0.050 m from the sheet? (b) What is the speed of the electron when it is 0.050 m from the sheet?

22.27 ••• CP CALC An insulating sphere of radius $R = 0.160$ m has uniform charge density $\rho = +7.20 \times 10^{-9}$ C/m^3. A small object that can be treated as a point charge is released from rest just outside the surface of the sphere. The small object has positive charge $q = 3.40 \times 10^{-6}$ C. How much work does the electric field of the sphere do on the object as the object moves to a point very far from the sphere?

22.28 • A conductor with an inner cavity, like that shown in Fig. 22.23c, carries a total charge of +5.00 nC. The charge within the cavity, insulated from the conductor, is -6.00 nC. How much charge is on (a) the inner surface of the conductor and (b) the outer surface of the conductor?

22.29 • Apply Gauss's law to the Gaussian surfaces S_2, S_3, and S_4 in Fig. 22.21b to calculate the electric field between and outside the plates.

22.30 • A square insulating sheet 80.0 cm on a side is held horizontally. The sheet has 7.50 nC of charge spread uniformly over its area. (a) Calculate the electric field at a point 0.100 mm above the center of the sheet. (b) Estimate the electric field at a point 100 m above the center of the sheet. (c) Would the answers to parts (a) and (b) be different if the sheet were made of a conducting material? Why or why not?

22.31 • An infinitely long cylindrical conductor has radius R and uniform surface charge density σ. (a) In terms of σ and R, what is the charge per unit length λ for the cylinder? (b) In terms of σ, what is the magnitude of the electric field produced by the charged cylinder at a distance $r > R$ from its axis? (c) Express the result of part (b) in terms of λ and show that the electric field outside the cylinder is the same as if all the charge were on the axis. Compare your result to the result for a line of charge in Example 22.6 (Section 22.4).

22.32 • Two very large, nonconducting plastic sheets, each 10.0 cm thick, carry uniform charge densities σ_1, σ_2, σ_3, and σ_4 on their surfaces, as shown in Fig. E22.32. These surface charge densities have the values $\sigma_1 = -6.00\ \mu C/m^2$, $\sigma_2 = +5.00\ \mu C/m^2$, $\sigma_3 = +2.00\ \mu C/m^2$, and $\sigma_4 = +4.00$ $\mu C/m^2$. Use Gauss's law to find the magnitude and direction of the electric field at the following points, far from

Figure **E22.32**

the edges of these sheets: (a) point A, 5.00 cm from the left face of the left-hand sheet; (b) point B, 1.25 cm from the inner surface of the right-hand sheet; (c) point C, in the middle of the right-hand sheet.

22.33 • A negative charge $-Q$ is placed inside the cavity of a hollow metal solid. The outside of the solid is grounded by connecting a conducting wire between it and the earth. (a) Is there any excess charge induced on the inner surface of the piece of metal? If so, find its sign and magnitude. (b) Is there any excess charge on the outside of the piece of metal? Why or why not? (c) Is there an electric field in the cavity? Explain. (d) Is there an electric field within the metal? Why or why not? Is there an electric field outside the piece of metal? Explain why or why not. (e) Would someone outside the solid measure an electric field due to the charge $-Q$? Is it reasonable to say that the grounded conductor has *shielded* the region from the effects of the charge $-Q$? In principle, could the same thing be done for gravity? Why or why not?

PROBLEMS

22.34 •• A cube has sides of length $L = 0.300$ m. It is placed with one corner at the origin as shown in Fig. E22.6. The electric field is not uniform but is given by $\vec{E} = (-5.00\ \text{N/C} \cdot \text{m})x\hat{\imath} + (3.00\ \text{N/C} \cdot \text{m})z\hat{k}$. (a) Find the electric flux through each of the six cube faces S_1, S_2, S_3, S_4, S_5, and S_6. (b) Find the total electric charge inside the cube.

22.35 • The electric field $\vec{E}$ in Fig. P22.35 is everywhere parallel to the x-axis, so the components E_y and E_z are zero. The x-component of the field E_x depends on x but not on y and z. At points in the yz-plane (where $x = 0$), $E_x = 125$ N/C. (a) What is the electric flux through surface I in Fig. P22.35? (b) What is the electric flux through surface II? (c) The volume shown in the figure is a small section of a

Figure **P22.35**

very large insulating slab 1.0 m thick. If there is a total charge of -24.0 nC within the volume shown, what are the magnitude and direction of $\vec{E}$ at the face opposite surface I? (d) Is the electric field produced only by charges within the slab, or is the field also due to charges outside the slab? How can you tell?

22.36 •• **CALC** In a region of space there is an electric field $\vec{E}$ that is in the z-direction and that has magnitude $E = (964\ \text{N}/(\text{C} \cdot \text{m}))x$. Find the flux for this field through a square in the xy-plane at $z = 0$ and with side length 0.350 m. One side of the square is along the +x-axis and another side is along the +y-axis.

22.37 •• The electric field $\vec{E}_1$ at one face of a parallelepiped is uniform over the entire face and is directed out of the face. At the opposite face, the electric field $\vec{E}_2$ is also uniform over the entire face and is directed into that face (Fig. P22.37). The two faces in question are inclined at 30.0° from the horizontal, while $\vec{E}_1$ and $\vec{E}_2$ are both horizontal; $\vec{E}_1$ has a magnitude of 2.50×10^4 N/C, and $\vec{E}_2$ has a magnitude of 7.00×10^4 N/C. (a) Assuming that no other electric field lines cross the surfaces of the parallelepiped, determine the net charge contained within. (b) Is the electric field produced only by the charges within the parallelepiped, or is the field also due to charges outside the parallelepiped? How can you tell?

Figure **P22.37**

22.38 • A long line carrying a uniform linear charge density $+50.0\ \mu C/m$ runs parallel to and 10.0 cm from the surface of a large, flat plastic sheet that has a uniform surface charge density of $-100\ \mu C/m^2$ on one side. Find the location of all points where an α particle would feel no force due to this arrangement of charged objects.

22.39 • **The Coaxial Cable.** A long coaxial cable consists of an inner cylindrical conductor with radius a and an outer coaxial cylinder with inner radius b and outer radius c. The outer cylinder is mounted on insulating supports and has no net charge. The inner cylinder has a uniform positive charge per unit length λ. Calculate the electric field (a) at any point between the cylinders a distance r from the axis and (b) at any point outside the outer cylinder. (c) Graph the magnitude of the electric field as a function of the distance r from the axis of the cable, from $r = 0$ to $r = 2c$. (d) Find the charge per unit length on the inner surface and on the outer surface of the outer cylinder.

22.40 • A very long conducting tube (hollow cylinder) has inner radius a and outer radius b. It carries charge per unit length $+\alpha$, where α is a positive constant with units of C/m. A line of charge lies along the axis of the tube. The line of charge has charge per unit length $+\alpha$. (a) Calculate the electric field in terms of α and the distance r from the axis of the tube for (i) $r < a$; (ii) $a < r < b$; (iii) $r > b$. Show your results in a graph of E as a function of r. (b) What is the charge per unit length on (i) the inner surface of the tube and (ii) the outer surface of the tube?

22.41 • Repeat Problem 22.40, but now let the conducting tube have charge per unit length $-\alpha$. As in Problem 22.40, the line of charge has charge per unit length $+\alpha$.

22.42 • A very long, solid cylinder with radius R has positive charge uniformly distributed throughout it, with charge per unit volume ρ. (a) Derive the expression for the electric field inside the volume at a distance r from the axis of the cylinder in terms of the charge density ρ. (b) What is the electric field at a point outside the volume in terms of the charge per unit length λ in the cylinder? (c) Compare the answers to parts (a) and (b) for $r = R$. (d) Graph the electric-field magnitude as a function of r from $r = 0$ to $r = 3R$.

22.43 •• **CP** A small sphere with a mass of 4.00×10^{-6} kg and carrying a charge of 5.00×10^{-8} C hangs from a thread near a very large, charged insulating

Figure **P22.43**

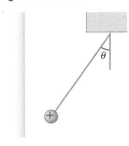

sheet, as shown in Fig. P22.43. The charge density on the surface of the sheet is uniform and equal to $2.50 \times 10^{-9}\,\text{C/m}^2$. Find the angle of the thread.

22.44 • **A Sphere in a Sphere.** A solid conducting sphere carrying charge q has radius a. It is inside a concentric hollow conducting sphere with inner radius b and outer radius c. The hollow sphere has no net charge. (a) Derive expressions for the electric-field magnitude in terms of the distance r from the center for the regions $r < a$, $a < r < b$, $b < r < c$, and $r > c$. (b) Graph the magnitude of the electric field as a function of r from $r = 0$ to $r = 2c$. (c) What is the charge on the inner surface of the hollow sphere? (d) On the outer surface? (e) Represent the charge of the small sphere by four plus signs. Sketch the field lines of the system within a spherical volume of radius $2c$.

22.45 • A solid conducting sphere with radius R that carries positive charge Q is concentric with a very thin insulating shell of radius $2R$ that also carries charge Q. The charge Q is distributed uniformly over the insulating shell. (a) Find the electric field (magnitude and direction) in each of the regions $0 < r < R$, $R < r < 2R$, and $r > 2R$. (b) Graph the electric-field magnitude as a function of r.

22.46 • A conducting spherical shell with inner radius a and outer radius b has a positive point charge Q located at its center. The total charge on the shell is $-3Q$, and it is insulated from its surroundings (Fig. P22.46). (a) Derive expressions for the electric-field magnitude in terms of the distance r from the center for the regions $r < a$, $a < r < b$, and $r > b$. (b) What is the surface charge density on the inner surface of the conducting shell? (c) What is the surface charge density on the outer surface of the conducting shell? (d) Sketch the electric field lines and the location of all charges. (e) Graph the electric-field magnitude as a function of r.

Figure **P22.46**

22.47 • **Concentric Spherical Shells.** A small conducting spherical shell with inner radius a and outer radius b is concentric with a larger conducting spherical shell with inner radius c and outer radius d (Fig. P22.47). The inner shell has total charge $+2q$, and the outer shell has charge $+4q$. (a) Calculate the electric field (magnitude and direction) in terms of q and the distance r from the common center of the two shells for (i) $r < a$; (ii) $a < r < b$; (iii) $b < r < c$; (iv) $c < r < d$; (v) $r > d$. Show your results in a graph of the radial component of $\vec{E}$ as a function of r. (b) What is the total charge on the (i) inner surface of the small shell; (ii) outer surface of the small shell; (iii) inner surface of the large shell; (iv) outer surface of the large shell?

Figure **P22.47**

22.48 • Repeat Problem 22.47, but now let the outer shell have charge $-2q$. As in Problem 22.47, the inner shell has charge $+2q$.

22.49 • Repeat Problem 22.47, but now let the outer shell have charge $-4q$. As in Problem 22.47, the inner shell has charge $+2q$.

22.50 • A solid conducting sphere with radius R carries a positive total charge Q. The sphere is surrounded by an insulating shell with inner radius R and outer radius $2R$. The insulating shell has a uniform charge density ρ. (a) Find the value of ρ so that the net charge of the entire system is zero. (b) If ρ has the value found in part (a), find the electric field (magnitude and direction) in each of the regions $0 < r < R$, $R < r < 2R$, and $r > 2R$. Show your results in a graph of the radial component of $\vec{E}$ as a function of r. (c) As a general rule, the electric field is discontinuous only at locations where there is a thin sheet of charge. Explain how your results in part (b) agree with this rule.

22.51 • Negative charge $-Q$ is distributed uniformly over the surface of a thin spherical insulating shell with radius R. Calculate the force (magnitude and direction) that the shell exerts on a positive point charge q located (a) a distance $r > R$ from the center of the shell (outside the shell) and (b) a distance $r < R$ from the center of the shell (inside the shell).

22.52 •• (a) How many excess electrons must be distributed uniformly within the volume of an isolated plastic sphere 30.0 cm in diameter to produce an electric field of 1390 N/C just outside the surface of the sphere? (b) What is the electric field at a point 10.0 cm outside the surface of the sphere?

22.53 ••• **CALC** An insulating hollow sphere has inner radius a and outer radius b. Within the insulating material the volume charge density is given by $\rho(r) = \frac{\alpha}{r}$, where α is a positive constant. (a) In terms of α and a, what is the magnitude of the electric field at a distance r from the center of the shell, where $a < r < b$? (b) A point charge q is placed at the center of the hollow space, at $r = 0$. In terms of α and a, what value must q have (sign and magnitude) in order for the electric field to be constant in the region $a < r < b$, and what then is the value of the constant field in this region?

22.54 •• **CP** **Thomson's Model of the Atom.** In the early years of the 20th century, a leading model of the structure of the atom was that of the English physicist J. J. Thomson (the discoverer of the electron). In Thomson's model, an atom consisted of a sphere of positively charged material in which were embedded negatively charged electrons, like chocolate chips in a ball of cookie dough. Consider such an atom consisting of one electron with mass m and charge $-e$, which may be regarded as a point charge, and a uniformly charged sphere of charge $+e$ and radius R. (a) Explain why the equilibrium position of the electron is at the center of the nucleus. (b) In Thomson's model, it was assumed that the positive material provided little or no resistance to the motion of the electron. If the electron is displaced from equilibrium by a distance less than R, show that the resulting motion of the electron will be simple harmonic, and calculate the frequency of oscillation. (*Hint:* Review the definition of simple harmonic motion in Section 14.2. If it can be shown that the net force on the electron is of this form, then it follows that the motion is simple harmonic. Conversely, if the net force on the electron does not follow this form, the motion is not simple harmonic.) (c) By Thomson's time, it was known that excited atoms emit light waves of only certain frequencies. In his model, the frequency of emitted light is the same as the oscillation frequency of the electron or electrons in the atom. What would the radius of a Thomson-model atom have to be for it to produce red light of frequency 4.57×10^{14} Hz? Compare your answer to the radii of real atoms, which are of the order of 10^{-10} m (see Appendix F for data about the electron). (d) If the electron were displaced from equilibrium by a distance greater than R, would the electron oscillate? Would its motion be simple harmonic? Explain your reasoning. (*Historical note:* In 1910, the atomic nucleus was discovered, proving the Thomson model to be incorrect. An atom's positive charge is not spread over its volume as Thomson supposed, but is concentrated in the tiny nucleus of radius 10^{-14} to 10^{-15} m.)

22.55 • **Thomson's Model of the Atom, Continued.** Using Thomson's (outdated) model of the atom described in Problem 22.54, consider an atom consisting of two electrons, each of charge $-e$, embedded in a sphere of charge $+2e$ and radius R. In

Figure **P22.55**

equilibrium, each electron is a distance d from the center of the atom (Fig. P22.55). Find the distance d in terms of the other properties of the atom.

22.56 • **A Uniformly Charged Slab.** A slab of insulating material has thickness $2d$ and is oriented so that its faces are parallel to the yz-plane and given by the planes $x = d$ and $x = -d$. The y- and z-dimensions of the slab are very large compared to d and may be treated as essentially infinite. The slab has a uniform positive charge density ρ. (a) Explain why the electric field due to the slab is zero at the center of the slab ($x = 0$). (b) Using Gauss's law, find the electric field due to the slab (magnitude and direction) at all points in space.

22.57 • **CALC A Nonuniformly Charged Slab.** Repeat Problem 22.56, but now let the charge density of the slab be given by $\rho(x) = \rho_0(x/d)^2$, where ρ_0 is a positive constant.

22.58 • **CALC** A nonuniform, but spherically symmetric, distribution of charge has a charge density $\rho(r)$ given as follows:

$$\rho(r) = \rho_0(1 - 4r/3R) \qquad \text{for } r \leq R$$
$$\rho(r) = 0 \qquad \text{for } r \geq R$$

where ρ_0 is a positive constant. (a) Find the total charge contained in the charge distribution. (b) Obtain an expression for the electric field in the region $r \geq R$. (c) Obtain an expression for the electric field in the region $r \leq R$. (d) Graph the electric-field magnitude E as a function of r. (e) Find the value of r at which the electric field is maximum, and find the value of that maximum field.

22.59 • **CP CALC Gauss's Law for Gravitation.** The gravitational force between two point masses separated by a distance r is proportional to $1/r^2$, just like the electric force between two point charges. Because of this similarity between gravitational and electric interactions, there is also a Gauss's law for gravitation. (a) Let $\vec{g}$ be the acceleration due to gravity caused by a point mass m at the origin, so that $\vec{g} = -(Gm/r^2)\hat{r}$. Consider a spherical Gaussian surface with radius r centered on this point mass, and show that the flux of $\vec{g}$ through this surface is given by

$$\oint \vec{g} \cdot d\vec{A} = -4\pi Gm$$

(b) By following the same logical steps used in Section 22.3 to obtain Gauss's law for the electric field, show that the flux of $\vec{g}$ through *any* closed surface is given by

$$\oint \vec{g} \cdot d\vec{A} = -4\pi GM_{\text{encl}}$$

where M_{encl} is the total mass enclosed within the closed surface.

22.60 • **CP Applying Gauss's Law for Gravitation.** Using Gauss's law for gravitation (derived in part (b) of Problem 22.59), show that the following statements are true: (a) For any spherically symmetric mass distribution with total mass M, the acceleration due to gravity outside the distribution is the same as though all the mass were concentrated at the center. (*Hint:* See Example 22.5 in Section 22.4.) (b) At any point inside a spherically symmetric shell of mass, the acceleration due to gravity is zero. (*Hint:* See Example 22.5.) (c) If we could drill a hole through a spherically symmetric planet to its center, and if the density were uniform, we would find that the magnitude of $\vec{g}$ is directly proportional to the distance r from the center. (*Hint:* See Example 22.9 in Section 22.4.) We proved these results in Section 13.6 using some fairly strenuous analysis; the proofs using Gauss's law for gravitation are *much* easier.

22.61 • (a) An insulating sphere with radius a has a uniform charge density ρ. The sphere is not centered at the origin but at $\vec{r} = \vec{b}$. Show that the electric field inside the sphere is given by

$\vec{E} = \rho(\vec{r} - \vec{b})/3\epsilon_0$. (b) An insulating sphere of radius R has a spherical hole of radius a located within its volume and centered a distance b from the center of the sphere, where $a < b < R$ (a cross section of the sphere is shown in Fig. P22.61). The solid part of the sphere has a uniform volume charge density ρ. Find the magnitude and direction of the electric field $\vec{E}$ inside the hole, and show that $\vec{E}$ is uniform over the entire hole. [*Hint:* Use the principle of superposition and the result of part (a).]

Figure **P22.61**

Charge density ρ

22.62 • A very long, solid insulating cylinder with radius R has a cylindrical hole with radius a bored along its entire length. The axis of the hole is a distance b from the axis of the cylinder, where $a < b < R$ (Fig. P22.62). The solid material of the cylinder has a uniform volume charge density ρ. Find the magnitude and direction of the electric field $\vec{E}$ inside the hole, and show that $\vec{E}$ is uniform over the entire hole. (*Hint:* See Problem 22.61.)

Figure **P22.62**

Charge density ρ

22.63 • Positive charge Q is distributed uniformly over each of two spherical volumes with radius R. One sphere of charge is centered at the origin and the other at $x = 2R$ (Fig. P22.63). Find the magnitude and direction of the net electric field due to these two distributions of charge at the following points on the x-axis: (a) $x = 0$; (b) $x = R/2$; (c) $x = R$; (d) $x = 3R$.

Figure **P22.63**

22.64 • Repeat Problem 22.63, but now let the left-hand sphere have positive charge Q and let the right-hand sphere have negative charge $-Q$.

22.65 •• **CALC** A nonuniform, but spherically symmetric, distribution of charge has a charge density $\rho(r)$ given as follows:

$$\rho(r) = \rho_0(1 - r/R) \qquad \text{for } r \leq R$$
$$\rho(r) = 0 \qquad \text{for } r \geq R$$

where $\rho_0 = 3Q/\pi R^3$ is a positive constant. (a) Show that the total charge contained in the charge distribution is Q. (b) Show that the electric field in the region $r \geq R$ is identical to that produced by a point charge Q at $r = 0$. (c) Obtain an expression for the electric field in the region $r \leq R$. (d) Graph the electric-field magnitude E as a function of r. (e) Find the value of r at which the electric field is maximum, and find the value of that maximum field.

CHALLENGE PROBLEMS

22.66 ••• **CP CALC** A region in space contains a total positive charge Q that is distributed spherically such that the volume charge density $\rho(r)$ is given by

$$\rho(r) = \alpha \qquad \text{for } r \leq R/2$$
$$\rho(r) = 2\alpha(1 - r/R) \qquad \text{for } R/2 \leq r \leq R$$
$$\rho(r) = 0 \qquad \text{for } r \geq R$$

Here α is a positive constant having units of C/m^3. (a) Determine α in terms of Q and R. (b) Using Gauss's law, derive an expression for the magnitude of $\vec{E}$ as a function of r. Do this separately for all three regions. Express your answers in terms of the total charge Q. Be sure to check that your results agree on the boundaries of the regions. (c) What fraction of the total charge is contained within the region $r \leq R/2$? (d) If an electron with charge $q' = -e$ is oscillating back and forth about $r = 0$ (the center of the distribution) with an amplitude less than $R/2$, show that the motion is simple harmonic. (*Hint:* Review the discussion of simple harmonic motion in Section 14.2. If, and only if, the net force on the electron is proportional to its displacement from equilibrium, then the motion is simple harmonic.) (e) What is the period of the motion in part (d)? (f) If the amplitude of the motion described in part (e) is greater than $R/2$, is the motion still simple harmonic? Why or why not?

22.67 ••• **CP CALC** A region in space contains a total positive charge Q that is distributed spherically such that the volume charge density $\rho(r)$ is given by

$$\rho(r) = 3\alpha r/(2R) \qquad \text{for } r \leq R/2$$
$$\rho(r) = \alpha[1 - (r/R)^2] \qquad \text{for } R/2 \leq r \leq R$$
$$\rho(r) = 0 \qquad \text{for } r \geq R$$

Here α is a positive constant having units of C/m^3. (a) Determine α in terms of Q and R. (b) Using Gauss's law, derive an expression for the magnitude of the electric field as a function of r. Do this separately for all three regions. Express your answers in terms of the total charge Q. (c) What fraction of the total charge is contained within the region $R/2 \leq r \leq R$? (d) What is the magnitude of $\vec{E}$ at $r = R/2$? (e) If an electron with charge $q' = -e$ is released from rest at any point in any of the three regions, the resulting motion will be oscillatory but not simple harmonic. Why? (See Challenge Problem 22.66.)

Answers

Chapter Opening Question **?**

No. The electric field inside a cavity within a conductor is zero, so there is no electric effect on the child. (See Section 22.5.)

Test Your Understanding Questions

22.1 Answer: (iii) Each part of the surface of the box will be three times farther from the charge $+q$, so the electric field will be $\left(\frac{1}{3}\right)^2 = \frac{1}{9}$ as strong. But the area of the box will increase by a factor of $3^2 = 9$. Hence the electric flux will be multiplied by a factor of $\left(\frac{1}{9}\right)(9) = 1$. In other words, the flux will be unchanged.

22.2 Answer: (iv), (ii), (i), (iii) In each case the electric field is uniform, so the flux is $\Phi_E = \vec{E} \cdot \vec{A}$. We use the relationships for the scalar products of unit vectors: $\hat{\imath} \cdot \hat{\imath} = \hat{\jmath} \cdot \hat{\jmath} = 1$, $\hat{\imath} \cdot \hat{\jmath} = 0$. In case (i) we have $\Phi_E = (4.0\ \text{N/C})(6.0\ \text{m}^2)\hat{\imath} \cdot \hat{\jmath} = 0$ (the electric field and vector area are perpendicular, so there is zero flux). In case (ii) we have $\Phi_E [(4.0\ \text{N/C})\hat{\imath} + (2.0\ \text{N/C})\hat{\jmath}] \cdot (3.0\ \text{m}^2)\hat{\jmath} = (2.0\ \text{N/C}) \cdot (3.0\ \text{m}^2) = 6.0\ \text{N} \cdot \text{m}^2/\text{C}$. Similarly, in case (iii) we have $\Phi_E = [(4.0\,\text{N/C})\hat{\imath} - (2.0\,\text{N/C})\hat{\jmath}] \cdot [(3.0\ \text{m}^2)\hat{\imath} + (7.0\ \text{m}^2)\hat{\jmath}] = (4.0\ \text{N/C})(3.0\ \text{m}^2) - (2.0\ \text{N/C})(7.0\ \text{m}^2) = -2\ \text{N} \cdot \text{m}^2/\text{C}$, and in case (iv) we have $\Phi_E = [(4.0\,\text{N/C})\hat{\imath} - (2.0\,\text{N/C})\hat{\jmath}] \cdot [(3.0\ \text{m}^2)\hat{\imath} - (7.0\ \text{m}^2)\hat{\jmath}] = (4.0\ \text{N/C})(3.0\ \text{m}^2) + (2.0\ \text{N/C}) \cdot (7.0\ \text{m}^2) = 26\ \text{N} \cdot \text{m}^2/\text{C}$.

22.3 Answer: S_2, S_5, S_4, S_1 and S_3 (tie) Gauss's law tells us that the flux through a closed surface is proportional to the amount of charge enclosed within that surface. So an ordering of these surfaces by their fluxes is the same as an ordering by the amount of enclosed charge. Surface S_1 encloses no charge, surface S_2 encloses $9.0\ \mu\text{C} + 5.0\ \mu\text{C} + (-7.0\ \mu\text{C}) = 7.0\ \mu\text{C}$, surface S_3 encloses $9.0\ \mu\text{C} + 1.0\ \mu\text{C} + (-10.0\ \mu\text{C}) = 0$, surface S_4 encloses $8.0\ \mu\text{C} + (-7.0\ \mu\text{C}) = 1.0\ \mu\text{C}$, and surface S_5 encloses $8.0\ \mu\text{C} + (-7.0\ \mu\text{C}) + (-10.0\ \mu\text{C}) + (1.0\ \mu\text{C}) + (9.0\ \mu\text{C}) + (5.0\ \mu\text{C}) = 6.0\ \mu\text{C}$.

22.4 Answer: no You might be tempted to draw a Gaussian surface that is an enlarged version of the conductor, with the same shape and placed so that it completely encloses the conductor.

While you know the flux through this Gaussian surface (by Gauss's law, it's $\Phi_E = Q/\epsilon_0$), the direction of the electric field need not be perpendicular to the surface and the magnitude of the field need not be the same at all points on the surface. It's not possible to do the flux integral $\oint E_\perp\ dA$, and we can't calculate the electric field. Gauss's law is useful for calculating the electric field only when the charge distribution is *highly* symmetric.

22.5 Answer: no Before you connect the wire to the sphere, the presence of the point charge will induce a charge $-q$ on the inner surface of the hollow sphere and a charge q on the outer surface (the net charge on the sphere is zero). There will be an electric field outside the sphere due to the charge on the outer surface. Once you touch the conducting wire to the sphere, however, electrons will flow from ground to the outer surface of the sphere to neutralize the charge there (see Fig. 21.7c). As a result the sphere will have no charge on its outer surface and no electric field outside.

Bridging Problem

Answers: (a) $Q(r) = Qe^{-2r/a_0}[2(r/a_0)^2 + 2(r/a_0) + 1]$

(b) $E = \dfrac{kQe^{-2r/a_0}}{r^2}[2(r/a_0)^2 + 2(r/a_0) + 1]$

(c)

23 ELECTRIC POTENTIAL

LEARNING GOALS

By studying this chapter, you will learn:

- How to calculate the electric potential energy of a collection of charges.

- The meaning and significance of electric potential.

- How to calculate the electric potential that a collection of charges produces at a point in space.

- How to use equipotential surfaces to visualize how the electric potential varies in space.

- How to use electric potential to calculate the electric field.

? In one type of welding, electric charge flows between the welding tool and the metal pieces that are to be joined together. This produces a glowing arc whose high temperature fuses the pieces together. Why must the tool be held close to the pieces being welded?

This chapter is about energy associated with electrical interactions. Every time you turn on a light, listen to an MP3 player, or talk on a mobile phone, you are using electrical energy, an indispensable ingredient of our technological society. In Chapters 6 and 7 we introduced the concepts of *work* and *energy* in the context of mechanics; now we'll combine these concepts with what we've learned about electric charge, electric forces, and electric fields. Just as we found for many problems in mechanics, using energy ideas makes it easier to solve a variety of problems in electricity.

When a charged particle moves in an electric field, the field exerts a force that can do *work* on the particle. This work can always be expressed in terms of electric potential energy. Just as gravitational potential energy depends on the height of a mass above the earth's surface, electric potential energy depends on the position of the charged particle in the electric field. We'll describe electric potential energy using a new concept called *electric potential,* or simply *potential.* In circuits, a difference in potential from one point to another is often called *voltage.* The concepts of potential and voltage are crucial to understanding how electric circuits work and have equally important applications to electron beams used in cancer radiotherapy, high-energy particle accelerators, and many other devices.

23.1 Electric Potential Energy

The concepts of work, potential energy, and conservation of energy proved to be extremely useful in our study of mechanics. In this section we'll show that these concepts are just as useful for understanding and analyzing electrical interactions.

Let's begin by reviewing three essential points from Chapters 6 and 7. First, when a force $\vec{F}$ acts on a particle that moves from point a to point b, the work $W_{a\to b}$ done by the force is given by a *line integral*:

$$W_{a\to b} = \int_a^b \vec{F} \cdot d\vec{l} = \int_a^b F\cos\phi \, dl \quad \text{(work done by a force)} \qquad (23.1)$$

where $d\vec{l}$ is an infinitesimal displacement along the particle's path and ϕ is the angle between $\vec{F}$ and $d\vec{l}$ at each point along the path.

Second, if the force $\vec{F}$ is *conservative*, as we defined the term in Section 7.3, the work done by $\vec{F}$ can always be expressed in terms of a **potential energy** U. When the particle moves from a point where the potential energy is U_a to a point where it is U_b, the change in potential energy is $\Delta U = U_b - U_a$ and the work $W_{a\to b}$ done by the force is

$$W_{a\to b} = U_a - U_b = -(U_b - U_a) = -\Delta U \quad \begin{matrix}\text{(work done by a}\\ \text{conservative force)}\end{matrix} \qquad (23.2)$$

When $W_{a\to b}$ is positive, U_a is greater than U_b, ΔU is negative, and the potential energy *decreases*. That's what happens when a baseball falls from a high point (a) to a lower point (b) under the influence of the earth's gravity; the force of gravity does positive work, and the gravitational potential energy decreases (Fig. 23.1). When a tossed ball is moving upward, the gravitational force does negative work during the ascent, and the potential energy increases.

Third, the work–energy theorem says that the change in kinetic energy $\Delta K = K_b - K_a$ during a displacement equals the *total* work done on the particle. If only conservative forces do work, then Eq. (23.2) gives the total work, and $K_b - K_a = -(U_b - U_a)$. We usually write this as

$$K_a + U_a = K_b + U_b \qquad (23.3)$$

That is, the total mechanical energy (kinetic plus potential) is *conserved* under these circumstances.

Electric Potential Energy in a Uniform Field

Let's look at an electrical example of these basic concepts. In Fig. 23.2 a pair of charged parallel metal plates sets up a uniform, downward electric field with magnitude E. The field exerts a downward force with magnitude $F = q_0 E$ on a positive test charge q_0. As the charge moves downward a distance d from point a to point b, the force on the test charge is constant and independent of its location. So the work done by the electric field is the product of the force magnitude and the component of displacement in the (downward) direction of the force:

$$W_{a\to b} = Fd = q_0 Ed \qquad (23.4)$$

This work is positive, since the force is in the same direction as the net displacement of the test charge.

The y-component of the electric force, $F_y = -q_0 E$, is constant, and there is no x- or z-component. This is exactly analogous to the gravitational force on a mass m near the earth's surface; for this force, there is a constant y-component $F_y = -mg$ and the x- and z-components are zero. Because of this analogy, we can conclude that the force exerted on q_0 by the uniform electric field in Fig. 23.2 is *conservative*, just as is the gravitational force. This means that the work $W_{a\to b}$ done by the field is independent of the path the particle takes from a to b. We can represent this work with a *potential-energy* function U, just as we did for gravitational potential energy

23.1 The work done on a baseball moving in a uniform gravitational field.

Object moving in a uniform gravitational field

$\vec{w} = m\vec{g}$

The work done by the gravitational force is the same for any path from a to b:
$W_{a\to b} = -\Delta U = mgh$

23.2 The work done on a point charge moving in a uniform electric field. Compare with Fig. 23.1.

Point charge moving in a uniform electric field

$\vec{E}$

q_0

$\vec{F} = q_0\vec{E}$

The work done by the electric force is the same for any path from a to b:
$W_{a\to b} = -\Delta U = q_0 Ed$

23.3 A positive charge moving (a) in the direction of the electric field $\vec{E}$ and (b) in the direction opposite $\vec{E}$.

(a) Positive charge moves in the direction of $\vec{E}$:
• Field does *positive* work on charge.
• *U decreases.*

(b) Positive charge moves opposite $\vec{E}$:
• Field does *negative* work on charge.
• *U increases.*

in Section 7.1. The potential energy for the gravitational force $F_y = -mg$ was $U = mgy$; hence the potential energy for the electric force $F_y = -q_0E$ is

$$U = q_0Ey \tag{23.5}$$

When the test charge moves from height y_a to height y_b, the work done on the charge by the field is given by

$$W_{a \to b} = -\Delta U = -(U_b - U_a) = -(q_0Ey_b - q_0Ey_a) = q_0E(y_a - y_b) \tag{23.6}$$

When y_a is greater than y_b (Fig. 23.3a), the positive test charge q_0 moves downward, in the same direction as $\vec{E}$; the displacement is in the same direction as the force $\vec{F} = q_0\vec{E}$, so the field does positive work and U decreases. [In particular, if $y_a - y_b = d$ as in Fig. 23.2, Eq. (23.6) gives $W_{a \to b} = q_0Ed$, in agreement with Eq. (23.4).] When y_a is less than y_b (Fig. 23.3b), the positive test charge q_0 moves upward, in the opposite direction to $\vec{E}$; the displacement is opposite the force, the field does negative work, and U increases.

If the test charge q_0 is *negative,* the potential energy increases when it moves with the field and decreases when it moves against the field (Fig. 23.4).

Whether the test charge is positive or negative, the following general rules apply: *U increases* if the test charge q_0 moves in the direction *opposite* the electric force $\vec{F} = q_0\vec{E}$ (Figs. 23.3b and 23.4a); *U decreases* if q_0 moves in the *same*

23.4 A negative charge moving (a) in the direction of the electric field $\vec{E}$ and (b) in the direction opposite $\vec{E}$. Compare with Fig. 23.3.

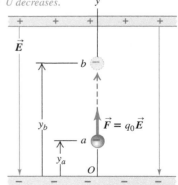

(a) Negative charge moves in the direction of $\vec{E}$:
• Field does *negative* work on charge.
• *U increases.*

(b) Negative charge moves opposite $\vec{E}$:
• Field does *positive* work on charge.
• *U decreases.*

direction as $\vec{F} = q_0\vec{E}$ (Figs. 23.3a and 23.4b). This is the same behavior as for gravitational potential energy, which increases if a mass m moves upward (opposite the direction of the gravitational force) and decreases if m moves downward (in the same direction as the gravitational force).

CAUTION **Electric potential energy** The relationship between electric potential energy change and motion in an electric field is an important one that we'll use often, but that takes some effort to truly understand. Take the time to carefully study the preceding paragraph as well as Figs. 23.3 and 23.4. Doing so now will help you tremendously later!

Electric Potential Energy of Two Point Charges

The idea of electric potential energy isn't restricted to the special case of a uniform electric field. Indeed, we can apply this concept to a point charge in *any* electric field caused by a static charge distribution. Recall from Chapter 21 that we can represent any charge distribution as a collection of point charges. Therefore it's useful to calculate the work done on a test charge q_0 moving in the electric field caused by a single, stationary point charge q.

We'll consider first a displacement along the *radial* line in Fig. 23.5. The force on q_0 is given by Coulomb's law, and its radial component is

$$F_r = \frac{1}{4\pi\epsilon_0}\frac{qq_0}{r^2} \qquad (23.7)$$

23.5 Test charge q_0 moves along a straight line extending radially from charge q. As it moves from a to b, the distance varies from r_a to r_b.

If q and q_0 have the same sign ($+$ or $-$) the force is repulsive and F_r is positive; if the two charges have opposite signs, the force is attractive and F_r is negative. The force is *not* constant during the displacement, and we have to integrate to calculate the work $W_{a\to b}$ done on q_0 by this force as q_0 moves from a to b:

$$W_{a\to b} = \int_{r_a}^{r_b} F_r\, dr = \int_{r_a}^{r_b}\frac{1}{4\pi\epsilon_0}\frac{qq_0}{r^2}dr = \frac{qq_0}{4\pi\epsilon_0}\left(\frac{1}{r_a}-\frac{1}{r_b}\right) \quad (23.8)$$

The work done by the electric force for this particular path depends only on the endpoints.

Now let's consider a more general displacement (Fig. 23.6) in which a and b do *not* lie on the same radial line. From Eq. (23.1) the work done on q_0 during this displacement is given by

$$W_{a\to b} = \int_{r_a}^{r_b} F\cos\phi\, dl = \int_{r_a}^{r_b}\frac{1}{4\pi\epsilon_0}\frac{qq_0}{r^2}\cos\phi\, dl$$

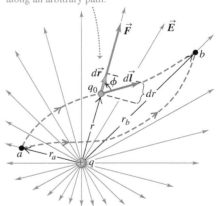

23.6 The work done on charge q_0 by the electric field of charge q does not depend on the path taken, but only on the distances r_a and r_b.

Test charge q_0 moves from a to b along an arbitrary path.

But Fig. 23.6 shows that $\cos\phi\, dl = dr$. That is, the work done during a small displacement $d\vec{l}$ depends only on the change dr in the distance r between the charges, which is the *radial component* of the displacement. Thus Eq. (23.8) is valid even for this more general displacement; the work done on q_0 by the electric field $\vec{E}$ produced by q depends only on r_a and r_b, not on the details of the path. Also, if q_0 returns to its starting point a by a different path, the total work done in the round-trip displacement is zero (the integral in Eq. (23.8) is from r_a back to r_a). These are the needed characteristics for a conservative force, as we defined it in Section 7.3. Thus the force on q_0 is a *conservative* force.

We see that Eqs. (23.2) and (23.8) are consistent if we define the potential energy to be $U_a = qq_0/4\pi\epsilon_0 r_a$ when q_0 is a distance r_a from q, and to be $U_b = qq_0/4\pi\epsilon_0 r_b$ when q_0 is a distance r_b from q. Thus the potential energy U when the test charge q_0 is at *any* distance r from charge q is

$$U = \frac{1}{4\pi\epsilon_0}\frac{qq_0}{r} \qquad \text{(electric potential energy of two point charges } q \text{ and } q_0\text{)} \qquad (23.9)$$

23.7 Graphs of the potential energy U of two point charges q and q_0 versus their separation r.

(a) q and q_0 have the same sign.

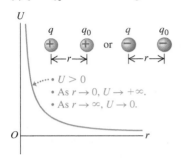

- $U > 0$
- As $r \to 0$, $U \to +\infty$.
- As $r \to \infty$, $U \to 0$.

(b) q and q_0 have opposite signs.

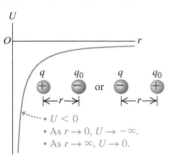

- $U < 0$
- As $r \to 0$, $U \to -\infty$.
- As $r \to \infty$, $U \to 0$.

Equation (23.9) is valid no matter what the signs of the charges q and q_0. The potential energy is positive if the charges q and q_0 have the same sign (Fig. 23.7a) and negative if they have opposite signs (Fig. 23.7b).

CAUTION **Electric potential energy vs. electric force** Don't confuse Eq. (23.9) for the potential energy of two point charges with the similar expression in Eq. (23.7) for the radial component of the electric force that one charge exerts on the other. Potential energy U is proportional to $1/r$, while the force component F_r is proportional to $1/r^2$. ▮

Potential energy is always defined relative to some reference point where $U = 0$. In Eq. (23.9), U is zero when q and q_0 are infinitely far apart and $r = \infty$. Therefore U represents the work that would be done on the test charge q_0 by the field of q if q_0 moved from an initial distance r to infinity. If q and q_0 have the same sign, the interaction is repulsive, this work is positive, and U is positive at any finite separation (Fig. 23.7a). If the charges have opposite signs, the interaction is attractive, the work done is negative, and U is negative (Fig. 23.7b).

We emphasize that the potential energy U given by Eq. (23.9) is a *shared* property of the two charges. If the distance between q and q_0 is changed from r_a to r_b, the change in potential energy is the same whether q is held fixed and q_0 is moved or q_0 is held fixed and q is moved. For this reason, we never use the phrase "the electric potential energy *of* a point charge." (Likewise, if a mass m is at a height h above the earth's surface, the gravitational potential energy is a shared property of the mass m and the earth. We emphasized this in Sections 7.1 and 13.3.)

Equation (23.9) also holds if the charge q_0 is outside a spherically symmetric charge *distribution* with total charge q; the distance r is from q_0 to the center of the distribution. That's because Gauss's law tells us that the electric field outside such a distribution is the same as if all of its charge q were concentrated at its center (see Example 22.9 in Section 22.4).

Example 23.1 **Conservation of energy with electric forces**

A positron (the electron's antiparticle) has mass 9.11×10^{-31} kg and charge $q_0 = +e = +1.60 \times 10^{-19}$ C. Suppose a positron moves in the vicinity of an α (alpha) particle, which has charge $q = +2e = 3.20 \times 10^{-19}$ C and mass 6.64×10^{-27} kg. The α particle's mass is more than 7000 times that of the positron, so we assume that the α particle remains at rest. When the positron is 1.00×10^{-10} m from the α particle, it is moving directly away from the α particle at 3.00×10^6 m/s. (a) What is the positron's speed when the particles are 2.00×10^{-10} m apart? (b) What is the positron's speed when it is very far from the α particle? (c) Suppose the initial conditions are the same but the moving particle is an electron (with the same mass as the positron but charge $q_0 = -e$). Describe the subsequent motion.

SOLUTION

IDENTIFY and SET UP: The electric force between a positron (or an electron) and an α particle is conservative, so mechanical energy (kinetic plus potential) is conserved. Equation (23.9) gives the potential energy U at any separation r: The potential-energy function for parts (a) and (b) looks like that of Fig. 23.7a, and the function for part (c) looks like that of Fig. 23.7b. We are given the positron speed $v_a = 3.00 \times 10^6$ m/s when the separation between the particles is $r_a = 1.00 \times 10^{-10}$ m. In parts (a) and (b) we use Eqs. (23.3) and (23.9) to find the speed for $r = r_b = 2.00 \times 10^{-10}$ m and $r = r_c \to \infty$, respectively. In part (c) we replace the positron with an electron and reconsider the problem.

EXECUTE: (a) Both particles have positive charge, so the positron speeds up as it moves away from the α particle. From the energy-conservation equation, Eq. (23.3), the final kinetic energy is

$$K_b = \tfrac{1}{2}mv_b^2 = K_a + U_a - U_b$$

In this expression,

$$K_a = \tfrac{1}{2}mv_a^2 = \tfrac{1}{2}(9.11 \times 10^{-31} \text{ kg})(3.00 \times 10^6 \text{ m/s})^2$$

$$= 4.10 \times 10^{-18} \text{ J}$$

$$U_a = \frac{1}{4\pi\epsilon_0}\frac{qq_0}{r_a} = (9.0 \times 10^9 \text{ N} \cdot \text{m}^2/\text{C}^2)$$

$$\times \frac{(3.20 \times 10^{-19} \text{ C})(1.60 \times 10^{-19} \text{ C})}{1.00 \times 10^{-10} \text{ m}}$$

$$= 4.61 \times 10^{-18} \text{ J}$$

$$U_b = \frac{1}{4\pi\epsilon_0}\frac{qq_0}{r_b} = 2.30 \times 10^{-18} \text{ J}$$

Hence the positron kinetic energy and speed at $r = r_b = 2.00 \times 10^{-10}$ m are

$$K_b = \tfrac{1}{2}mv_b^2 = 4.10 \times 10^{-18}\text{ J} + 4.61 \times 10^{-18}\text{ J} - 2.30 \times 10^{-18}\text{ J}$$

$$= 6.41 \times 10^{-18}\text{ J}$$

$$v_b = \sqrt{\frac{2K_b}{m}} = \sqrt{\frac{2(6.41 \times 10^{-18} \text{ J})}{9.11 \times 10^{-31} \text{ kg}}} = 3.8 \times 10^6 \text{ m/s}$$

(b) When the positron and α particle are very far apart so that $r = r_c \to \infty$, the final potential energy U_c approaches zero. Again from energy conservation, the final kinetic energy and speed of the positron in this case are

$$K_c = K_a + U_a - U_c = 4.10 \times 10^{-18}\,\text{J} + 4.61 \times 10^{-18}\,\text{J} - 0$$
$$= 8.71 \times 10^{-18}\,\text{J}$$

$$v_c = \sqrt{\frac{2K_c}{m}} = \sqrt{\frac{2(8.71 \times 10^{-18}\,\text{J})}{9.11 \times 10^{-31}\,\text{kg}}} = 4.4 \times 10^6\,\text{m/s}$$

(c) The electron and α particle have opposite charges, so the force is attractive and the electron slows down as it moves away. Changing the moving particle's sign from $+e$ to $-e$ means that the initial potential energy is now $U_a = -4.61 \times 10^{-18}$ J, which makes the total mechanical energy *negative*:

$$K_a + U_a = (4.10 \times 10^{-18}\,\text{J}) - (4.61 \times 10^{-18}\,\text{J})$$
$$= -0.51 \times 10^{-18}\,\text{J}$$

The total mechanical energy would have to be positive for the electron to move infinitely far away from the α particle. Like a rock thrown upward at low speed from the earth's surface, it will reach a maximum separation $r = r_d$ from the α particle before reversing direction. At this point its speed and its kinetic energy K_d are zero, so at separation r_d we have

$$U_d = K_a + U_a - K_d = (-0.51 \times 10^{-18}\,\text{J}) - 0$$

$$U_d = \frac{1}{4\pi\epsilon_0}\frac{qq_0}{r_d} = -0.51 \times 10^{-18}\,\text{J}$$

$$r_d = \frac{1}{U_d}\frac{qq_0}{4\pi\epsilon_0}$$

$$= \frac{(9.0 \times 10^9\,\text{N}\cdot\text{m}^2/\text{C}^2)}{-0.51 \times 10^{-18}\,\text{J}}(3.20 \times 10^{-19}\,\text{C})(-1.60 \times 10^{-19}\,\text{C})$$

$$= 9.0 \times 10^{-10}\,\text{m}$$

For $r_b = 2.00 \times 10^{-10}$ m we have $U_b = -2.30 \times 10^{-18}$ J, so the electron kinetic energy and speed at this point are

$$K_b = \tfrac{1}{2}mv_b^2 = 4.10 \times 10^{-18}\,\text{J} + (-4.61 \times 10^{-18}\,\text{J})$$
$$- (-2.30 \times 10^{-18}\,\text{J}) = 1.79 \times 10^{-18}\,\text{J}$$

$$v_b = \sqrt{\frac{2K_b}{m}} = \sqrt{\frac{2(1.79 \times 10^{-18}\,\text{J})}{9.11 \times 10^{-31}\,\text{kg}}} = 2.0 \times 10^6\,\text{m/s}$$

EVALUATE: Both particles behave as expected as they move away from the α particle: The positron speeds up, and the electron slows down and eventually turns around. How fast would an electron have to be moving at $r_a = 1.00 \times 10^{-10}$ m to travel infinitely far from the α particle? (*Hint:* See Example 13.4 in Section 13.3.)

Electric Potential Energy with Several Point Charges

Suppose the electric field $\vec{E}$ in which charge q_0 moves is caused by *several* point charges $q_1, q_2, q_3, \ldots$ at distances $r_1, r_2, r_3, \ldots$ from q_0, as in Fig. 23.8. For example, q_0 could be a positive ion moving in the presence of other ions (Fig. 23.9). The total electric field at each point is the *vector sum* of the fields due to the individual charges, and the total work done on q_0 during any displacement is the sum of the contributions from the individual charges. From Eq. (23.9) we conclude that the potential energy associated with the test charge q_0 at point a in Fig. 23.8 is the *algebraic* sum (*not* a vector sum):

23.8 The potential energy associated with a charge q_0 at point a depends on the other charges q_1, q_2, and q_3 and on their distances r_1, r_2, and r_3 from point a.

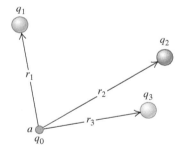

$$U = \frac{q_0}{4\pi\epsilon_0}\left(\frac{q_1}{r_1} + \frac{q_2}{r_2} + \frac{q_3}{r_3} + \cdots\right) = \frac{q_0}{4\pi\epsilon_0}\sum_i \frac{q_i}{r_i} \quad \begin{array}{l}\text{(point charge } q_0 \\ \text{and collection} \\ \text{of charges } q_i)\end{array} \quad (23.10)$$

When q_0 is at a different point b, the potential energy is given by the same expression, but $r_1, r_2, \ldots$ are the distances from $q_1, q_2, \ldots$ to point b. The work done on charge q_0 when it moves from a to b along any path is equal to the difference $U_a - U_b$ between the potential energies when q_0 is at a and at b.

We can represent *any* charge distribution as a collection of point charges, so Eq. (23.10) shows that we can always find a potential-energy function for *any* static electric field. It follows that **for every electric field due to a static charge distribution, the force exerted by that field is conservative.**

Equations (23.9) and (23.10) define U to be zero when all the distances $r_1, r_2, \ldots$ are infinite—that is, when the test charge q_0 is very far away from all the charges that produce the field. As with any potential-energy function, the point where $U = 0$ is arbitrary; we can always add a constant to make U equal zero at any point we choose. In electrostatics problems it's usually simplest to choose this point to be at infinity. When we analyze electric circuits in Chapters 25 and 26, other choices will be more convenient.

23.9 This ion engine for spacecraft uses electric forces to eject a stream of positive xenon ions (Xe^+) at speeds in excess of 30 km/s. The thrust produced is very low (about 0.09 newton) but can be maintained continuously for days, in contrast to chemical rockets, which produce a large thrust for a short time (see Fig. 8.33). Such ion engines have been used for maneuvering interplanetary spacecraft.

Equation (23.10) gives the potential energy associated with the presence of the test charge q_0 in the $\vec{E}$ field produced by $q_1, q_2, q_3, \dots$. But there is also potential energy involved in assembling these charges. If we start with charges $q_1, q_2, q_3, \dots$ all separated from each other by infinite distances and then bring them together so that the distance between q_i and q_j is r_{ij}, the *total* potential energy U is the sum of the potential energies of interaction for each pair of charges. We can write this as

$$U = \frac{1}{4\pi\epsilon_0} \sum_{i<j} \frac{q_i q_j}{r_{ij}} \qquad (23.11)$$

This sum extends over all *pairs* of charges; we don't let $i = j$ (because that would be an interaction of a charge with itself), and we include only terms with $i < j$ to make sure that we count each pair only once. Thus, to account for the interaction between q_3 and q_4, we include a term with $i = 3$ and $j = 4$ but not a term with $i = 4$ and $j = 3$.

Interpreting Electric Potential Energy

As a final comment, here are two viewpoints on electric potential energy. We have defined it in terms of the work done *by the electric field* on a charged particle moving in the field, just as in Chapter 7 we defined potential energy in terms of the work done by gravity or by a spring. When a particle moves from point a to point b, the work done on it by the electric field is $W_{a\rightarrow b} = U_a - U_b$. Thus the potential-energy difference $U_a - U_b$ equals *the work that is done by the electric force when the particle moves from a to b*. When U_a is greater than U_b, the field does positive work on the particle as it "falls" from a point of higher potential energy (a) to a point of lower potential energy (b).

An alternative but equivalent viewpoint is to consider how much work we would have to do to "raise" a particle from a point b where the potential energy is U_b to a point a where it has a greater value U_a (pushing two positive charges closer together, for example). To move the particle slowly (so as not to give it any kinetic energy), we need to exert an additional external force $\vec{F}_{\text{ext}}$ that is equal and opposite to the electric-field force and does positive work. The potential-energy difference $U_a - U_b$ is then defined as *the work that must be done by an external force to move the particle slowly from b to a against the electric force*. Because $\vec{F}_{\text{ext}}$ is the negative of the electric-field force and the displacement is in the opposite direction, this definition of the potential difference $U_a - U_b$ is equivalent to that given above. This alternative viewpoint also works if U_a is less than U_b, corresponding to "lowering" the particle; an example is moving two positive charges away from each other. In this case, $U_a - U_b$ is again equal to the work done by the external force, but now this work is negative.

We will use both of these viewpoints in the next section to interpret what is meant by electric *potential,* or potential energy per unit charge.

Example 23.2 **A system of point charges**

Two point charges are located on the x-axis, $q_1 = -e$ at $x = 0$ and $q_2 = +e$ at $x = a$. (a) Find the work that must be done by an external force to bring a third point charge $q_3 = +e$ from infinity to $x = 2a$. (b) Find the total potential energy of the system of three charges.

SOLUTION

IDENTIFY and SET UP: Figure 23.10 shows the final arrangement of the three charges. In part (a) we need to find the work W that must be done on q_3 by an external force $\vec{F}_{\text{ext}}$ to bring q_3 in from

infinity to $x = 2a$. We do this by using Eq. (23.10) to find the potential energy associated with q_3 in the presence of q_1 and q_2. In part (b) we use Eq. (23.11), the expression for the potential energy of a collection of point charges, to find the total potential energy of the system.

23.10 Our sketch of the situation after the third charge has been brought in from infinity.

$$q_1 = -e \qquad q_2 = +e \qquad q_3 = +e$$

$$\underset{x=0}{\ominus} \quad\quad \underset{x=a}{\oplus} \quad\quad \underset{x=2a}{\oplus} \longrightarrow x$$

EXECUTE: (a) The work W equals the difference between (i) the potential energy U associated with q_3 when it is at $x = 2a$ and (ii) the potential energy when it is infinitely far away. The second of these is zero, so the work required is equal to U. The distances between the charges are $r_{13} = 2a$ and $r_{23} = a$, so from Eq. (23.10),

$$W = U = \frac{q_3}{4\pi\epsilon_0}\left(\frac{q_1}{r_{13}} + \frac{q_2}{r_{23}}\right) = \frac{+e}{4\pi\epsilon_0}\left(\frac{-e}{2a} + \frac{+e}{a}\right) = \frac{+e^2}{8\pi\epsilon_0 a}$$

This is positive, just as we should expect. If we bring q_3 in from infinity along the $+x$-axis, it is attracted by q_1 but is repelled more strongly by q_2. Hence we must do positive work to push q_3 to the position at $x = 2a$.

(b) From Eq. (23.11), the total potential energy of the three-charge system is

$$U = \frac{1}{4\pi\epsilon_0}\sum_{i<j}\frac{q_i q_j}{r_{ij}} = \frac{1}{4\pi\epsilon_0}\left(\frac{q_1 q_2}{r_{12}} + \frac{q_1 q_3}{r_{13}} + \frac{q_2 q_3}{r_{23}}\right)$$

$$= \frac{1}{4\pi\epsilon_0}\left[\frac{(-e)(e)}{a} + \frac{(-e)(e)}{2a} + \frac{(e)(e)}{a}\right] = \frac{-e^2}{8\pi\epsilon_0 a}$$

EVALUATE: Our negative result in part (b) means that the system has lower potential energy than it would if the three charges were infinitely far apart. An external force would have to do *negative* work to bring the three charges from infinity to assemble this entire arrangement and would have to do *positive* work to move the three charges back to infinity.

Test Your Understanding of Section 23.1   Consider the system of three point charges in Example 21.4 (Section 21.3) and shown in Fig. 21.14. (a) What is the sign of the total potential energy of this system? (i) positive; (ii) negative; (iii) zero. (b) What is the sign of the total amount of work you would have to do to move these charges infinitely far from each other? (i) positive; (ii) negative; (iii) zero.   ∎

23.2 Electric Potential

In Section 23.1 we looked at the potential energy U associated with a test charge q_0 in an electric field. Now we want to describe this potential energy on a "per unit charge" basis, just as electric field describes the force per unit charge on a charged particle in the field. This leads us to the concept of *electric potential,* often called simply *potential.* This concept is very useful in calculations involving energies of charged particles. It also facilitates many electric-field calculations because electric potential is closely related to the electric field $\vec{E}$. When we need to determine an electric field, it is often easier to determine the potential first and then find the field from it.

Potential is *potential energy per unit charge.* We define the potential V at any point in an electric field as the potential energy U *per unit charge* associated with a test charge q_0 at that point:

$$V = \frac{U}{q_0} \quad \text{or} \quad U = q_0 V \qquad (23.12)$$

Potential energy and charge are both scalars, so potential is a scalar. From Eq. (23.12) its units are the units of energy divided by those of charge. The SI unit of potential, called one **volt** (1 V) in honor of the Italian electrical experimenter Alessandro Volta (1745–1827), equals 1 joule per coulomb:

$$1 \text{ V} = 1 \text{ volt} = 1 \text{ J/C} = 1 \text{ joule/coulomb}$$

Let's put Eq. (23.2), which equates the work done by the electric force during a displacement from a to b to the quantity $-\Delta U = -(U_b - U_a)$, on a "work per unit charge" basis. We divide this equation by q_0, obtaining

$$\frac{W_{a\to b}}{q_0} = -\frac{\Delta U}{q_0} = -\left(\frac{U_b}{q_0} - \frac{U_a}{q_0}\right) = -(V_b - V_a) = V_a - V_b \qquad (23.13)$$

where $V_a = U_a/q_0$ is the potential energy per unit charge at point a and similarly for V_b. We call V_a and V_b the *potential at point a* and *potential at point b,* respectively. Thus the work done per unit charge by the electric force when a charged body moves from a to b is equal to the potential at a minus the potential at b.

Mastering**PHYSICS**

PhET: Charges and Fields
ActivPhysics 11.13: Electrical Potential Energy and Potential

23.11 The voltage of this battery equals the difference in potential $V_{ab} = V_a - V_b$ between its positive terminal (point a) and its negative terminal (point b).

Point a (positive terminal)

ENERGY PLUS

ALKALINE

LONGER LASTING

$V_{ab} = 1.5$ volts

Point b (negative terminal)

The difference $V_a - V_b$ is called the *potential of a with respect to b*; we sometimes abbreviate this difference as $V_{ab} = V_a - V_b$ (note the order of the subscripts). This is often called the potential difference between a and b, but that's ambiguous unless we specify which is the reference point. In electric circuits, which we will analyze in later chapters, the potential difference between two points is often called **voltage** (Fig. 23.11). Equation (23.13) then states: V_{ab}, **the potential of a with respect to b, equals the work done by the electric force when a UNIT charge moves from a to b.**

Another way to interpret the potential difference V_{ab} in Eq. (23.13) is to use the alternative viewpoint mentioned at the end of Section 23.1. In that viewpoint, $U_a - U_b$ is the amount of work that must be done by an *external* force to move a particle of charge q_0 slowly from b to a against the electric force. The work that must be done *per unit charge* by the external force is then $(U_a - U_b)/q_0 = V_a - V_b = V_{ab}$. In other words: V_{ab}, **the potential of a with respect to b, equals the work that must be done to move a UNIT charge slowly from b to a against the electric force.**

An instrument that measures the difference of potential between two points is called a *voltmeter*. (In Chapter 26 we'll discuss how these devices work.) Voltmeters that can measure a potential difference of 1 μV are common, and sensitivities down to 10^{-12} V can be attained.

Calculating Electric Potential

To find the potential V due to a single point charge q, we divide Eq. (23.9) by q_0:

$$V = \frac{U}{q_0} = \frac{1}{4\pi\epsilon_0}\frac{q}{r} \quad \text{(potential due to a point charge)} \quad [23.14]$$

where r is the distance from the point charge q to the point at which the potential is evaluated. If q is positive, the potential that it produces is positive at all points; if q is negative, it produces a potential that is negative everywhere. In either case, V is equal to zero at $r = \infty$, an infinite distance from the point charge. Note that potential, like electric field, is independent of the test charge q_0 that we use to define it.

Similarly, we divide Eq. (23.10) by q_0 to find the potential due to a collection of point charges:

$$V = \frac{U}{q_0} = \frac{1}{4\pi\epsilon_0}\sum_i \frac{q_i}{r_i} \quad \begin{array}{l}\text{(potential due to a collection}\\ \text{of point charge)}\end{array} \quad [23.15]$$

In this expression, r_i is the distance from the ith charge, q_i, to the point at which V is evaluated. Just as the electric field due to a collection of point charges is the *vector* sum of the fields produced by each charge, the electric potential due to a collection of point charges is the *scalar* sum of the potentials due to each charge. When we have a continuous distribution of charge along a line, over a surface, or through a volume, we divide the charge into elements dq, and the sum in Eq. (23.15) becomes an integral:

$$V = \frac{1}{4\pi\epsilon_0}\int \frac{dq}{r} \quad \begin{array}{l}\text{(potential due to a continuous}\\ \text{distribution of charge)}\end{array} \quad [23.16]$$

where r is the distance from the charge element dq to the field point where we are finding V. We'll work out several examples of such cases. The potential defined by Eqs. (23.15) and (23.16) is zero at points that are infinitely far away from *all* the charges. Later we'll encounter cases in which the charge distribution itself

Application **Electrocardiography**
The electrodes used in an electrocardiogram—EKG or ECG for short—measure the potential differences (typically no greater than 1 mV = 10^{-3} V) between different parts of the patient's skin. These are indicative of the potential differences between regions of the heart, and so provide a sensitive way to detect any abnormalities in the electrical activity that drives cardiac function.

extends to infinity. We'll find that in such cases we cannot set $V = 0$ at infinity, and we'll need to exercise care in using and interpreting Eqs. (23.15) and (23.16).

CAUTION **What is electric potential?** Before getting too involved in the details of how to calculate electric potential, you should stop and remind yourself what potential is. The electric *potential* at a certain point is the potential energy that would be associated with a *unit* charge placed at that point. That's why potential is measured in joules per coulomb, or volts. Keep in mind, too, that there doesn't have to be a charge at a given point for a potential V to exist at that point. (In the same way, an electric field can exist at a given point even if there's no charge there to respond to it.) ▮

Finding Electric Potential from Electric Field

When we are given a collection of point charges, Eq. (23.15) is usually the easiest way to calculate the potential V. But in some problems in which the electric field is known or can be found easily, it is easier to determine V from $\vec{E}$. The force $\vec{F}$ on a test charge q_0 can be written as $\vec{F} = q_0\vec{E}$, so from Eq. (23.1) the work done by the electric force as the test charge moves from a to b is given by

$$W_{a \to b} = \int_a^b \vec{F} \cdot d\vec{l} = \int_a^b q_0\vec{E} \cdot d\vec{l}$$

If we divide this by q_0 and compare the result with Eq. (23.13), we find

$$V_a - V_b = \int_a^b \vec{E} \cdot d\vec{l} = \int_a^b E\cos\phi\, dl \quad \begin{array}{l}\text{(potential difference}\\ \text{as an integral of } \vec{E}\text{)}\end{array} \quad \text{(23.17)}$$

The value of $V_a - V_b$ is independent of the path taken from a to b, just as the value of $W_{a \to b}$ is independent of the path. To interpret Eq. (23.17), remember that $\vec{E}$ is the electric force per unit charge on a test charge. If the line integral $\int_a^b \vec{E} \cdot d\vec{l}$ is positive, the electric field does positive work on a positive test charge as it moves from a to b. In this case the electric potential energy decreases as the test charge moves, so the potential energy per unit charge decreases as well; hence V_b is less than V_a and $V_a - V_b$ is positive.

As an illustration, consider a positive point charge (Fig. 23.12a). The electric field is directed away from the charge, and $V = q/4\pi\epsilon_0 r$ is positive at any finite distance from the charge. If you move away from the charge, in the direction of $\vec{E}$, you move toward lower values of V; if you move toward the charge, in the direction opposite $\vec{E}$, you move toward greater values of V. For the negative point charge in Fig. 23.12b, $\vec{E}$ is directed toward the charge and $V = q/4\pi\epsilon_0 r$ is negative at any finite distance from the charge. In this case, if you move toward the charge, you are moving in the direction of $\vec{E}$ and in the direction of decreasing (more negative) V. Moving away from the charge, in the direction opposite $\vec{E}$, moves you toward increasing (less negative) values of V. The general rule, valid for *any* electric field, is: Moving *with* the direction of $\vec{E}$ means moving in the direction of *decreasing* V, and moving *against* the direction of $\vec{E}$ means moving in the direction of *increasing* V.

Also, a positive test charge q_0 experiences an electric force in the direction of $\vec{E}$, toward lower values of V; a negative test charge experiences a force opposite $\vec{E}$, toward higher values of V. Thus a positive charge tends to "fall" from a high-potential region to a lower-potential region. The opposite is true for a negative charge.

Notice that Eq. (23.17) can be rewritten as

$$V_a - V_b = -\int_b^a \vec{E} \cdot d\vec{l} \quad \text{(23.18)}$$

This has a negative sign compared to the integral in Eq. (23.17), and the limits are reversed; hence Eqs. (23.17) and (23.18) are equivalent. But Eq. (23.18) has a slightly different interpretation. To move a unit charge slowly against the electric

23.12 If you move in the direction of $\vec{E}$, electric potential V decreases; if you move in the direction opposite $\vec{E}$, V increases.

(a) A positive point charge

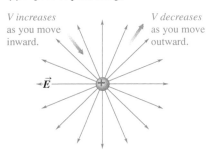

V increases as you move inward.

V decreases as you move outward.

(b) A negative point charge

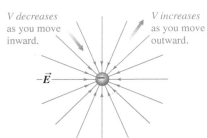

V decreases as you move inward.

V increases as you move outward.

force, we must apply an *external* force per unit charge equal to $-\vec{E}$, equal and opposite to the electric force per unit charge $\vec{E}$. Equation (23.18) says that $V_a - V_b = V_{ab}$, the potential of a with respect to b, equals the work done per unit charge by this external force to move a unit charge from b to a. This is the same alternative interpretation we discussed under Eq. (23.13).

Equations (23.17) and (23.18) show that the unit of potential difference (1 V) is equal to the unit of electric field (1 N/C) multiplied by the unit of distance (1 m). Hence the unit of electric field can be expressed as 1 *volt per meter* (1 V/m), as well as 1 N/C:

$$1 \text{ V/m} = 1 \text{ volt/meter} = 1 \text{ N/C} = 1 \text{ newton/coulomb}$$

In practice, the volt per meter is the usual unit of electric-field magnitude.

Electron Volts

The magnitude e of the electron charge can be used to define a unit of energy that is useful in many calculations with atomic and nuclear systems. When a particle with charge q moves from a point where the potential is V_b to a point where it is V_a, the change in the potential energy U is

$$U_a - U_b = q(V_a - V_b) = qV_{ab}$$

If the charge q equals the magnitude e of the electron charge, 1.602×10^{-19} C, and the potential difference is $V_{ab} = 1$ V, the change in energy is

$$U_a - U_b = (1.602 \times 10^{-19} \text{ C})(1 \text{ V}) = 1.602 \times 10^{-19} \text{ J}$$

This quantity of energy is defined to be 1 **electron volt** (1 eV):

$$1 \text{ eV} = 1.602 \times 10^{-19} \text{ J}$$

The multiples meV, keV, MeV, GeV, and TeV are often used.

CAUTION **Electron volts vs. volts** Remember that the electron volt is a unit of energy, *not* a unit of potential or potential difference!

When a particle with charge e moves through a potential difference of 1 volt, the change in potential *energy* is 1 eV. If the charge is some multiple of e—say Ne—the change in potential energy in electron volts is N times the potential difference in volts. For example, when an alpha particle, which has charge $2e$, moves between two points with a potential difference of 1000 V, the change in potential energy is $2(1000 \text{ eV}) = 2000$ eV. To confirm this, we write

$$U_a - U_b = qV_{ab} = (2e)(1000 \text{ V}) = (2)(1.602 \times 10^{-19} \text{ C})(1000 \text{ V})$$
$$= 3.204 \times 10^{-16} \text{ J} = 2000 \text{ eV}$$

Although we have defined the electron volt in terms of *potential* energy, we can use it for *any* form of energy, such as the kinetic energy of a moving particle. When we speak of a "one-million-electron-volt proton," we mean a proton with a kinetic energy of one million electron volts (1 MeV), equal to $(10^6)(1.602 \times 10^{-19} \text{ J}) = 1.602 \times 10^{-13}$ J. The Large Hadron Collider near Geneva, Switzerland, is designed to accelerate protons to a kinetic energy of 7 TeV (7×10^{12} eV).

Example 23.3 **Electric force and electric potential**

A proton (charge $+e = 1.602 \times 10^{-19}$ C) moves a distance $d = 0.50$ m in a straight line between points a and b in a linear accelerator. The electric field is uniform along this line, with magnitude $E = 1.5 \times 10^7$ V/m $= 1.5 \times 10^7$ N/C in the direction from a to b. Determine (a) the force on the proton; (b) the work done on it by the field; (c) the potential difference $V_a - V_b$.

SOLUTION

IDENTIFY and SET UP: This problem uses the relationship between electric field and electric force. It also uses the relationship among force, work, and potential-energy difference. We are given the electric field, so it is straightforward to find the electric force on the proton. Calculating the work is also straightforward because $\vec{E}$ is uniform, so the force on the proton is constant. Once the work is known, we find $V_a - V_b$ using Eq. (23.13).

EXECUTE: (a) The force on the proton is in the same direction as the electric field, and its magnitude is

$$F = qE = (1.602 \times 10^{-19}\,\text{C})(1.5 \times 10^7\,\text{N/C})$$
$$= 2.4 \times 10^{-12}\,\text{N}$$

(b) The force is constant and in the same direction as the displacement, so the work done on the proton is

$$W_{a \to b} = Fd = (2.4 \times 10^{-12}\,\text{N})(0.50\,\text{m}) = 1.2 \times 10^{-12}\,\text{J}$$

$$= (1.2 \times 10^{-12}\,\text{J})\frac{1\,\text{eV}}{1.602 \times 10^{-19}\,\text{J}}$$

$$= 7.5 \times 10^6\,\text{eV} = 7.5\,\text{MeV}$$

(c) From Eq. (23.13) the potential difference is the work per unit charge, which is

$$V_a - V_b = \frac{W_{a \to b}}{q} = \frac{1.2 \times 10^{-12}\,\text{J}}{1.602 \times 10^{-19}\,\text{C}}$$

$$= 7.5 \times 10^6\,\text{J/C} = 7.5 \times 10^6\,\text{V}$$

$$= 7.5\,\text{MV}$$

We can get this same result even more easily by remembering that 1 electron volt equals 1 volt multiplied by the charge e. The work done is 7.5×10^6 eV and the charge is e, so the potential difference is $(7.5 \times 10^6\,\text{eV})/e = 7.5 \times 10^6$ V.

EVALUATE: We can check our result in part (c) by using Eq. (23.17) or Eq. (23.18). The angle ϕ between the constant field $\vec{E}$ and the displacement is zero, so Eq. (23.17) becomes

$$V_a - V_b = \int_a^b E\cos\phi\,dl = \int_a^b E\,dl = E\int_a^b dl$$

The integral of dl from a to b is just the distance d, so we again find

$$V_a - V_b = Ed = (1.5 \times 10^7\,\text{V/m})(0.50\,\text{m}) = 7.5 \times 10^6\,\text{V}$$

Example 23.4 Potential due to two point charges

An electric dipole consists of point charges $q_1 = +12$ nC and $q_2 = -12$ nC placed 10.0 cm apart (Fig. 23.13). Compute the electric potentials at points a, b, and c.

SOLUTION

IDENTIFY and SET UP: This is the same arrangement as in Example 21.8, in which we calculated the electric *field* at each point by doing a *vector* sum. Here our target variable is the electric *potential* V at three points, which we find by doing the *algebraic* sum in Eq. (23.15).

EXECUTE: At point a we have $r_1 = 0.060$ m and $r_2 = 0.040$ m, so Eq. (23.15) becomes

$$V_a = \frac{1}{4\pi\epsilon_0}\sum_i \frac{q_i}{r_i} = \frac{1}{4\pi\epsilon_0}\frac{q_1}{r_1} + \frac{1}{4\pi\epsilon_0}\frac{q_2}{r_2}$$

$$= (9.0 \times 10^9\,\text{N}\cdot\text{m}^2/\text{C}^2)\frac{12 \times 10^{-9}\,\text{C}}{0.060\,\text{m}}$$

$$+ (9.0 \times 10^9\,\text{N}\cdot\text{m}^2/\text{C}^2)\frac{(-12 \times 10^{-9}\,\text{C})}{0.040\,\text{m}}$$

$$= 1800\,\text{N}\cdot\text{m/C} + (-2700\,\text{N}\cdot\text{m/C})$$

$$= 1800\,\text{V} + (-2700\,\text{V}) = -900\,\text{V}$$

In a similar way you can show that the potential at point b (where $r_1 = 0.040$ m and $r_2 = 0.140$ m) is $V_b = 1930$ V and that the potential at point c (where $r_1 = r_2 = 0.130$ m) is $V_c = 0$.

EVALUATE: Let's confirm that these results make sense. Point a is closer to the -12-nC charge than to the $+12$-nC charge, so the potential at a is negative. The potential is positive at point b, which

23.13 What are the potentials at points a, b, and c due to this electric dipole?

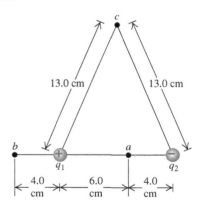

is closer to the $+12$-nC charge than the -12-nC charge. Finally, point c is equidistant from the $+12$-nC charge and the -12-nC charge, so the potential there is zero. (The potential is also equal to zero at a point infinitely far from both charges.)

Comparing this example with Example 21.8 shows that it's much easier to calculate electric potential (a scalar) than electric field (a vector). We'll take advantage of this simplification whenever possible.

Example 23.5 **Potential and potential energy**

Compute the potential energy associated with a +4.0-nC point charge if it is placed at points a, b, and c in Fig. 23.13.

SOLUTION

IDENTIFY and SET UP: The potential energy U associated with a point charge q at a location where the electric potential is V is $U = qV$. We use the values of V from Example 23.4.

EXECUTE: At the three points we find

$$U_a = qV_a = (4.0 \times 10^{-9}\,\text{C})(-900\,\text{J/C}) = -3.6 \times 10^{-6}\,\text{J}$$
$$U_b = qV_b = (4.0 \times 10^{-9}\,\text{C})(1930\,\text{J/C}) = 7.7 \times 10^{-6}\,\text{J}$$
$$U_c = qV_c = 0$$

All of these values correspond to U and V being zero at infinity.

EVALUATE: Note that *zero* net work is done on the 4.0-nC charge if it moves from point c to infinity *by any path*. In particular, let the path be along the perpendicular bisector of the line joining the other two charges q_1 and q_2 in Fig. 23.13. As shown in Example 21.8 (Section 21.5), at points on the bisector, the direction of $\vec{E}$ is perpendicular to the bisector. Hence the force on the 4.0-nC charge is perpendicular to the path, and no work is done in any displacement along it.

Example 23.6 **Finding potential by integration**

By integrating the electric field as in Eq. (23.17), find the potential at a distance r from a point charge q.

SOLUTION

IDENTIFY and SET UP: We let point a in Eq. (23.17) be at distance r and let point b be at infinity (Fig. 23.14). As usual, we choose the potential to be zero at an infinite distance from the charge q.

EXECUTE: To carry out the integral, we can choose any path we like between points a and b. The most convenient path is a radial line as shown in Fig. 23.14, so that $d\vec{l}$ is in the radial direction and has magnitude dr. Writing $d\vec{l} = \hat{r}\,dr$, we have from Eq. (23.17)

$$V - 0 = V = \int_r^\infty \vec{E} \cdot d\vec{l}$$
$$= \int_r^\infty \frac{1}{4\pi\epsilon_0}\frac{q}{r^2}\hat{r}\cdot\hat{r}\,dr = \int_r^\infty \frac{q}{4\pi\epsilon_0 r^2}\,dr$$
$$= -\frac{q}{4\pi\epsilon_0 r}\Big|_r^\infty = 0 - \left(-\frac{q}{4\pi\epsilon_0 r}\right)$$
$$V = \frac{q}{4\pi\epsilon_0 r}$$

23.14 Calculating the potential by integrating $\vec{E}$ for a single point charge.

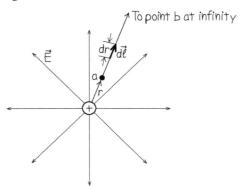

EVALUATE: Our result agrees with Eq. (23.14) and is correct for positive or negative q.

Example 23.7 **Moving through a potential difference**

In Fig. 23.15 a dust particle with mass $m = 5.0 \times 10^{-9}\,\text{kg}$ $= 5.0\ \mu\text{g}$ and charge $q_0 = 2.0\,\text{nC}$ starts from rest and moves in a straight line from point a to point b. What is its speed v at point b?

SOLUTION

IDENTIFY and SET UP: Only the conservative electric force acts on the particle, so mechanical energy is conserved: $K_a + U_a = K_b + U_b$. We get the potential energies U from the

23.15 The particle moves from point a to point b; its acceleration is not constant.

corresponding potentials V using Eq. (23.12): $U_a = q_0 V_a$ and $U_b = q_0 V_b$.

EXECUTE: We have $K_a = 0$ and $K_b = \frac{1}{2}mv^2$. We substitute these and our expressions for U_a and U_b into the energy-conservation equation, then solve for v. We find

$$0 + q_0V_a = \tfrac{1}{2}mv^2 + q_0V_b$$

$$v = \sqrt{\frac{2q_0(V_a - V_b)}{m}}$$

We calculate the potentials using Eq. (23.15), $V = q/4\pi\epsilon_0 r$:

$$V_a = (9.0 \times 10^9 \text{ N} \cdot \text{m}^2/\text{C}^2)\left(\frac{3.0 \times 10^{-9} \text{ C}}{0.010 \text{ m}}\right.$$

$$\left. + \frac{(-3.0 \times 10^{-9} \text{ C})}{0.020 \text{ m}}\right)$$

$$= 1350 \text{ V}$$

$$V_b = (9.0 \times 10^9 \text{ N} \cdot \text{m}^2/\text{C}^2)\left(\frac{3.0 \times 10^{-9} \text{ C}}{0.020 \text{ m}}\right.$$

$$\left. + \frac{(-3.0 \times 10^{-9} \text{ C})}{0.010 \text{ m}}\right)$$

$$= -1350 \text{ V}$$

$$V_a - V_b = (1350 \text{ V}) - (-1350 \text{ V}) = 2700 \text{ V}$$

Finally,

$$v = \sqrt{\frac{2(2.0 \times 10^{-9} \text{ C})(2700 \text{ V})}{5.0 \times 10^{-9} \text{ kg}}} = 46 \text{ m/s}$$

EVALUATE: Our result makes sense: The positive test charge speeds up as it moves away from the positive charge and toward the negative charge. To check unit consistency in the final line of the calculation, note that 1 V = 1 J/C, so the numerator under the radical has units of J or $\text{kg} \cdot \text{m}^2/\text{s}^2$.

Test Your Understanding of Section 23.2 If the electric *potential* at a certain point is zero, does the electric *field* at that point have to be zero? (*Hint:* Consider point c in Example 23.4 and Example 21.8.) ❙

23.3 Calculating Electric Potential

When calculating the potential due to a charge distribution, we usually follow one of two routes. If we know the charge distribution, we can use Eq. (23.15) or (23.16). Or if we know how the electric field depends on position, we can use Eq. (23.17), defining the potential to be zero at some convenient place. Some problems require a combination of these approaches.

As you read through these examples, compare them with the related examples of calculating electric *field* in Section 21.5. You'll see how much easier it is to calculate scalar electric potentials than vector electric fields. The moral is clear: Whenever possible, solve problems using an energy approach (using electric potential and electric potential energy) rather than a dynamics approach (using electric fields and electric forces).

Problem-Solving Strategy 23.1 **Calculating Electric Potential**

IDENTIFY *the relevant concepts:* Remember that electric potential is *potential energy per unit charge.*

SET UP *the problem* using the following steps:
1. Make a drawing showing the locations and values of the charges (which may be point charges or a continuous distribution of charge) and your choice of coordinate axes.
2. Indicate on your drawing the position of the point at which you want to calculate the electric potential V. Sometimes this position will be an arbitrary one (say, a point a distance r from the center of a charged sphere).

EXECUTE *the solution* as follows:
1. To find the potential due to a collection of point charges, use Eq. (23.15). If you are given a continuous charge distribution, devise a way to divide it into infinitesimal elements and use Eq. (23.16). Carry out the integration, using appropriate limits to include the entire charge distribution.
2. If you are given the electric field, or if you can find it using any of the methods presented in Chapter 21 or 22, it may be

easier to find the potential difference between points a and b using Eq. (23.17) or (23.18). When appropriate, make use of your freedom to define V to be zero at some convenient place, and choose this place to be point b. (For point charges, this will usually be at infinity. For other distributions of charge—especially those that themselves extend to infinity—it may be necessary to define V_b to be zero at some finite distance from the charge distribution.) Then the potential at any other point, say a, can by found from Eq. (23.17) or (23.18) with $V_b = 0$.
3. Although potential V is a *scalar* quantity, you may have to use components of the vectors $\vec{E}$ and $d\vec{l}$ when you use Eq. (23.17) or (23.18) to calculate V.

EVALUATE *your answer:* Check whether your answer agrees with your intuition. If your result gives V as a function of position, graph the function to see whether it makes sense. If you know the electric field, you can make a rough check of your result for V by verifying that V decreases if you move in the direction of $\vec{E}$.

Example 23.8 **A charged conducting sphere**

A solid conducting sphere of radius R has a total charge q. Find the electric potential everywhere, both outside and inside the sphere.

SOLUTION

IDENTIFY and SET UP: In Example 22.5 (Section 22.4) we used Gauss's law to find the electric *field* at all points for this charge distribution. We can use that result to determine the corresponding potential.

EXECUTE: From Example 22.5, the field *outside* the sphere is the same as if the sphere were removed and replaced by a point charge q. We take $V = 0$ at infinity, as we did for a point charge. Then the potential at a point outside the sphere at a distance r from its center is the same as that due to a point charge q at the center:

$$V = \frac{1}{4\pi\epsilon_0} \frac{q}{r}$$

The potential at the surface of the sphere is $V_{surface} = q/4\pi\epsilon_0 R$.

Inside the sphere, $\vec{E}$ is zero everywhere. Hence no work is done on a test charge that moves from any point to any other point inside the sphere. This means that the potential is the same at every point inside the sphere and is equal to its value $q/4\pi\epsilon_0 R$ at the surface.

EVALUATE: Figure 23.16 shows the field and potential for a positive charge q. In this case the electric field points radially away

from the sphere. As you move away from the sphere, in the direction of $\vec{E}$, V decreases (as it should).

23.16 Electric-field magnitude E and potential V at points inside and outside a positively charged spherical conductor.

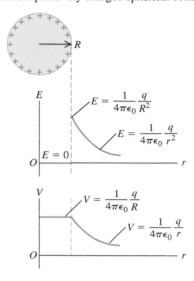

$$E = \frac{1}{4\pi\epsilon_0} \frac{q}{R^2}$$

$$E = \frac{1}{4\pi\epsilon_0} \frac{q}{r^2}$$

$$E = 0$$

$$V = \frac{1}{4\pi\epsilon_0} \frac{q}{R}$$

$$V = \frac{1}{4\pi\epsilon_0} \frac{q}{r}$$

Ionization and Corona Discharge

The results of Example 23.8 have numerous practical consequences. One consequence relates to the maximum potential to which a conductor in air can be raised. This potential is limited because air molecules become *ionized*, and air becomes a conductor, at an electric-field magnitude of about 3×10^6 V/m. Assume for the moment that q is positive. When we compare the expressions in Example 23.8 for the potential $V_{surface}$ and field magnitude $E_{surface}$ at the surface of a charged conducting sphere, we note that $V_{surface} = E_{surface}R$. Thus, if E_m represents the electric-field magnitude at which air becomes conductive (known as the *dielectric strength* of air), then the maximum potential V_m to which a spherical conductor can be raised is

$$V_m = RE_m$$

For a conducting sphere 1 cm in radius in air, $V_m = (10^{-2} \text{ m})(3 \times 10^6 \text{ V/m}) =$ 30,000 V. No amount of "charging" could raise the potential of a conducting sphere of this size in air higher than about 30,000 V; attempting to raise the potential further by adding extra charge would cause the surrounding air to become ionized and conductive, and the extra added charge would leak into the air.

To attain even higher potentials, high-voltage machines such as Van de Graaff generators use spherical terminals with very large radii (see Fig. 22.26 and the photograph that opens Chapter 22). For example, a terminal of radius $R = 2$ m has a maximum potential $V_m = (2 \text{ m})(3 \times 10^6 \text{ V/m}) = 6 \times 10^6 \text{ V} = 6 \text{ MV}$.

Our result in Example 23.8 also explains what happens with a charged conductor with a very *small* radius of curvature, such as a sharp point or thin wire. Because the maximum potential is proportional to the radius, even relatively small potentials applied to sharp points in air produce sufficiently high fields just outside the point to ionize the surrounding air, making it become a conductor. The resulting current and its associated glow (visible in a dark room) are called *corona*. Laser printers and photocopying machines use corona from fine wires to spray charge on the imaging drum (see Fig. 21.2).

A large-radius conductor is used in situations where it's important to *prevent* corona. An example is the metal ball at the end of a car radio antenna, which prevents the static that would be caused by corona. Another example is the blunt end of a metal lightning rod (Fig. 23.17). If there is an excess charge in the atmosphere, as happens during thunderstorms, a substantial charge of the opposite sign can build up on this blunt end. As a result, when the atmospheric charge is discharged through a lightning bolt, it tends to be attracted to the charged lightning rod rather than to other nearby structures that could be damaged. (A conducting wire connecting the lightning rod to the ground then allows the acquired charge to dissipate harmlessly.) A lightning rod with a sharp end would allow less charge buildup and hence would be less effective.

23.17 The metal mast at the top of the Empire State Building acts as a lightning rod. It is struck by lightning as many as 500 times each year.

Example 23.9   Oppositely charged parallel plates

Find the potential at any height y between the two oppositely charged parallel plates discussed in Section 23.1 (Fig. 23.18).

SOLUTION

IDENTIFY and SET UP: We discussed this situation in Section 23.1. From Eq. (23.5), we know the electric *potential energy* U for a test charge q_0 is $U = q_0 Ey$. (We set $y = 0$ and $U = 0$ at the bottom plate.) We use Eq. (23.12), $U = q_0 V$, to find the electric *potential* V as a function of y.

EXECUTE: The potential $V(y)$ at coordinate y is the potential energy per unit charge:

$$V(y) = \frac{U(y)}{q_0} = \frac{q_0 Ey}{q_0} = Ey$$

The potential decreases as we move in the direction of $\vec{E}$ from the upper to the lower plate. At point a, where $y = d$ and $V(y) = V_a$,

$$V_a - V_b = Ed \quad \text{and} \quad E = \frac{V_a - V_b}{d} = \frac{V_{ab}}{d}$$

where V_{ab} is the potential of the positive plate with respect to the negative plate. That is, the electric field equals the potential difference between the plates divided by the distance between them. For a given potential difference V_{ab}, the smaller the distance d between the two plates, the greater the magnitude E of the electric field. (This relationship between E and V_{ab} holds *only* for the planar geometry

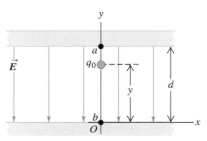

23.18 The charged parallel plates from Fig. 23.2.

we have described. It does *not* work for situations such as concentric cylinders or spheres in which the electric field is not uniform.)

EVALUATE: Our result shows that $V = 0$ at the bottom plate (at $y = 0$). This is consistent with our choice that $U = q_0 V = 0$ for a test charge placed at the bottom plate.

CAUTION   *"Zero potential" is arbitrary* You might think that if a conducting body has zero potential, it must necessarily also have zero net charge. But that just isn't so! As an example, the plate at $y = 0$ in Fig. 23.18 has zero potential ($V = 0$) but has a nonzero charge per unit area $-\sigma$. There's nothing particularly special about the place where potential is zero; we can *define* this place to be wherever we want it to be. ∎

Example 23.10   An infinite line charge or charged conducting cylinder

Find the potential at a distance r from a very long line of charge with linear charge density (charge per unit length) λ.

SOLUTION

IDENTIFY and SET UP: In both Example 21.10 (Section 21.5) and Example 22.6 (Section 22.4) we found that the electric field at a

radial distance r from a long straight-line charge (Fig. 23.19a) has only a radial component given by $E_r = \lambda/2\pi\epsilon_0 r$. We use this expression to find the potential by integrating $\vec{E}$ as in Eq. (23.17).

EXECUTE: Since the field has only a radial component, we have $\vec{E} \cdot d\vec{l} = E_r\, dr$. Hence from Eq. (23.17) the potential of any point a

Continued

with respect to any other point b, at radial distances r_a and r_b from the line of charge, is

$$V_a - V_b = \int_a^b \vec{E} \cdot d\vec{l} = \int_a^b E_r \, dr = \frac{\lambda}{2\pi\epsilon_0} \int_{r_a}^{r_b} \frac{dr}{r} = \frac{\lambda}{2\pi\epsilon_0} \ln \frac{r_b}{r_a}$$

If we take point b at infinity and set $V_b = 0$, we find that V_a is *infinite* for any finite distance r_a from the line charge: $V_a = (\lambda/2\pi\epsilon_0) \ln (\infty/r_a) = \infty$. This is *not* a useful way to define V for this problem! The difficulty is that the charge distribution itself extends to infinity.

Instead, as recommended in Problem-Solving Strategy 23.1, we set $V_b = 0$ at point b at an arbitrary but *finite* radial distance r_0. Then the potential $V = V_a$ at point a at a radial distance r is given by $V - 0 = (\lambda/2\pi\epsilon_0) \ln (r_0/r)$, or

$$V = \frac{\lambda}{2\pi\epsilon_0} \ln \frac{r_0}{r}$$

EVALUATE: According to our result, if λ is positive, then V decreases as r increases. This is as it should be: V decreases as we move in the direction of $\vec{E}$.

From Example 22.6, the expression for E_r with which we started also applies outside a long, charged conducting cylinder with charge per unit length λ (Fig. 23.19b). Hence our result also gives the potential for such a cylinder, but only for values

23.19 Electric field outside (a) a long, positively charged wire and (b) a long, positively charged cylinder.

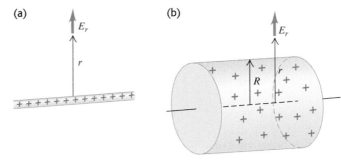

(a)   (b)

of r (the distance from the cylinder axis) equal to or greater than the radius R of the cylinder. If we choose r_0 to be the cylinder radius R, so that $V = 0$ when $r = R$, then at any point for which $r > R$,

$$V = \frac{\lambda}{2\pi\epsilon_0} \ln \frac{R}{r}$$

Inside the cylinder, $\vec{E} = 0$, and V has the same value (zero) as on the cylinder's surface.

Example 23.11   A ring of charge

Electric charge Q is distributed uniformly around a thin ring of radius a (Fig. 23.20). Find the potential at a point P on the ring axis at a distance x from the center of the ring.

SOLUTION

IDENTIFY and SET UP: We divide the ring into infinitesimal segments and use Eq. (23.16) to find V. All parts of the ring (and therefore all elements of the charge distribution) are at the same distance from P.

EXECUTE: Figure 23.20 shows that the distance from each charge element dq to P is $r = \sqrt{x^2 + a^2}$. Hence we can take the factor $1/r$ outside the integral in Eq. (23.16), and

$$V = \frac{1}{4\pi\epsilon_0} \int \frac{dq}{r} = \frac{1}{4\pi\epsilon_0} \frac{1}{\sqrt{x^2 + a^2}} \int dq = \frac{1}{4\pi\epsilon_0} \frac{Q}{\sqrt{x^2 + a^2}}$$

EVALUATE: When x is much larger than a, our expression for V becomes approximately $V = Q/4\pi\epsilon_0 x$, which is the potential at a distance x from a point charge Q. Very far away from a charged

23.20 All the charge in a ring of charge Q is the same distance r from a point P on the ring axis.

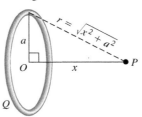

ring, its electric potential looks like that of a point charge. We drew a similar conclusion about the electric *field* of a ring in Example 21.9 (Section 21.5).

We know the electric field at all points along the x-axis from Example 21.9 (Section 21.5), so we can also find V along this axis by integrating $\vec{E} \cdot d\vec{l}$ as in Eq. (23.17).

Example 23.12   Potential of a line of charge

Positive electric charge Q is distributed uniformly along a line of length $2a$ lying along the y-axis between $y = -a$ and $y = +a$ (Fig. 23.21). Find the electric potential at a point P on the x-axis at a distance x from the origin.

SOLUTION

IDENTIFY and SET UP: This is the same situation as in Example 21.10 (Section 21.5), where we found an expression for the electric field $\vec{E}$ at an arbitrary point on the x-axis. We can find V at point P by integrating over the charge distribution using Eq. (23.16). Unlike the situation in Example 23.11, each charge element dQ is a *different* distance from point P, so the integration will take a little more effort.

EXECUTE: As in Example 21.10, the element of charge dQ corresponding to an element of length dy on the rod is $dQ = (Q/2a)dy$. The distance from dQ to P is $\sqrt{x^2 + y^2}$, so the contribution dV that the charge element makes to the potential at P is

$$dV = \frac{1}{4\pi\epsilon_0} \frac{Q}{2a} \frac{dy}{\sqrt{x^2 + y^2}}$$

To find the potential at P due to the entire rod, we integrate dV over the length of the rod from $y = -a$ to $y = a$:

$$V = \frac{1}{4\pi\epsilon_0} \frac{Q}{2a} \int_{-a}^{a} \frac{dy}{\sqrt{x^2 + y^2}}$$

You can look up the integral in a table. The final result is

$$V = \frac{1}{4\pi\epsilon_0} \frac{Q}{2a} \ln\left(\frac{\sqrt{a^2 + x^2} + a}{\sqrt{a^2 + x^2} - a}\right)$$

23.21 Our sketch for this problem.

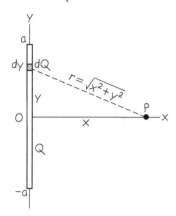

EVALUATE: We can check our result by letting x approach infinity. In this limit the point P is infinitely far from all of the charge, so we expect V to approach zero; you can verify that it does.

We know the electric field at all points along the x-axis from Example 21.10. We invite you to use this information to find V along this axis by integrating $\vec{E}$ as in Eq. (23.17).

Test Your Understanding of Section 23.3 If the electric *field* at a certain point is zero, does the electric *potential* at that point have to be zero? (*Hint:* Consider the center of the ring in Example 23.11 and Example 21.9.)

23.4 Equipotential Surfaces

Field lines (see Section 21.6) help us visualize electric fields. In a similar way, the potential at various points in an electric field can be represented graphically by *equipotential surfaces*. These use the same fundamental idea as topographic maps like those used by hikers and mountain climbers (Fig. 23.22). On a topographic map, contour lines are drawn through points that are all at the same elevation. Any number of these could be drawn, but typically only a few contour lines are shown at equal spacings of elevation. If a mass m is moved over the terrain along such a contour line, the gravitational potential energy mgy does not change because the elevation y is constant. Thus contour lines on a topographic map are really curves of constant gravitational potential energy. Contour lines are close together where the terrain is steep and there are large changes in elevation over a small horizontal distance; the contour lines are farther apart where the terrain is gently sloping. A ball allowed to roll downhill will experience the greatest downhill gravitational force where contour lines are closest together.

By analogy to contour lines on a topographic map, an **equipotential surface** is a three-dimensional surface on which the *electric potential* V is the same at every point. If a test charge q_0 is moved from point to point on such a surface, the *electric potential energy* q_0V remains constant. In a region where an electric field is present, we can construct an equipotential surface through any point. In diagrams we usually show only a few representative equipotentials, often with equal potential differences between adjacent surfaces. No point can be at two different potentials, so equipotential surfaces for different potentials can never touch or intersect.

23.22 Contour lines on a topographic map are curves of constant elevation and hence of constant gravitational potential energy.

Equipotential Surfaces and Field Lines

Because potential energy does not change as a test charge moves over an equipotential surface, the electric field can do no work on such a charge. It follows that $\vec{E}$ must be perpendicular to the surface at every point so that the electric force $q_0\vec{E}$ is always perpendicular to the displacement of a charge moving on the surface.

23.23 Cross sections of equipotential surfaces (blue lines) and electric field lines (red lines) for assemblies of point charges. There are equal potential differences between adjacent surfaces. Compare these diagrams to those in Fig. 21.28, which showed only the electric field lines.

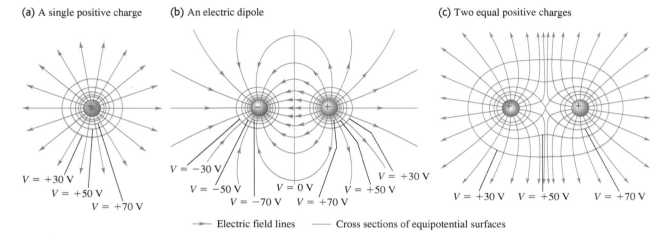

(a) A single positive charge

(b) An electric dipole

(c) Two equal positive charges

$V = +30$ V
$V = +50$ V
$V = +70$ V

$V = -30$ V
$V = -50$ V $V = 0$ V $V = +30$ V
$V = -70$ V $V = +70$ V $V = +50$ V

$V = +30$ V $V = +50$ V $V = +70$ V

→— Electric field lines   —— Cross sections of equipotential surfaces

Field lines and equipotential surfaces are always mutually perpendicular. In general, field lines are curves, and equipotentials are curved surfaces. For the special case of a *uniform* field, in which the field lines are straight, parallel, and equally spaced, the equipotentials are parallel *planes* perpendicular to the field lines.

Figure 23.23 shows three arrangements of charges. The field lines in the plane of the charges are represented by red lines, and the intersections of the equipotential surfaces with this plane (that is, cross sections of these surfaces) are shown as blue lines. The actual equipotential surfaces are three-dimensional. At each crossing of an equipotential and a field line, the two are perpendicular.

In Fig. 23.23 we have drawn equipotentials so that there are equal potential differences between adjacent surfaces. In regions where the magnitude of $\vec{E}$ is large, the equipotential surfaces are close together because the field does a relatively large amount of work on a test charge in a relatively small displacement. This is the case near the point charge in Fig. 23.23a or between the two point charges in Fig. 23.23b; note that in these regions the field lines are also closer together. This is directly analogous to the downhill force of gravity being greatest in regions on a topographic map where contour lines are close together. Conversely, in regions where the field is weaker, the equipotential surfaces are farther apart; this happens at larger radii in Fig. 23.23a, to the left of the negative charge or the right of the positive charge in Fig. 23.23b, and at greater distances from both charges in Fig. 23.23c. (It may appear that two equipotential surfaces intersect at the center of Fig. 23.23c, in violation of the rule that this can never happen. In fact this is a single figure-8–shaped equipotential surface.)

CAUTION *E need not be constant over an equipotential surface* On a given equipotential surface, the potential V has the same value at every point. In general, however, the electric-field magnitude E is *not* the same at all points on an equipotential surface. For instance, on the equipotential surface labeled "$V = -30$ V" in Fig. 23.23b, the magnitude E is less to the left of the negative charge than it is between the two charges. On the figure-8–shaped equipotential surface in Fig. 23.23c, $E = 0$ at the middle point halfway between the two charges; at any other point on this surface, E is nonzero. ▍

Equipotentials and Conductors

Here's an important statement about equipotential surfaces: **When all charges are at rest, the surface of a conductor is always an equipotential surface.**

Since the electric field $\vec{E}$ is always perpendicular to an equipotential surface, we can prove this statement by proving that **when all charges are at rest, the electric field just outside a conductor must be perpendicular to the surface at every point** (Fig. 23.24). We know that $\vec{E} = 0$ everywhere inside the conductor; otherwise, charges would move. In particular, at any point just inside the surface the component of $\vec{E}$ tangent to the surface is zero. It follows that the tangential component of $\vec{E}$ is also zero just *outside* the surface. If it were not, a charge could move around a rectangular path partly inside and partly outside (Fig. 23.25) and return to its starting point with a net amount of work having been done on it. This would violate the conservative nature of electrostatic fields, so the tangential component of $\vec{E}$ just outside the surface must be zero at every point on the surface. Thus $\vec{E}$ is perpendicular to the surface at each point, proving our statement.

It also follows that **when all charges are at rest, the entire solid volume of a conductor is at the same potential.** Equation (23.17) states that the potential difference between two points a and b within the conductor's solid volume, $V_a - V_b$, is equal to the line integral $\int_a^b \vec{E} \cdot d\vec{l}$ of the electric field from a to b. Since $\vec{E} = 0$ everywhere inside the conductor, the integral is guaranteed to be zero for any two such points a and b. Hence the potential is the same for any two points within the solid volume of the conductor. We describe this by saying that the solid volume of the conductor is an *equipotential volume.*

Finally, we can now prove a theorem that we quoted without proof in Section 22.5. The theorem is as follows: In an electrostatic situation, if a conductor contains a cavity and if no charge is present inside the cavity, then there can be no net charge *anywhere* on the surface of the cavity. This means that if you're inside a charged conducting box, you can safely touch any point on the inside walls of the box without being shocked. To prove this theorem, we first prove that *every point in the cavity is at the same potential.* In Fig. 23.26 the conducting surface A of the cavity is an equipotential surface, as we have just proved. Suppose point P in the cavity is at a different potential; then we can construct a different equipotential surface B including point P.

Now consider a Gaussian surface, shown in Fig. 23.26, between the two equipotential surfaces. Because of the relationship between $\vec{E}$ and the equipotentials, we know that the field at every point between the equipotentials is from A toward B, or else at every point it is from B toward A, depending on which equipotential surface is at higher potential. In either case the flux through this Gaussian surface is certainly not zero. But then Gauss's law says that the charge enclosed by the Gaussian surface cannot be zero. This contradicts our initial assumption that there is *no* charge in the cavity. So the potential at P *cannot* be different from that at the cavity wall.

The entire region of the cavity must therefore be at the same potential. But for this to be true, *the electric field inside the cavity must be zero everywhere.* Finally, Gauss's law shows that the electric field at any point on the surface of a conductor is proportional to the surface charge density σ at that point. We conclude that *the surface charge density on the wall of the cavity is zero at every point.* This chain of reasoning may seem tortuous, but it is worth careful study.

CAUTION   **Equipotential surfaces vs. Gaussian surfaces**   Don't confuse equipotential surfaces with the Gaussian surfaces we encountered in Chapter 22. Gaussian surfaces have relevance only when we are using Gauss's law, and we can choose *any* Gaussian surface that's convenient. We are *not* free to choose the shape of equipotential surfaces; the shape is determined by the charge distribution. ▮

Test Your Understanding of Section 23.4   Would the shapes of the equipotential surfaces in Fig. 23.23 change if the sign of each charge were reversed? ▮

23.24 When charges are at rest, a conducting surface is always an equipotential surface. Field lines are perpendicular to a conducting surface.

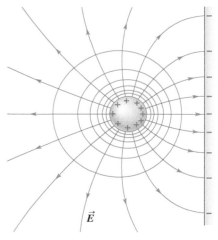

—— Cross sections of equipotential surfaces
→— Electric field lines

23.25 At all points on the surface of a conductor, the electric field must be perpendicular to the surface. If $\vec{E}$ had a tangential component, a net amount of work would be done on a test charge by moving it around a loop as shown here—which is impossible because the electric force is conservative.

An impossible electric field
If the electric field just outside a conductor had a tangential component $E_∥$, a charge could move in a loop with net work done.

23.26 A cavity in a conductor. If the cavity contains no charge, every point in the cavity is at the same potential, the electric field is zero everywhere in the cavity, and there is no charge anywhere on the surface of the cavity.

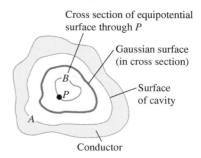

Mastering**PHYSICS**

ActivPhysics 11.12.3: Electrical Potential, Field, and Force

23.5 Potential Gradient

Electric field and potential are closely related. Equation (23.17), restated here, expresses one aspect of that relationship:

$$V_a - V_b = \int_a^b \vec{E} \cdot d\vec{l}$$

If we know $\vec{E}$ at various points, we can use this equation to calculate potential differences. In this section we show how to turn this around; if we know the potential V at various points, we can use it to determine $\vec{E}$. Regarding V as a function of the coordinates (x, y, z) of a point in space, we will show that the components of $\vec{E}$ are related to the *partial derivatives* of V with respect to x, y, and z.

In Eq. (23.17), $V_a - V_b$ is the potential of a with respect to b—that is, the change of potential encountered on a trip from b to a. We can write this as

$$V_a - V_b = \int_b^a dV = -\int_a^b dV$$

where dV is the infinitesimal change of potential accompanying an infinitesimal element $d\vec{l}$ of the path from b to a. Comparing to Eq. (23.17), we have

$$-\int_a^b dV = \int_a^b \vec{E} \cdot d\vec{l}$$

These two integrals must be equal for *any* pair of limits a and b, and for this to be true the *integrands* must be equal. Thus, for *any* infinitesimal displacement $d\vec{l}$,

$$-dV = \vec{E} \cdot d\vec{l}$$

To interpret this expression, we write $\vec{E}$ and $d\vec{l}$ in terms of their components: $\vec{E} = \hat{\imath} E_x + \hat{\jmath} E_y + \hat{k} E_z$ and $d\vec{l} = \hat{\imath} dx + \hat{\jmath} dy + \hat{k} dz$. Then we have

$$-dV = E_x dx + E_y dy + E_z dz$$

Suppose the displacement is parallel to the x-axis, so $dy = dz = 0$. Then $-dV = E_x dx$ or $E_x = -(dV/dx)_{y, z \text{ constant}}$, where the subscript reminds us that only x varies in the derivative; recall that V is in general a function of x, y, and z. But this is just what is meant by the partial derivative $\partial V / \partial x$. The y- and z-components of $\vec{E}$ are related to the corresponding derivatives of V in the same way, so we have

$$E_x = -\frac{\partial V}{\partial x} \qquad E_y = -\frac{\partial V}{\partial y} \qquad E_z = -\frac{\partial V}{\partial z} \qquad \begin{array}{l}\text{(components of } \vec{E} \\ \text{in terms of } V)\end{array} \qquad (23.19)$$

This is consistent with the units of electric field being V/m. In terms of unit vectors we can write $\vec{E}$ as

$$\vec{E} = -\left(\hat{\imath} \frac{\partial V}{\partial x} + \hat{\jmath} \frac{\partial V}{\partial y} + \hat{k} \frac{\partial V}{\partial z} \right) \qquad (\vec{E} \text{ in terms of } V) \qquad (23.20)$$

In vector notation the following operation is called the **gradient** of the function f:

$$\vec{\nabla} f = \left(\hat{\imath} \frac{\partial}{\partial x} + \hat{\jmath} \frac{\partial}{\partial y} + \hat{k} \frac{\partial}{\partial z} \right) f \qquad (23.21)$$

The operator denoted by the symbol $\vec{\nabla}$ is called "grad" or "del." Thus in vector notation,

$$\vec{E} = -\vec{\nabla} V \qquad (23.22)$$

This is read "$\vec{E}$ is the negative of the gradient of V" or "$\vec{E}$ equals negative grad V." The quantity $\vec{\nabla} V$ is called the *potential gradient*.

Application Potential Gradient Across a Cell Membrane
The interior of a human cell is at a lower electric potential V than the exterior. (The potential difference when the cell is inactive is about –70 mV in neurons and about –95 mV in skeletal muscle cells.) Hence there is a potential gradient $\vec{\nabla} V$ that points from the *interior* to the *exterior* of the cell membrane, and an electric field $\vec{E} = -\vec{\nabla} V$ that points from the *exterior* to the *interior*. This field affects how ions flow into or out of the cell through special channels in the membrane.

● Calcium (Ca)
● Potassium (K)
● Sodium (Na)

At each point, the potential gradient points in the direction in which V *increases* most rapidly with a change in position. Hence at each point the direction of $\vec{E}$ is the direction in which V *decreases* most rapidly and is always perpendicular to the equipotential surface through the point. This agrees with our observation in Section 23.2 that moving in the direction of the electric field means moving in the direction of decreasing potential.

Equation (23.22) doesn't depend on the particular choice of the zero point for V. If we were to change the zero point, the effect would be to change V at every point by the same amount; the derivatives of V would be the same.

If $\vec{E}$ is radial with respect to a point or an axis and r is the distance from the point or the axis, the relationship corresponding to Eqs. (23.19) is

$$E_r = -\frac{\partial V}{\partial r} \quad \text{(radial electric field)} \qquad (23.23)$$

Often we can compute the electric field caused by a charge distribution in either of two ways: directly, by adding the $\vec{E}$ fields of point charges, or by first calculating the potential and then taking its gradient to find the field. The second method is often easier because potential is a *scalar* quantity, requiring at worst the integration of a scalar function. Electric field is a *vector* quantity, requiring computation of components for each element of charge and a separate integration for each component. Thus, quite apart from its fundamental significance, potential offers a very useful computational technique in field calculations. Below, we present two examples in which a knowledge of V is used to find the electric field.

We stress once more that if we know $\vec{E}$ as a function of position, we can calculate V using Eq. (23.17) or (23.18), and if we know V as a function of position, we can calculate $\vec{E}$ using Eq. (23.19), (23.20), or (23.23). Deriving V from $\vec{E}$ requires integration, and deriving $\vec{E}$ from V requires differentiation.

Example 23.13   Potential and field of a point charge

From Eq. (23.14) the potential at a radial distance r from a point charge q is $V = q/4\pi\epsilon_0 r$. Find the vector electric field from this expression for V.

SOLUTION

IDENTIFY and SET UP: This problem uses the general relationship between the electric potential as a function of position and the electric-field vector. By symmetry, the electric field here has only a radial component E_r. We use Eq. (23.23) to find this component.

EXECUTE: From Eq. (23.23),

$$E_r = -\frac{\partial V}{\partial r} = -\frac{\partial}{\partial r}\left(\frac{1}{4\pi\epsilon_0}\frac{q}{r}\right) = \frac{1}{4\pi\epsilon_0}\frac{q}{r^2}$$

so the vector electric field is

$$\vec{E} = \hat{r}E_r = \frac{1}{4\pi\epsilon_0}\frac{q}{r^2}\hat{r}$$

EVALUATE: Our result agrees with Eq. (21.7), as it must.

An alternative approach is to ignore the radial symmetry, write the radial distance as $r = \sqrt{x^2 + y^2 + z^2}$, and take the derivatives of V with respect to x, y, and z as in Eq. (23.20). We find

$$\frac{\partial V}{\partial x} = \frac{\partial}{\partial x}\left(\frac{1}{4\pi\epsilon_0}\frac{q}{\sqrt{x^2 + y^2 + z^2}}\right) = -\frac{1}{4\pi\epsilon_0}\frac{qx}{(x^2 + y^2 + z^2)^{3/2}}$$

$$= -\frac{qx}{4\pi\epsilon_0 r^3}$$

and similarly

$$\frac{\partial V}{\partial y} = -\frac{qy}{4\pi\epsilon_0 r^3} \qquad \frac{\partial V}{\partial z} = -\frac{qz}{4\pi\epsilon_0 r^3}$$

Then from Eq. (23.20),

$$\vec{E} = -\left[\hat{i}\left(-\frac{qx}{4\pi\epsilon_0 r^3}\right) + \hat{j}\left(-\frac{qy}{4\pi\epsilon_0 r^3}\right) + \hat{k}\left(-\frac{qz}{4\pi\epsilon_0 r^3}\right)\right]$$

$$= \frac{1}{4\pi\epsilon_0}\frac{q}{r^2}\left(\frac{x\hat{i} + y\hat{j} + z\hat{k}}{r}\right) = \frac{1}{4\pi\epsilon_0}\frac{q}{r^2}\hat{r}$$

This approach gives us the same answer, but with more effort. Clearly it's best to exploit the symmetry of the charge distribution whenever possible.

Example 23.14 Potential and field of a ring of charge

In Example 23.11 (Section 23.3) we found that for a ring of charge with radius a and total charge Q, the potential at a point P on the ring's symmetry axis a distance x from the center is

$$V = \frac{1}{4\pi\epsilon_0} \frac{Q}{\sqrt{x^2 + a^2}}$$

Find the electric field at P.

SOLUTION

IDENTIFY and SET UP: Figure 23.20 shows the situation. We are given V as a function of x along the x-axis, and we wish to find the electric field at a point on this axis. From the symmetry of the charge distribution, the electric field along the symmetry (x-) axis of the ring can have only an x-component. We find it using the first of Eqs. (23.19).

EXECUTE: The x-component of the electric field is

$$E_x = -\frac{\partial V}{\partial x} = \frac{1}{4\pi\epsilon_0} \frac{Qx}{(x^2 + a^2)^{3/2}}$$

EVALUATE: This agrees with our result in Example 21.9.

CAUTION Don't use expressions where they don't apply In this example, V is not a function of y or z on the ring axis, so that $\partial V/\partial y = \partial V/\partial z = 0$ and $E_y = E_z = 0$. But that does not mean that it's true *everywhere*; our expressions for V and E_x are valid *only on the ring axis*. If we had an expression for V valid at *all* points in space, we could use it to find the components of $\vec{E}$ at any point using Eqs. (23.19). ∎

Test Your Understanding of Section 23.5 In a certain region of space the potential is given by $V = A + Bx + Cy^3 + Dxy$, where A, B, C, and D are positive constants. Which of these statements about the electric field $\vec{E}$ in this region of space is correct? (There may be more than one correct answer.) (i) Increasing the value of A will increase the value of $\vec{E}$ at all points; (ii) increasing the value of A will decrease the value of $\vec{E}$ at all points; (iii) $\vec{E}$ has no z-component; (iv) the electric field is zero at the origin ($x = 0, y = 0, z = 0$). ∎

Electric potential energy: The electric force caused by any collection of charges at rest is a conservative force. The work W done by the electric force on a charged particle moving in an electric field can be represented by the change in a potential-energy function U.

The electric potential energy for two point charges q and q_0 depends on their separation r. The electric potential energy for a charge q_0 in the presence of a collection of charges q_1, q_2, q_3 depends on the distance from q_0 to each of these other charges. (See Examples 23.1 and 23.2.)

$$W_{a \to b} = U_a - U_b \qquad (23.2)$$

$$U = \frac{1}{4\pi\epsilon_0} \frac{qq_0}{r} \qquad (23.9)$$

(two point charges)

$$U = \frac{q_0}{4\pi\epsilon_0} \left(\frac{q_1}{r_1} + \frac{q_2}{r_2} + \frac{q_3}{r_3} + \cdots \right)$$

$$= \frac{q_0}{4\pi\epsilon_0} \sum_i \frac{q_i}{r_i} \qquad (23.10)$$

(q_0 in presence of other point charges)

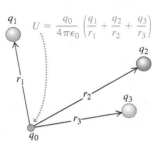

Electric potential: Potential, denoted by V, is potential energy per unit charge. The potential difference between two points equals the amount of work that would be required to move a unit positive test charge between those points. The potential V due to a quantity of charge can be calculated by summing (if the charge is a collection of point charges) or by integrating (if the charge is a distribution). (See Examples 23.3, 23.4, 23.5, 23.7, 23.11, and 23.12.)

The potential difference between two points a and b, also called the potential of a with respect to b, is given by the line integral of $\vec{E}$. The potential at a given point can be found by first finding $\vec{E}$ and then carrying out this integral. (See Examples 23.6, 23.8, 23.9, and 23.10.)

$$V = \frac{U}{q_0} = \frac{1}{4\pi\epsilon_0} \frac{q}{r} \qquad (23.14)$$

(due to a point charge)

$$V = \frac{U}{q_0} = \frac{1}{4\pi\epsilon_0} \sum_i \frac{q_i}{r_i} \qquad (23.15)$$

(due to a collection of point charges)

$$V = \frac{1}{4\pi\epsilon_0} \int \frac{dq}{r} \qquad (23.16)$$

(due to a charge distribution)

$$V_a - V_b = \int_a^b \vec{E} \cdot d\vec{l} = \int_a^b E \cos\phi \, dl \qquad (23.17)$$

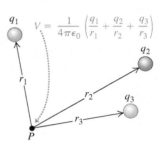

Equipotential surfaces: An equipotential surface is a surface on which the potential has the same value at every point. At a point where a field line crosses an equipotential surface, the two are perpendicular. When all charges are at rest, the surface of a conductor is always an equipotential surface and all points in the interior of a conductor are at the same potential. When a cavity within a conductor contains no charge, the entire cavity is an equipotential region and there is no surface charge anywhere on the surface of the cavity.

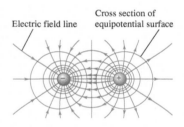

Electric field line

Cross section of equipotential surface

Finding electric field from electric potential: If the potential V is known as a function of the coordinates x, y, and z, the components of electric field $\vec{E}$ at any point are given by partial derivatives of V. (See Examples 23.13 and 23.14.)

$$E_x = -\frac{\partial V}{\partial x} \quad E_y = -\frac{\partial V}{\partial y} \quad E_z = -\frac{\partial V}{\partial z} \qquad (23.19)$$

$$\vec{E} = -\left(\hat{i}\frac{\partial V}{\partial x} + \hat{j}\frac{\partial V}{\partial y} + \hat{k}\frac{\partial V}{\partial z} \right) \qquad (23.20)$$

(vector form)

BRIDGING PROBLEM   **A Point Charge and a Line of Charge**

Positive electric charge Q is distributed uniformly along a thin rod of length $2a$. The rod lies along the x-axis between $x = -a$ and $x = +a$. Calculate how much work you must do to bring a positive point charge q from infinity to the point $x = +L$ on the x-axis, where $L > a$.

SOLUTION GUIDE

See MasteringPhysics® study area for a Video Tutor solution.

IDENTIFY and SET UP

1. In this problem you must first calculate the potential V at $x = +L$ due to the charged rod. You can then find the change in potential energy involved in bringing the point charge q from infinity (where $V = 0$) to $x = +L$.
2. To find V, divide the rod into infinitesimal segments of length dx'. How much charge is on such a segment? Consider one such segment located at $x = x'$, where $-a \leq x' \leq a$. What is the potential dV at $x = +L$ due to this segment?

3. The total potential at $x = +L$ is the integral of dV, including contributions from all of the segments for x' from $-a$ to $+a$. Set up this integral.

EXECUTE

4. Integrate your expression from step 3 to find the potential V at $x = +L$. A simple, standard substitution will do the trick; use a table of integrals only as a last resort.
5. Use your result from step 4 to find the potential energy for a point charge q placed at $x = +L$.
6. Use your result from step 5 to find the work you must do to bring the point charge from infinity to $x = +L$.

EVALUATE

7. What does your result from step 5 become in the limit $a \to 0$? Does this make sense?
8. Suppose the point charge q were negative rather than positive. How would this affect your result in step 4? In step 5?

Problems

For instructor-assigned homework, go to www.masteringphysics.com

•, ••, •••: Problems of increasing difficulty. **CP**: Cumulative problems incorporating material from earlier chapters. **CALC**: Problems requiring calculus. **BIO**: Biosciences problems.

DISCUSSION QUESTIONS

Q23.1 A student asked, "Since electrical potential is always proportional to potential energy, why bother with the concept of potential at all?" How would you respond?

Q23.2 The potential (relative to a point at infinity) midway between two charges of equal magnitude and opposite sign is zero. Is it possible to bring a test charge from infinity to this midpoint in such a way that no work is done in any part of the displacement? If so, describe how it can be done. If it is not possible, explain why.

Q23.3 Is it possible to have an arrangement of two point charges separated by a finite distance such that the electric potential energy of the arrangement is the same as if the two charges were infinitely far apart? Why or why not? What if there are three charges? Explain your reasoning.

Q23.4 Since potential can have any value you want depending on the choice of the reference level of zero potential, how does a voltmeter know what to read when you connect it between two points?

Q23.5 If $\vec{E}$ is zero everywhere along a certain path that leads from point A to point B, what is the potential difference between those two points? Does this mean that $\vec{E}$ is zero everywhere along *any* path from A to B? Explain.

Q23.6 If $\vec{E}$ is zero throughout a certain region of space, is the potential necessarily also zero in this region? Why or why not? If not, what *can* be said about the potential?

Q23.7 If you carry out the integral of the electric field $\int \vec{E} \cdot d\vec{l}$ for a *closed* path like that shown in Fig. Q23.7, the integral will *always* be equal to zero, independent of the shape of the

Figure **Q23.7**

path and independent of where charges may be located relative to the path. Explain why.

Q23.8 The potential difference between the two terminals of an AA battery (used in flashlights and portable stereos) is 1.5 V. If two AA batteries are placed end to end with the positive terminal of one battery touching the negative terminal of the other, what is the potential difference between the terminals at the exposed ends of the combination? What if the two positive terminals are touching each other? Explain your reasoning.

Q23.9 It is easy to produce a potential difference of several thousand volts between your body and the floor by scuffing your shoes across a nylon carpet. When you touch a metal doorknob, you get a mild shock. Yet contact with a power line of comparable voltage would probably be fatal. Why is there a difference?

Q23.10 If the electric potential at a single point is known, can $\vec{E}$ at that point be determined? If so, how? If not, why not?

Q23.11 Because electric field lines and equipotential surfaces are always perpendicular, two equipotential surfaces can never cross; if they did, the direction of $\vec{E}$ would be ambiguous at the crossing points. Yet two equipotential surfaces appear to cross at the center of Fig. 23.23c. Explain why there is no ambiguity about the direction of $\vec{E}$ in this particular case.

Q23.12 A uniform electric field is directed due east. Point B is 2.00 m west of point A, point C is 2.00 m east of point A, and point D is 2.00 m south of A. For each point, B, C, and D, is the potential at that point larger, smaller, or the same as at point A? Give the reasoning behind your answers.

Q23.13 We often say that if point A is at a higher potential than point B, A is at positive potential and B is at negative potential. Does it necessarily follow that a point at positive potential is positively charged, or that a point at negative potential is negatively charged? Illustrate your answers with clear, simple examples.

Q23.14 A conducting sphere is to be charged by bringing in positive charge a little at a time until the total charge is Q. The total work required for this process is alleged to be proportional to Q^2. Is this correct? Why or why not?

Q23.15 Three pairs of parallel metal plates (A, B, and C) are connected as shown in Fig. Q23.15, and a battery maintains a potential of 1.5 V across ab. What can you say about the potential difference across each pair of plates? Why?

Figure **Q23.15**

Q23.16 A conducting sphere is placed between two charged parallel plates such as those shown in Fig. 23.2. Does the electric field inside the sphere depend on precisely where between the plates the sphere is placed? What about the electric potential inside the sphere? Do the answers to these questions depend on whether or not there is a net charge on the sphere? Explain your reasoning.

Q23.17 A conductor that carries a net charge Q has a hollow, empty cavity in its interior. Does the potential vary from point to point within the material of the conductor? What about within the cavity? How does the potential inside the cavity compare to the potential within the material of the conductor?

Q23.18 A high-voltage dc power line falls on a car, so the entire metal body of the car is at a potential of 10,000 V with respect to the ground. What happens to the occupants (a) when they are sitting in the car and (b) when they step out of the car? Explain your reasoning.

Q23.19 When a thunderstorm is approaching, sailors at sea sometimes observe a phenomenon called "St. Elmo's fire," a bluish flickering light at the tips of masts. What causes this? Why does it occur at the tips of masts? Why is the effect most pronounced when the masts are wet? (*Hint:* Seawater is a good conductor of electricity.)

Q23.20 A positive point charge is placed near a very large conducting plane. A professor of physics asserted that the field caused by this configuration is the same as would be obtained by removing the plane and placing a negative point charge of equal magnitude in the mirror-image position behind the initial position of the plane. Is this correct? Why or why not? (*Hint:* Inspect Fig. 23.23b.)

Q23.21 In electronics it is customary to define the potential of ground (thinking of the earth as a large conductor) as zero. Is this consistent with the fact that the earth has a net electric charge that is not zero? (Refer to Exercise 21.32.)

EXERCISES

Section 23.1 Electric Potential Energy

23.1 •• A point charge $q_1 = +2.40\ \mu C$ is held stationary at the origin. A second point charge $q_2 = -4.30\ \mu C$ moves from the point $x = 0.150$ m, $y = 0$ to the point $x = 0.250$ m, $y = 0.250$ m. How much work is done by the electric force on q_2?

23.2 • A point charge q_1 is held stationary at the origin. A second charge q_2 is placed at point a, and the electric potential energy of the pair of charges is $+5.4 \times 10^{-8}$ J. When the second charge is moved to point b, the electric force on the charge does -1.9×10^{-8} J of work. What is the electric potential energy of the pair of charges when the second charge is at point b?

23.3 •• **Energy of the Nucleus.** How much work is needed to assemble an atomic nucleus containing three protons (such as Be) if we model it as an equilateral triangle of side 2.00×10^{-15} m

with a proton at each vertex? Assume the protons started from very far away.

23.4 •• (a) How much work would it take to push two protons very slowly from a separation of 2.00×10^{-10} m (a typical atomic distance) to 3.00×10^{-15} m (a typical nuclear distance)? (b) If the protons are both released from rest at the closer distance in part (a), how fast are they moving when they reach their original separation?

23.5 •• A small metal sphere, carrying a net charge of $q_1 = -2.80\ \mu C$, is held in a stationary position by insulating supports. A second small metal sphere, with a net charge of $q_2 = -7.80\ \mu C$ and mass 1.50 g, is projected toward q_1.

Figure **E23.5**

When the two spheres are 0.800 m apart, q_2 is moving toward q_1 with speed 22.0 m/s (Fig. E23.5). Assume that the two spheres can be treated as point charges. You can ignore the force of gravity. (a) What is the speed of q_2 when the spheres are 0.400 m apart? (b) How close does q_2 get to q_1?

23.6 •• **BIO** **Energy of DNA Base Pairing, I.** (See Exercise 21.23.) (a) Calculate the electric potential energy of the adenine–thymine bond, using the same combinations of molecules ($O-H-N$ and $N-H-N$) as in Exercise 21.23. (b) Compare this energy with the potential energy of the proton–electron pair in the hydrogen atom.

23.7 •• **BIO** **Energy of DNA Base Pairing, II.** (See Exercise 21.24.) Calculate the electric potential energy of the guanine–cytosine bond, using the same combinations of molecules ($O-H-O$, $N-H-N$, and $O-H-N$) as in Exercise 21.24.

23.8 •• Three equal 1.20-μC point charges are placed at the corners of an equilateral triangle whose sides are 0.500 m long. What is the potential energy of the system? (Take as zero the potential energy of the three charges when they are infinitely far apart.)

23.9 •• Two protons are released from rest when they are 0.750 nm apart. (a) What is the maximum speed they will reach? When does this speed occur? (b) What is the maximum acceleration they will achieve? When does this acceleration occur?

23.10 •• Four electrons are located at the corners of a square 10.0 nm on a side, with an alpha particle at its midpoint. How much work is needed to move the alpha particle to the midpoint of one of the sides of the square?

23.11 •• Three point charges, which initially are infinitely far apart, are placed at the corners of an equilateral triangle with sides d. Two of the point charges are identical and have charge q. If zero net work is required to place the three charges at the corners of the triangle, what must the value of the third charge be?

23.12 •• Starting from a separation of several meters, two protons are aimed directly toward each other by a cyclotron accelerator with speeds of 1000 km/s, measured relative to the earth. Find the maximum electrical force that these protons will exert on each other.

Section 23.2 Electric Potential

23.13 • A small particle has charge $-5.00\ \mu C$ and mass 2.00×10^{-4} kg. It moves from point A, where the electric potential is $V_A = +200$ V, to point B, where the electric potential is $V_B = +800$ V. The electric force is the only force acting on the particle. The particle has speed 5.00 m/s at point A. What is its speed at point B? Is it moving faster or slower at B than at A? Explain.

23.14 • A particle with a charge of +4.20 nC is in a uniform electric field $\vec{E}$ directed to the left. It is released from rest and moves to the left; after it has moved 6.00 cm, its kinetic energy is found to be $+1.50 \times 10^{-6}$ J. (a) What work was done by the electric force? (b) What is the potential of the starting point with respect to the end point? (c) What is the magnitude of $\vec{E}$?

23.15 • A charge of 28.0 nC is placed in a uniform electric field that is directed vertically upward and has a magnitude of 4.00×10^4 V/m. What work is done by the electric force when the charge moves (a) 0.450 m to the right; (b) 0.670 m upward; (c) 2.60 m at an angle of 45.0° downward from the horizontal?

23.16 • Two stationary point charges +3.00 nC and +2.00 nC are separated by a distance of 50.0 cm. An electron is released from rest at a point midway between the two charges and moves along the line connecting the two charges. What is the speed of the electron when it is 10.0 cm from the +3.00-nC charge?

23.17 •• Point charges $q_1 = +2.00 \ \mu$C and $q_2 = -2.00 \ \mu$C are placed at adjacent corners of a square for which the length of each side is 3.00 cm. Point a is at the center of the square, and point b is at the empty corner closest to q_2. Take the electric potential to be zero at a distance far from both charges. (a) What is the electric potential at point a due to q_1 and q_2? (b) What is the electric potential at point b? (c) A point charge $q_3 = -5.00 \ \mu$C moves from point a to point b. How much work is done on q_3 by the electric forces exerted by q_1 and q_2? Is this work positive or negative?

23.18 • Two charges of equal magnitude Q are held a distance d apart. Consider only points on the line passing through both charges. (a) If the two charges have the same sign, find the location of all points (if there are any) at which (i) the potential (relative to infinity) is zero (is the electric field zero at these points?), and (ii) the electric field is zero (is the potential zero at these points?). (b) Repeat part (a) for two charges having opposite signs.

23.19 • Two point charges $q_1 = +2.40$ nC and $q_2 = -6.50$ nC are 0.100 m apart. Point A is midway between them; point B is 0.080 m from q_1 and 0.060 m from q_2 (Fig. E23.19). Take the electric potential to be zero at infinity. Find (a) the potential at point A;

Figure **E23.19**

(b) the potential at point B; (c) the work done by the electric field on a charge of 2.50 nC that travels from point B to point A.

23.20 • A positive charge $+q$ is located at the point $x = 0$, $y = -a$, and a negative charge $-q$ is located at the point $x = 0$, $y = +a$. (a) Derive an expression for the potential V at points on the y-axis as a function of the coordinate y. Take V to be zero at an infinite distance from the charges. (b) Graph V at points on the y-axis as a function of y over the range from $y = -4a$ to $y = +4a$. (c) Show that for $y > a$, the potential at a point on the positive y-axis is given by $V = -(1/4\pi\epsilon_0)2qa/y^2$. (d) What are the answers to parts (a) and (c) if the two charges are interchanged so that $+q$ is at $y = +a$ and $-q$ is at $y = -a$?

23.21 •• A positive charge q is fixed at the point $x = 0$, $y = 0$, and a negative charge $-2q$ is fixed at the point $x = a$, $y = 0$. (a) Show the positions of the charges in a diagram. (b) Derive an expression for the potential V at points on the x-axis as a function of the coordinate x. Take V to be zero at an infinite distance from the charges. (c) At which positions on the x-axis is $V = 0$? (d) Graph V at points on the x-axis as a function of x in the range from $x = -2a$ to $x = +2a$. (e) What does the answer to 'part (b) become when $x \gg a$? Explain why this result is obtained.

23.22 •• Consider the arrangement of point charges described in Exercise 23.21. (a) Derive an expression for the potential V at points on the y-axis as a function of the coordinate y. Take V to be zero at an infinite distance from the charges. (b) At which positions on the y-axis is $V = 0$? (c) Graph V at points on the y-axis as a function of y in the range from $y = -2a$ to $y = +2a$. (d) What does the answer to part (a) become when $y > a$? Explain why this result is obtained.

23.23 •• (a) An electron is to be accelerated from 3.00×10^6 m/s to 8.00×10^6 m/s. Through what potential difference must the electron pass to accomplish this? (b) Through what potential difference must the electron pass if it is to be slowed from 8.00×10^6 m/s to a halt?

23.24 • At a certain distance from a point charge, the potential and electric-field magnitude due to that charge are 4.98 V and 12.0 V/m, respectively. (Take the potential to be zero at infinity.) (a) What is the distance to the point charge? (b) What is the magnitude of the charge? (c) Is the electric field directed toward or away from the point charge?

23.25 • A uniform electric field has magnitude E and is directed in the negative x-direction. The potential difference between point a (at $x = 0.60$ m) and point b (at $x = 0.90$ m) is 240 V. (a) Which point, a or b, is at the higher potential? (b) Calculate the value of E. (c) A negative point charge $q = -0.200 \ \mu$C is moved from b to a. Calculate the work done on the point charge by the electric field.

23.26 • For each of the following arrangements of two point charges, find all the points along the line passing through both charges for which the electric potential V is zero (take $V = 0$ infinitely far from the charges) and for which the electric field E is zero: (a) charges $+Q$ and $+2Q$ separated by a distance d, and (b) charges $-Q$ and $+2Q$ separated by a distance d. (c) Are both V and E zero at the same places? Explain.

Section 23.3 Calculating Electric Potential

23.27 •• A thin spherical shell with radius $R_1 = 3.00$ cm is concentric with a larger thin spherical shell with radius $R_2 = 5.00$ cm. Both shells are made of insulating material. The smaller shell has charge $q_1 = +6.00$ nC distributed uniformly over its surface, and the larger shell has charge $q_2 = -9.00$ nC distributed uniformly over its surface. Take the electric potential to be zero at an infinite distance from both shells. (a) What is the electric potential due to the two shells at the following distance from their common center: (i) $r = 0$; (ii) $r = 4.00$ cm; (iii) $r = 6.00$ cm? (b) What is the magnitude of the potential difference between the surfaces of the two shells? Which shell is at higher potential: the inner shell or the outer shell?

23.28 • A total electric charge of 3.50 nC is distributed uniformly over the surface of a metal sphere with a radius of 24.0 cm. If the potential is zero at a point at infinity, find the value of the potential at the following distances from the center of the sphere: (a) 48.0 cm; (b) 24.0 cm; (c) 12.0 cm.

23.29 •• A uniformly charged, thin ring has radius 15.0 cm and total charge +24.0 nC. An electron is placed on the ring's axis a distance 30.0 cm from the center of the ring and is constrained to stay on the axis of the ring. The electron is then released from rest. (a) Describe the subsequent motion of the electron. (b) Find the speed of the electron when it reaches the center of the ring.

23.30 •• An infinitely long line of charge has linear charge density 5.00×10^{-12} C/m. A proton (mass 1.67×10^{-27} kg, charge $+1.60 \times 10^{-19}$ C) is 18.0 cm from the line and moving directly toward the line at 1.50×10^3 m/s. (a) Calculate the proton's initial kinetic energy. (b) How close does the proton get to the line of charge?

23.31 • A very long wire carries a uniform linear charge density λ. Using a voltmeter to measure potential difference, you find that when one probe of the meter is placed 2.50 cm from the wire and the other probe is 1.00 cm farther from the wire, the meter reads 575 V. (a) What is λ? (b) If you now place one probe at 3.50 cm from the wire and the other probe 1.00 cm farther away, will the voltmeter read 575 V? If not, will it read more or less than 575 V? Why? (c) If you place both probes 3.50 cm from the wire but 17.0 cm from each other, what will the voltmeter read?

23.32 •• A very long insulating cylinder of charge of radius 2.50 cm carries a uniform linear density of 15.0 nC/m. If you put one probe of a voltmeter at the surface, how far from the surface must the other probe be placed so that the voltmeter reads 175 V?

23.33 •• A very long insulating cylindrical shell of radius 6.00 cm carries charge of linear density 8.50 μC/m spread uniformly over its outer surface. What would a voltmeter read if it were connected between (a) the surface of the cylinder and a point 4.00 cm above the surface, and (b) the surface and a point 1.00 cm from the central axis of the cylinder?

23.34 • A ring of diameter 8.00 cm is fixed in place and carries a charge of +5.00 μC uniformly spread over its circumference. (a) How much work does it take to move a tiny +3.00-μC charged ball of mass 1.50 g from very far away to the center of the ring? (b) Is it necessary to take a path along the axis of the ring? Why? (c) If the ball is slightly displaced from the center of the ring, what will it do and what is the maximum speed it will reach?

23.35 •• A very small sphere with positive charge $q = +8.00$ μC is released from rest at a point 1.50 cm from a very long line of uniform linear charge density $\lambda = +3.00$ μC/m. What is the kinetic energy of the sphere when it is 4.50 cm from the line of charge if the only force on it is the force exerted by the line of charge?

23.36 • Charge $Q = 5.00$ μC is distributed uniformly over the volume of an insulating sphere that has radius $R = 12.0$ cm. A small sphere with charge $q = +3.00$ μC and mass 6.00×10^{-5} kg is projected toward the center of the large sphere from an initial large distance. The large sphere is held at a fixed position and the small sphere can be treated as a point charge. What minimum speed must the small sphere have in order to come within 8.00 cm of the surface of the large sphere?

23.37 • BIO **Axons.** Neurons are the basic units of the nervous system. They contain long tubular structures called *axons* that propagate electrical signals away from the ends of the neurons. The axon contains a solution of potassium (K^+) ions and large negative organic ions. The axon membrane prevents the large ions from leaking out, but the smaller K^+ ions are able to penetrate the membrane to some degree (Fig. E23.37). This leaves an excess negative charge on the inner surface of the axon membrane and an excess positive charge on the outer surface, resulting in a potential difference across the membrane that prevents further K^+ ions from leaking out. Measurements show that this potential difference is typically about 70 mV. The thickness of the axon membrane itself varies from about 5 to 10 nm, so we'll use an average of 7.5 nm. We can model the membrane as a large sheet having equal and opposite charge densities on its faces. (a) Find the electric field inside the axon membrane, assuming (not too realistically) that it is filled with air. Which way does it point: into or out of the axon?

Figure **E23.37**

↓ 7.5 nm

K^+ K^+ Axon membrane

(b) Which is at a higher potential: the inside surface or the outside surface of the axon membrane?

23.38 • CP Two large, parallel conducting plates carrying opposite charges of equal magnitude are separated by 2.20 cm. (a) If the surface charge density for each plate has magnitude 47.0 nC/m², what is the magnitude of $\vec{E}$ in the region between the plates? (b) What is the potential difference between the two plates? (c) If the separation between the plates is doubled while the surface charge density is kept constant at the value in part (a), what happens to the magnitude of the electric field and to the potential difference?

23.39 • Two large, parallel, metal plates carry opposite charges of equal magnitude. They are separated by 45.0 mm, and the potential difference between them is 360 V. (a) What is the magnitude of the electric field (assumed to be uniform) in the region between the plates? (b) What is the magnitude of the force this field exerts on a particle with charge +2.40 nC? (c) Use the results of part (b) to compute the work done by the field on the particle as it moves from the higher-potential plate to the lower. (d) Compare the result of part (c) to the change of potential energy of the same charge, computed from the electric potential.

23.40 • BIO **Electrical Sensitivity of Sharks.** Certain sharks can detect an electric field as weak as 1.0 μV/m. To grasp how weak this field is, if you wanted to produce it between two parallel metal plates by connecting an ordinary 1.5-V AA battery across these plates, how far apart would the plates have to be?

23.41 •• (a) Show that V for a spherical shell of radius R, that has charge q distributed uniformly over its surface, is the same as V for a solid conductor with radius R and charge q. (b) You rub an inflated balloon on the carpet and it acquires a potential that is 1560 V lower than its potential before it became charged. If the charge is uniformly distributed over the surface of the balloon and if the radius of the balloon is 15 cm, what is the net charge on the balloon? (c) In light of its 1200-V potential difference relative to you, do you think this balloon is dangerous? Explain.

23.42 •• (a) How much excess charge must be placed on a copper sphere 25.0 cm in diameter so that the potential of its center, relative to infinity, is 1.50 kV? (b) What is the potential of the sphere's surface relative to infinity?

23.43 • The electric field at the surface of a charged, solid, copper sphere with radius 0.200 m is 3800 N/C, directed toward the center of the sphere. What is the potential at the center of the sphere, if we take the potential to be zero infinitely far from the sphere?

Section 23.4 Equipotential Surfaces and Section 23.5 Potential Gradient

23.44 • A very large plastic sheet carries a uniform charge density of −6.00 nC/m² on one face. (a) As you move away from the sheet along a line perpendicular to it, does the potential increase or decrease? How do you know, without doing any calculations? Does your answer depend on where you choose the reference point for potential? (b) Find the spacing between equipotential surfaces that differ from each other by 1.00 V. What type of surfaces are these?

23.45 • CALC In a certain region of space, the electric potential is $V(x, y, z) = Axy - Bx^2 + Cy$, where A, B, and C are positive constants. (a) Calculate the x-, y-, and z-components of the electric field. (b) At which points is the electric field equal to zero?

23.46 • CALC In a certain region of space the electric potential is given by $V = +Ax^2y - Bxy^2$, where $A = 5.00$ V/m³ and $B = 8.00$ V/m³. Calculate the magnitude and direction of the electric field at the point in the region that has coordinates $x = 2.00$ m, $y = 0.400$ m, and $z = 0$.

23.47 •• **CALC** A metal sphere with radius r_a is supported on an insulating stand at the center of a hollow, metal, spherical shell with radius r_b. There is charge $+q$ on the inner sphere and charge $-q$ on the outer spherical shell. (a) Calculate the potential $V(r)$ for (i) $r < r_a$; (ii) $r_a < r < r_b$; (iii) $r > r_b$. (*Hint:* The net potential is the sum of the potentials due to the individual spheres.) Take V to be zero when r is infinite. (b) Show that the potential of the inner sphere with respect to the outer is

$$V_{ab} = \frac{q}{4\pi\epsilon_0}\left(\frac{1}{r_a} - \frac{1}{r_b}\right)$$

(c) Use Eq. (23.23) and the result from part (a) to show that the electric field at any point between the spheres has magnitude

$$E(r) = \frac{V_{ab}}{(1/r_a - 1/r_b)}\frac{1}{r^2}$$

(d) Use Eq. (23.23) and the result from part (a) to find the electric field at a point outside the larger sphere at a distance r from the center, where $r > r_b$. (e) Suppose the charge on the outer sphere is not $-q$ but a negative charge of different magnitude, say $-Q$. Show that the answers for parts (b) and (c) are the same as before but the answer for part (d) is different.

23.48 • A metal sphere with radius $r_a = 1.20$ cm is supported on an insulating stand at the center of a hollow, metal, spherical shell with radius $r_b = 9.60$ cm. Charge $+q$ is put on the inner sphere and charge $-q$ on the outer spherical shell. The magnitude of q is chosen to make the potential difference between the spheres 500 V, with the inner sphere at higher potential. (a) Use the result of Exercise 23.47(b) to calculate q. (b) With the help of the result of Exercise 23.47(a), sketch the equipotential surfaces that correspond to 500, 400, 300, 200, 100, and 0 V. (c) In your sketch, show the electric field lines. Are the electric field lines and equipotential surfaces mutually perpendicular? Are the equipotential surfaces closer together when the magnitude of $\vec{E}$ is largest?

23.49 • A very long cylinder of radius 2.00 cm carries a uniform charge density of 1.50 nC/m. (a) Describe the shape of the equipotential surfaces for this cylinder. (b) Taking the reference level for the zero of potential to be the surface of the cylinder, find the radius of equipotential surfaces having potentials of 10.0 V, 20.0 V, and 30.0 V. (c) Are the equipotential surfaces equally spaced? If not, do they get closer together or farther apart as r increases?

PROBLEMS

23.50 • **CP** A point charge $q_1 = +5.00$ μC is held fixed in space. From a horizontal distance of 6.00 cm, a small sphere with mass 4.00×10^{-3} kg and charge $q_2 = +2.00$ μC is fired toward the fixed charge with an initial speed of 40.0 m/s. Gravity can be neglected. What is the acceleration of the sphere at the instant when its speed is 25.0 m/s?

23.51 ••• A point charge $q_1 = 4.00$ nC is placed at the origin, and a second point charge $q_2 = -3.00$ nC is placed on the x-axis at $x = +20.0$ cm. A third point charge $q_3 = 2.00$ nC is to be placed on the x-axis between q_1 and q_2. (Take as zero the potential energy of the three charges when they are infinitely far apart.) (a) What is the potential energy of the system of the three charges if q_3 is placed at $x = +10.0$ cm? (b) Where should q_3 be placed to make the potential energy of the system equal to zero?

23.52 ••• A small sphere with mass 5.00×10^{-7} kg and charge $+3.00$ μC is released from rest a distance of 0.400 m above a large horizontal insulating sheet of charge that has uniform surface charge density $\sigma = +8.00$ pC/m^2. Using energy methods, calculate the speed of the sphere when it is 0.100 m above the sheet of charge?

23.53 •• **Determining the Size of the Nucleus.** When radium-226 decays radioactively, it emits an alpha particle (the nucleus of helium), and the end product is radon-222. We can model this decay by thinking of the radium-226 as consisting of an alpha particle emitted from the surface of the spherically symmetric radon-222 nucleus, and we can treat the alpha particle as a point charge. The energy of the alpha particle has been measured in the laboratory and has been found to be 4.79 MeV when the alpha particle is essentially infinitely far from the nucleus. Since radon is much heavier than the alpha particle, we can assume that there is no appreciable recoil of the radon after the decay. The radon nucleus contains 86 protons, while the alpha particle has 2 protons and the radium nucleus has 88 protons. (a) What was the electric potential energy of the alpha–radon combination just before the decay, in MeV and in joules? (b) Use your result from part (a) to calculate the radius of the radon nucleus.

23.54 •• **CP** A proton and an alpha particle are released from rest when they are 0.225 nm apart. The alpha particle (a helium nucleus) has essentially four times the mass and two times the charge of a proton. Find the maximum *speed* and maximum *acceleration* of each of these particles. When do these maxima occur: just following the release of the particles or after a very long time?

23.55 • A particle with charge $+7.60$ nC is in a uniform electric field directed to the left. Another force, in addition to the electric force, acts on the particle so that when it is released from rest, it moves to the right. After it has moved 8.00 cm, the additional force has done 6.50×10^{-5} J of work and the particle has 4.35×10^{-5} J of kinetic energy. (a) What work was done by the electric force? (b) What is the potential of the starting point with respect to the end point? (c) What is the magnitude of the electric field?

23.56 • **CP** In the *Bohr model* of the hydrogen atom, a single electron revolves around a single proton in a circle of radius r. Assume that the proton remains at rest. (a) By equating the electric force to the electron mass times its acceleration, derive an expression for the electron's speed. (b) Obtain an expression for the electron's kinetic energy, and show that its magnitude is just half that of the electric potential energy. (c) Obtain an expression for the total energy, and evaluate it using $r = 5.29 \times 10^{-11}$ m. Give your numerical result in joules and in electron volts.

23.57 •• **CALC** A vacuum tube diode consists of concentric cylindrical electrodes, the negative cathode and the positive anode. Because of the accumulation of charge near the cathode, the electric potential between the electrodes is not a linear function of the position, even with planar geometry, but is given by

$$V(x) = Cx^{4/3}$$

where x is the distance from the cathode and C is a constant, characteristic of a particular diode and operating conditions. Assume that the distance between the cathode and anode is 13.0 mm and the potential difference between electrodes is 240 V. (a) Determine the value of C. (b) Obtain a formula for the electric field between the electrodes as a function of x. (c) Determine the force on an electron when the electron is halfway between the electrodes.

23.58 •• Two oppositely charged, identical insulating spheres, each 50.0 cm in diameter and carrying a uniform charge of magnitude 250 μC, are placed 1.00 m apart center to center (Fig. P23.58). (a) If a voltmeter is connected between the nearest points (a and b) on their surfaces, what will it read? (b) Which point, a or b, is at the higher potential? How can you know this without any calculations?

Figure **P23.58**

23.59 •• **An Ionic Crystal.** Figure P23.59 shows eight point charges arranged at the corners of a cube with sides of length d. The values of the charges are $+q$ and $-q$, as shown. This is a model of one cell of a cubic ionic crystal. In sodium chloride (NaCl), for instance, the positive ions are Na$^+$ and the negative ions are Cl$^-$. (a) Calculate the potential energy U of this arrangement. (Take as zero the potential energy of the eight charges when they are infinitely far apart.) (b) In part (a), you should have found that $U < 0$. Explain the relationship between this result and the observation that such ionic crystals exist in nature.

Figure **P23.59**

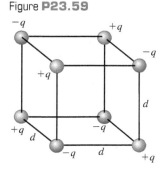

23.60 • (a) Calculate the potential energy of a system of two small spheres, one carrying a charge of 2.00 μC and the other a charge of -3.50 μC, with their centers separated by a distance of 0.250 m. Assume zero potential energy when the charges are infinitely separated. (b) Suppose that one of the spheres is held in place and the other sphere, which has a mass of 1.50 g, is shot away from it. What minimum initial speed would the moving sphere need in order to escape completely from the attraction of the fixed sphere? (To escape, the moving sphere would have to reach a velocity of zero when it was infinitely distant from the fixed sphere.)

23.61 •• **The H$_2^+$ Ion.** The H$_2^+$ ion is composed of two protons, each of charge $+e = 1.60 \times 10^{-19}$ C, and an electron of charge $-e$ and mass 9.11×10^{-31} kg. The separation between the protons is 1.07×10^{-10} m. The protons and the electron may be treated as point charges. (a) Suppose the electron is located at the point midway between the two protons. What is the potential energy of the interaction between the electron and the two protons? (Do not include the potential energy due to the interaction between the two protons.) (b) Suppose the electron in part (a) has a velocity of magnitude 1.50×10^6 m/s in a direction along the perpendicular bisector of the line connecting the two protons. How far from the point midway between the two protons can the electron move? Because the masses of the protons are much greater than the electron mass, the motions of the protons are very slow and can be ignored. (*Note:* A realistic description of the electron motion requires the use of quantum mechanics, not Newtonian mechanics.)

23.62 •• **CP** A small sphere with mass 1.50 g hangs by a thread between two parallel vertical plates 5.00 cm apart (Fig. P23.62). The plates are insulating and have uniform

Figure **P23.62**

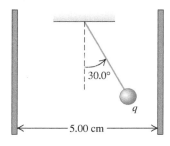

surface charge densities $+\sigma$ and $-\sigma$. The charge on the sphere is $q = 8.90 \times 10^{-6}$ C. What potential difference between the plates will cause the thread to assume an angle of 30.0° with the vertical?

23.63 • **CALC Coaxial Cylinders.** A long metal cylinder with radius a is supported on an insulating stand on the axis of a long, hollow, metal tube with radius b. The positive charge per unit length on the inner cylinder is λ, and there is an equal negative charge per unit length on the outer cylinder. (a) Calculate the potential $V(r)$ for (i) $r < a$; (ii) $a < r < b$; (iii) $r > b$. (*Hint:* The net potential is the sum of the potentials due to the individual conductors.) Take $V = 0$ at $r = b$. (b) Show that the potential of the inner cylinder with respect to the outer is

$$V_{ab} = \frac{\lambda}{2\pi\epsilon_0} \ln\frac{b}{a}$$

(c) Use Eq. (23.23) and the result from part (a) to show that the electric field at any point between the cylinders has magnitude

$$E(r) = \frac{V_{ab}}{\ln(b/a)} \frac{1}{r}$$

(d) What is the potential difference between the two cylinders if the outer cylinder has no net charge?

23.64 •• A *Geiger counter* detects radiation such as alpha particles by using the fact that the radiation ionizes the air along its path. A thin wire lies on the axis of a hollow metal cylinder and is insulated from it (Fig. P23.64). A large potential difference is established between the wire and the outer cylinder, with the wire at higher potential; this sets up a strong electric field directed radially outward. When ionizing radiation enters the device, it ionizes a few air molecules. The free electrons produced are accelerated by the electric field toward the wire and, on the way there, ionize many more air molecules. Thus a current pulse is produced that can be detected by appropriate electronic circuitry and converted to an audible "click." Suppose the radius of the central wire is 145 μm and the radius of the hollow cylinder is 1.80 cm. What potential difference between the wire and the cylinder produces an electric field of 2.00×10^4 V/m at a distance of 1.20 cm from the axis of the wire? (The wire and cylinder are both very long in comparison to their radii, so the results of Problem 23.63 apply.)

Figure **P23.64**

23.65 • **CP Deflection in a CRT.** Cathode-ray tubes (CRTs) are often found in oscilloscopes and computer monitors. In Fig. P23.65 an electron with an initial speed of 6.50×10^6 m/s is projected along the axis midway between the deflection plates of a cathode-ray tube. The potential difference between the two plates is 22.0 V and the lower plate is the one at higher potential. (a) What is the force (magnitude and direction) on the electron when it is between the plates? (b) What is the acceleration of the electron (magnitude and direction) when acted on by the force in part (a)? (c) How far below the axis has the electron moved when it reaches the end of the plates? (d) At what angle with the axis is it moving as it leaves the plates? (e) How far below the axis will it strike the fluorescent screen S?

Figure **P23.65**

23.66 •• **CP Deflecting Plates of an Oscilloscope.** The vertical deflecting plates of a typical classroom oscilloscope are a pair of parallel square metal plates carrying equal but opposite charges. Typical dimensions are about 3.0 cm on a side, with a separation of about 5.0 mm. The potential difference between the plates is 25.0 V. The plates are close enough that we can ignore fringing at the ends. Under these conditions: (a) how much charge is on each plate, and (b) how strong is the electric field between the plates? (c) If an electron is ejected at rest from the negative plate, how fast is it moving when it reaches the positive plate?

23.67 •• *Electrostatic precipitators* use electric forces to remove pollutant particles from smoke, in particular in the smokestacks of coal-burning power plants. One form of precipitator consists of a vertical, hollow, metal cylinder with a thin wire, insulated from the cylinder, running along its axis (Fig. P23.67). A large potential difference is established between the wire and the outer cylinder, with the wire at lower potential. This sets up a strong radial electric field directed inward.

Figure **P23.67**

The field produces a region of ionized air near the wire. Smoke enters the precipitator at the bottom, ash and dust in it pick up electrons, and the charged pollutants are accelerated toward the outer cylinder wall by the electric field. Suppose the radius of the central wire is 90.0 μm, the radius of the cylinder is 14.0 cm, and a potential difference of 50.0 kV is established between the wire and the cylinder. Also assume that the wire and cylinder are both very long in comparison to the cylinder radius, so the results of Problem 23.63 apply. (a) What is the magnitude of the electric field midway between the wire and the cylinder wall? (b) What magnitude of charge must a 30.0-μg ash particle have if the electric field computed in part (a) is to exert a force ten times the weight of the particle?

23.68 •• **CALC** A disk with radius R has uniform surface charge density σ. (a) By regarding the disk as a series of thin concentric rings, calculate the electric potential V at a point on the disk's axis a distance x from the center of the disk. Assume that the potential is zero at infinity. (*Hint:* Use the result of Example 23.11 in Section 23.3.) (b) Calculate $-\partial V/\partial x$. Show that the result agrees with the expression for E_x calculated in Example 21.11 (Section 21.5).

23.69 •• **CALC** (a) From the expression for E obtained in Problem 22.42, find the expressions for the electric potential V as a function of r, both inside and outside the cylinder. Let $V = 0$ at the surface of the cylinder. In each case, express your result in terms of the charge per unit length λ of the charge distribution. (b) Graph V and E as functions of r from $r = 0$ to $r = 3R$.

23.70 • **CALC** A thin insulating rod is bent into a semicircular arc of radius a, and a total electric charge Q is distributed uniformly along the rod. Calculate the potential at the center of curvature of the arc if the potential is assumed to be zero at infinity.

23.71 ••• **CALC Self-Energy of a Sphere of Charge.** A solid sphere of radius R contains a total charge Q distributed uniformly throughout its volume. Find the energy needed to assemble this charge by bringing infinitesimal charges from far away. This energy is called the "self-energy" of the charge distribution. (*Hint:* After you have assembled a charge q in a sphere of radius r, how much energy would it take to add a spherical shell of thickness dr having charge dq? Then integrate to get the total energy.)

23.72 •• **CALC** (a) From the expression for E obtained in Example 22.9 (Section 22.4), find the expression for the electric potential V as a function of r both inside and outside the uniformly charged sphere. Assume that $V = 0$ at infinity. (b) Graph V and E as functions of r from $r = 0$ to $r = 3R$.

23.73 •• Charge $Q = +4.00$ μC is distributed uniformly over the volume of an insulating sphere that has radius $R = 5.00$ cm. What is the potential difference between the center of the sphere and the surface of the sphere?

23.74 • An insulating spherical shell with inner radius 25.0 cm and outer radius 60.0 cm carries a charge of $+150.0$ μC uniformly distributed over its outer surface (see Exercise 23.41). Point a is at the center of the shell, point b is on the inner surface, and point c is on the outer surface. (a) What will a voltmeter read if it is connected between the following points: (i) a and b; (ii) b and c; (iii) c and infinity; (iv) a and c? (b) Which is at higher potential: (i) a or b; (ii) b or c; (iii) a or c? (c) Which, if any, of the answers would change sign if the charge were -150 μC?

23.75 •• Exercise 23.41 shows that, outside a spherical shell with uniform surface charge, the potential is the same as if all the charge were concentrated into a point charge at the center of the sphere. (a) Use this result to show that for two uniformly charged insulating shells, the force they exert on each other and their mutual electrical energy are the same as if all the charge were concentrated at their centers. (*Hint:* See Section 13.6.) (b) Does this same result hold for solid insulating spheres, with charge distributed uniformly throughout their volume? (c) Does this same result hold for the force between two charged conducting shells? Between two charged solid conductors? Explain.

23.76 •• **CP** Two plastic spheres, each carrying charge uniformly distributed throughout its interior, are initially placed in contact and then released. One sphere is 60.0 cm in diameter, has mass 50.0 g, and contains -10.0 μC of charge. The other sphere is 40.0 cm in diameter, has mass 150.0 g, and contains -30.0 μC of charge. Find the maximum acceleration and the maximum speed achieved by each sphere (relative to the fixed point of their initial location in space), assuming that no other forces are acting on them. (*Hint:* The uniformly distributed charges behave as though they were concentrated at the centers of the two spheres.)

23.77 • **CALC** Use the electric field calculated in Problem 22.45 to calculate the potential difference between the solid conducting sphere and the thin insulating shell.

23.78 • **CALC** Consider a solid conducting sphere inside a hollow conducting sphere, with radii and charges specified in Problem 22.44. Take $V = 0$ as $r \rightarrow \infty$. Use the electric field calculated in Problem 22.44 to calculate the potential V at the following values of r: (a) $r = c$ (at the outer surface of the hollow sphere); (b) $r = b$ (at the inner surface of the hollow sphere); (c) $r = a$ (at the surface of the solid sphere); (d) $r = 0$ (at the center of the solid sphere).

23.79 • **CALC** Electric charge is distributed uniformly along a thin rod of length a, with total charge Q. Take the potential to be zero at infinity. Find the potential at the following points (Fig. P23.79): (a) point P, a distance x to the right of the rod, and (b) point R, a distance y above the right-hand end of the rod. (c) In parts (a) and (b), what does your result reduce to as x or y becomes much larger than a?

Figure **P23.79**

23.80 • (a) If a spherical raindrop of radius 0.650 mm carries a charge of -3.60 pC uniformly distributed over its volume, what is the potential at its surface? (Take the potential to be zero at an infinite distance from the raindrop.) (b) Two identical raindrops, each with radius and charge specified in part (a), collide and merge into one larger raindrop. What is the radius of this larger drop, and what is the potential at its surface, if its charge is uniformly distributed over its volume?

23.81 •• Two metal spheres of different sizes are charged such that the electric potential is the same at the surface of each. Sphere A has a radius three times that of sphere B. Let Q_A and Q_B be the charges on the two spheres, and let E_A and E_B be the electric-field magnitudes at the surfaces of the two spheres. What are (a) the ratio Q_B/Q_A and (b) the ratio E_B/E_A?

23.82 • An alpha particle with kinetic energy 11.0 MeV makes a head-on collision with a lead nucleus at rest. What is the distance of closest approach of the two particles? (Assume that the lead nucleus remains stationary and that it may be treated as a point charge. The atomic number of lead is 82. The alpha particle is a helium nucleus, with atomic number 2.)

23.83 • A metal sphere with radius R_1 has a charge Q_1. Take the electric potential to be zero at an infinite distance from the sphere. (a) What are the electric field and electric potential at the surface of the sphere? This sphere is now connected by a long, thin conducting wire to another sphere of radius R_2 that is several meters from the first sphere. Before the connection is made, this second sphere is uncharged. After electrostatic equilibrium has been reached, what are (b) the total charge on each sphere; (c) the electric potential at the surface of each sphere; (d) the electric field at the surface of each sphere? Assume that the amount of charge on the wire is much less than the charge on each sphere.

23.84 ••• **CALC** Use the charge distribution and electric field calculated in Problem 22.65. (a) Show that for $r \geq R$ the potential is identical to that produced by a point charge Q. (Take the potential to be zero at infinity.) (b) Obtain an expression for the electric potential valid in the region $r \leq R$.

23.85 •• **CP** Nuclear Fusion in the Sun. The source of the sun's energy is a sequence of nuclear reactions that occur in its core. The first of these reactions involves the collision of two protons, which fuse together to form a heavier nucleus and release energy. For this process, called *nuclear fusion,* to occur, the two protons must first approach until their surfaces are essentially in contact. (a) Assume both protons are moving with the same speed and they collide head-on. If the radius of the proton is 1.2×10^{-15} m, what is the minimum speed that will allow fusion to occur? The charge distribution within a proton is spherically symmetric, so the electric field and potential outside a proton are the same as if it were a point charge. The mass of the proton is 1.67×10^{-27} kg. (b) Another nuclear fusion reaction that occurs in the sun's core involves a collision between two helium nuclei, each of which has 2.99 times the mass of the proton, charge $+2e$, and radius 1.7×10^{-15} m. Assuming the same collision geometry as in part (a), what minimum speed is required for this fusion reaction to take place if the nuclei must approach a center-to-center distance of about 3.5×10^{-15} m? As for the proton, the charge of the helium nucleus is uniformly distributed throughout its volume. (c) In Section 18.3 it was shown that the average translational kinetic energy of a particle with mass m in a gas at absolute temperature T is $\frac{3}{2}kT$, where k is the Boltzmann constant (given in Appendix F). For two protons with kinetic energy equal to this average value to be able to undergo the process described in part (a), what absolute temperature is required? What absolute temperature is required for two average helium nuclei to be able to undergo the process described in part (b)? (At these temperatures, atoms are completely ionized, so nuclei and electrons move separately.) (d) The temperature in the sun's core is about 1.5×10^7 K. How does this compare to the temperatures calculated in parts (c)? How can the reactions described in parts (a) and (b) occur at all in the interior of the sun? (*Hint:* See the discussion of the distribution of molecular speeds in Section 18.5.)

23.86 • **CALC** The electric potential V in a region of space is given by

$$V(x, y, z) = A(x^2 - 3y^2 + z^2)$$

where A is a constant. (a) Derive an expression for the electric field $\vec{E}$ at any point in this region. (b) The work done by the field when a 1.50-μC test charge moves from the point $(x, y, z) = (0, 0, 0.250$ m$)$ to the origin is measured to be 6.00×10^{-5} J. Determine A. (c) Determine the electric field at the point $(0, 0, 0.250$ m$)$. (d) Show that in every plane parallel to the xz-plane the equipotential contours are circles. (e) What is the radius of the equipotential contour corresponding to $V = 1280$ V and $y = 2.00$ m?

23.87 •• **Nuclear Fission.** The unstable nucleus of uranium-236 can be regarded as a uniformly charged sphere of charge $Q = +92e$ and radius $R = 7.4 \times 10^{-15}$ m. In nuclear fission, this can divide into two smaller nuclei, each with half the charge and half the volume of the original uranium-236 nucleus. This is one of the reactions that occurred in the nuclear weapon that exploded over Hiroshima, Japan, in August 1945. (a) Find the radii of the two "daughter" nuclei of charge $+46e$. (b) In a simple model for the fission process, immediately after the uranium-236 nucleus has undergone fission, the "daughter" nuclei are at rest and just touching, as shown in Fig. P23.87. Calculate the kinetic energy that each of the "daughter" nuclei will have when they are very far apart. (c) In this model the sum of the kinetic energies of the two "daughter" nuclei, calculated in part (b), is the energy released by the fission of one uranium-236 nucleus. Calculate the energy released by the fission of 10.0 kg of uranium-236. The atomic mass of uranium-236 is 236 u, where 1 u = 1 atomic mass unit = 1.66×10^{-24} kg. Express your answer both in joules and in kilotons of TNT (1 kiloton of TNT releases 4.18×10^{12} J when it explodes). (d) In terms of this model, discuss why an atomic bomb could just as well be called an "electric bomb."

Figure **P23.87**

$Q = +92e$

BEFORE

$Q = +46e$ ⇩ $Q = +46e$

AFTER

CHALLENGE PROBLEMS

23.88 ••• **CP CALC** In a certain region, a charge distribution exists that is spherically symmetric but nonuniform. That is, the volume charge density $\rho(r)$ depends on the distance r from the center of the distribution but not on the spherical polar angles θ and ϕ. The electric potential $V(r)$ due to this charge distribution is

$$V(r) = \begin{cases} \dfrac{\rho_0 a^2}{18\epsilon_0}\left[1 - 3\left(\dfrac{r}{a}\right)^2 + 2\left(\dfrac{r}{a}\right)^3\right] & \text{for } r \leq a \\ 0 & \text{for } r \geq a \end{cases}$$

where ρ_0 is a constant having units of C/m^3 and a is a constant having units of meters. (a) Derive expressions for $\vec{E}$ for the regions $r \leq a$ and $r \geq a$. [*Hint:* Use Eq. (23.23).] Explain why $\vec{E}$ has only a radial component. (b) Derive an expression for $\rho(r)$ in each of the two regions $r \leq a$ and $r \geq a$. [*Hint:* Use Gauss's law for two spherical shells, one of radius r and the other of radius $r + dr$. The charge contained in the infinitesimal spherical shell of radius dr is $dq = 4\pi r^2 \rho(r)\,dr$.] (c) Show that the net charge contained in the volume of a sphere of radius greater than or equal to a is zero. [*Hint:* Integrate the expressions derived in part (b) for $\rho(r)$ over a spherical volume of radius greater than or equal to a.] Is this result consistent with the electric field for $r > a$ that you calculated in part (a)?

23.89 ••• **CP** In experiments in which atomic nuclei collide, head-on collisions like that described in Problem 23.82 do happen, but "near misses" are more common. Suppose the alpha particle in Problem 23.82 was not "aimed" at the center of the lead nucleus, but had an initial nonzero angular momentum (with respect to the stationary lead nucleus) of magnitude $L = p_0 b$, where p_0 is the magnitude of the initial momentum of the alpha particle and $b = 1.00 \times 10^{-12}$ m. What is the distance of closest approach? Repeat for $b = 1.00 \times 10^{-13}$ m and $b = 1.00 \times 10^{-14}$ m.

23.90 ••• **CALC** A hollow, thin-walled insulating cylinder of radius R and length L (like the cardboard tube in a roll of toilet paper) has charge Q uniformly distributed over its surface. (a) Calculate the electric potential at all points along the axis of the tube. Take the origin to be at the center of the tube, and take the potential to be zero at infinity. (b) Show that if $L \ll R$, the result of part (a) reduces to the potential on the axis of a ring of charge of radius R. (See Example 23.11 in Section 23.3.) (c) Use the result of part (a) to find the electric field at all points along the axis of the tube.

23.91 ••• **The Millikan Oil-Drop Experiment.** The charge of an electron was first measured by the American physicist Robert Millikan during 1909–1913. In his experiment, oil is sprayed in very fine drops (around 10^{-4} mm in diameter) into the space between two parallel horizontal plates separated by a distance d. A potential difference V_{AB} is maintained between the parallel plates, causing a downward electric field between them. Some of the oil drops acquire a negative charge because of frictional effects or because of ionization of the surrounding air by x rays or radioactivity. The drops are observed through a microscope. (a) Show that an oil drop of radius r at rest between the plates will remain at rest if the magnitude of its charge is

$$q = \frac{4\pi}{3}\frac{\rho r^3 g d}{V_{AB}}$$

where ρ is the density of the oil. (Ignore the buoyant force of the air.) By adjusting V_{AB} to keep a given drop at rest, the charge on that drop can be determined, provided its radius is known. (b) Millikan's oil drops were much too small to measure their radii directly. Instead, Millikan determined r by cutting off the electric field and measuring the *terminal speed* v_t of the drop as it fell. (We discussed the concept of terminal speed in Section 5.3.) The viscous force F on a sphere of radius r moving with speed v through a fluid with viscosity η is given by Stokes's law: $F = 6\pi\eta r v$. When the drop is falling at v_t, the viscous force just balances the weight $w = mg$ of the drop. Show that the magnitude of the charge on the drop is

$$q = 18\pi \frac{d}{V_{AB}}\sqrt{\frac{\eta^3 v_t^3}{2\rho g}}$$

Within the limits of their experimental error, every one of the thousands of drops that Millikan and his coworkers measured had a charge equal to some small integer multiple of a basic charge e. That is, they found drops with charges of $\pm 2e$, $\pm 5e$, and so on, but none with values such as $0.76e$ or $2.49e$. A drop with charge $-e$ has acquired one extra electron; if its charge is $-2e$, it has acquired two extra electrons, and so on. (c) A charged oil drop in a Millikan oil-drop apparatus is observed to fall 1.00 mm at constant speed in 39.3 s if $V_{AB} = 0$. The same drop can be held at rest between two plates separated by 1.00 mm if $V_{AB} = 9.16$ V. How many excess electrons has the drop acquired, and what is the radius of the drop? The viscosity of air is 1.81×10^{-5} N·s/m^2, and the density of the oil is 824 kg/m^3.

23.92 •• **CP** Two point charges are moving to the right along the x-axis. Point charge 1 has charge $q_1 = 2.00\ \mu C$, mass $m_1 = 6.00 \times 10^{-5}$ kg, and speed v_1. Point charge 2 is to the right of q_1 and has charge $q_2 = -5.00\ \mu C$, mass $m_2 = 3.00 \times 10^{-5}$ kg, and speed v_2. At a particular instant, the charges are separated by a distance of 9.00 mm and have speeds $v_1 = 400$ m/s and $v_2 = 1300$ m/s. The only forces on the particles are the forces they exert on each other. (a) Determine the speed v_{cm} of the center of mass of the system. (b) The *relative energy* E_{rel} of the system is defined as the total energy minus the kinetic energy contributed by the motion of the center of mass:

$$E_{rel} = E - \tfrac{1}{2}(m_1 + m_2)v_{cm}^2$$

where $E = \tfrac{1}{2}m_1 v_1^2 + \tfrac{1}{2}m_2 v_2^2 + q_1 q_2/4\pi\epsilon_0 r$ is the total energy of the system and r is the distance between the charges. Show that $E_{rel} = \tfrac{1}{2}\mu v^2 + q_1 q_2/4\pi\epsilon_0 r$, where $\mu = m_1 m_2/(m_1 + m_2)$ is called the *reduced mass* of the system and $v = v_2 - v_1$ is the relative speed of the moving particles. (c) For the numerical values given above, calculate the numerical value of E_{rel}. (d) Based on the result of part (c), for the conditions given above, will the particles escape from one another? Explain. (e) If the particles do escape, what will be their final relative speed when $r \to \infty$? If the particles do not escape, what will be their distance of maximum separation? That is, what will be the value of r when $v = 0$? (f) Repeat parts (c)–(e) for $v_1 = 400$ m/s and $v_2 = 1800$ m/s when the separation is 9.00 mm.

Answers

Chapter Opening Question ?

A large, constant potential difference V_{ab} is maintained between the welding tool (a) and the metal pieces to be welded (b). From Example 23.9 (Section 23.3) the electric field between two conductors separated by a distance d has magnitude $E = V_{ab}/d$. Hence d must be small in order for the field magnitude E to be large enough to ionize the gas between the conductors a and b (see Section 23.3) and produce an arc through this gas.

Test Your Understanding Questions

23.1 Answers: (a) (i), (b) (ii) The three charges q_1, q_2, and q_3 are all positive, so all three of the terms in the sum in Eq. (23.11)—q_1q_2/r_{12}, q_1q_3/r_{13}, and q_2q_3/r_{23}—are positive. Hence the total electric potential energy U is positive. This means that it would take positive work to bring the three charges from infinity to the positions shown in Fig. 21.14, and hence *negative* work to move the three charges from these positions back to infinity.

23.2 Answer: no If $V = 0$ at a certain point, $\vec{E}$ does *not* have to be zero at that point. An example is point c in Figs. 21.23 and 23.13, for which there is an electric field in the $+x$-direction (see Example 21.9 in Section 21.5) even though $V = 0$ (see Example 23.4). This isn't a surprising result because V and $\vec{E}$ are quite different quantities: V is the net amount of work required to bring a unit charge from infinity to the point in question, whereas $\vec{E}$ is the electric force that acts on a unit charge when it arrives at that point.

23.3 Answer: no If $\vec{E} = 0$ at a certain point, V does *not* have to be zero at that point. An example is point O at the center of the charged ring in Figs. 21.23 and 23.21. From Example 21.9 (Section 21.5), the electric field is zero at O because the electric-field contributions from different parts of the ring completely cancel. From Example 23.11, however, the potential at O is *not* zero: This point corresponds to $x = 0$, so $V = (1/4\pi\epsilon_0)(Q/a)$. This value of V corresponds to the work that would have to be done to move a unit positive test charge along a path from infinity to point O; it is nonzero because the charged ring repels the test charge, so positive work must be done to move the test charge toward the ring.

23.4 Answer: no If the positive charges in Fig. 23.23 were replaced by negative charges, and vice versa, the equipotential surfaces would be the same but the sign of the potential would be reversed. For example, the surfaces in Fig. 23.23b with potential $V = +30$ V and $V = -50$ V would have potential $V = -30$ V and $V = +50$ V, respectively.

23.5 Answer: (iii) From Eqs. (23.19), the components of the electric field are $E_x = -\partial V/\partial x = B + Dy$, $E_y = -\partial V/\partial y = 3Cy^2 + Dx$, and $E_z = -\partial V/\partial z = 0$. The value of A has no effect, which means that we can add a constant to the electric potential at all points without changing $\vec{E}$ or the potential difference between two points. The potential does not depend on z, so the z-component of $\vec{E}$ is zero. Note that at the origin the electric field is not zero because it has a nonzero x-component: $E_x = B, E_y = 0, E_z = 0$.

Bridging Problem

Answer: $\dfrac{qQ}{8\pi\epsilon_0 a} \ln\left(\dfrac{L + a}{L - a}\right)$

24 CAPACITANCE AND DIELECTRICS

LEARNING GOALS

By studying this chapter, you will learn:

- The nature of capacitors, and how to calculate a quantity that measures their ability to store charge.

- How to analyze capacitors connected in a network.

- How to calculate the amount of energy stored in a capacitor.

- What dielectrics are, and how they make capacitors more effective.

? The energy used in a camera's flash unit is stored in a capacitor, which consists of two closely spaced conductors that carry opposite charges. If the amount of charge on the conductors is doubled, by what factor does the stored energy increase?

When you set an old-fashioned spring mousetrap or pull back the string of an archer's bow, you are storing mechanical energy as elastic potential energy. A capacitor is a device that stores *electric* potential energy and electric charge. To make a capacitor, just insulate two conductors from each other. To store energy in this device, transfer charge from one conductor to the other so that one has a negative charge and the other has an equal amount of positive charge. Work must be done to move the charges through the resulting potential difference between the conductors, and the work done is stored as electric potential energy.

Capacitors have a tremendous number of practical applications in devices such as electronic flash units for photography, pulsed lasers, air bag sensors for cars, and radio and television receivers. We'll encounter many of these applications in later chapters (particularly Chapter 31, in which we'll see the crucial role played by capacitors in the alternating-current circuits that pervade our technological society). In this chapter, however, our emphasis is on the fundamental properties of capacitors. For a particular capacitor, the ratio of the charge on each conductor to the potential difference between the conductors is a constant, called the *capacitance.* The capacitance depends on the sizes and shapes of the conductors and on the insulating material (if any) between them. Compared to the case in which there is only vacuum between the conductors, the capacitance increases when an insulating material (a *dielectric*) is present. This happens because a redistribution of charge, called *polarization,* takes place within the insulating material. Studying polarization will give us added insight into the electrical properties of matter.

Capacitors also give us a new way to think about electric potential energy. The energy stored in a charged capacitor is related to the electric field in the space between the conductors. We will see that electric potential energy can be regarded as being stored *in the field itself.* The idea that the electric field is itself a storehouse of energy is at the heart of the theory of electromagnetic waves and our modern understanding of the nature of light, to be discussed in Chapter 32.

24.1 Capacitors and Capacitance

Any two conductors separated by an insulator (or a vacuum) form a **capacitor** (Fig. 24.1). In most practical applications, each conductor initially has zero net charge and electrons are transferred from one conductor to the other; this is called *charging* the capacitor. Then the two conductors have charges with equal magnitude and opposite sign, and the *net* charge on the capacitor as a whole remains zero. We will assume throughout this chapter that this is the case. When we say that a capacitor has charge Q, or that a charge Q is *stored* on the capacitor, we mean that the conductor at higher potential has charge $+Q$ and the conductor at lower potential has charge $-Q$ (assuming that Q is positive). Keep this in mind in the following discussion and examples.

In circuit diagrams a capacitor is represented by either of these symbols:

In either symbol the vertical lines (straight or curved) represent the conductors and the horizontal lines represent wires connected to either conductor. One common way to charge a capacitor is to connect these two wires to opposite terminals of a battery. Once the charges Q and $-Q$ are established on the conductors, the battery is disconnected. This gives a fixed *potential difference* V_{ab} between the conductors (that is, the potential of the positively charged conductor a with respect to the negatively charged conductor b) that is just equal to the voltage of the battery.

The electric field at any point in the region between the conductors is proportional to the magnitude Q of charge on each conductor. It follows that the potential difference V_{ab} between the conductors is also proportional to Q. If we double the magnitude of charge on each conductor, the charge density at each point doubles, the electric field at each point doubles, and the potential difference between conductors doubles; however, the *ratio* of charge to potential difference does not change. This ratio is called the **capacitance** C of the capacitor:

$$ C = \frac{Q}{V_{ab}} \qquad \text{(definition of capacitance)} \qquad (24.1) $$

The SI unit of capacitance is called one **farad** (1 F), in honor of the 19th-century English physicist Michael Faraday. From Eq. (24.1), one farad is equal to one *coulomb per volt* (1 C/V):

$$ 1\ \text{F} = 1\ \text{farad} = 1\ \text{C/V} = 1\ \text{coulomb/volt} $$

CAUTION **Capacitance vs. coulombs** Don't confuse the symbol C for capacitance (which is always in italics) with the abbreviation C for coulombs (which is never italicized). ▮

The greater the capacitance C of a capacitor, the greater the magnitude Q of charge on either conductor for a given potential difference V_{ab} and hence the greater the amount of stored energy. (Remember that potential is potential energy per unit charge.) Thus *capacitance is a measure of the ability of a capacitor to store energy.* We will see that the value of the capacitance depends only on the shapes and sizes of the conductors and on the nature of the insulating material between them. (The above remarks about capacitance being independent of Q and V_{ab} do not apply to certain special types of insulating materials. We won't discuss these materials in this book, however.)

Calculating Capacitance: Capacitors in Vacuum

We can calculate the capacitance C of a given capacitor by finding the potential difference V_{ab} between the conductors for a given magnitude of charge Q and

24.1 Any two conductors a and b insulated from each other form a capacitor.

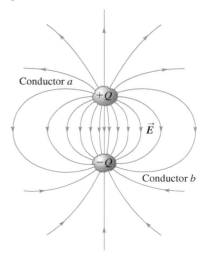

Conductor a
$+Q$
$\vec{E}$
$-Q$
Conductor b

MasteringPHYSICS

ActivPhysics 11.11.6: Electric Potential: Qualitative Introduction
ActivPhysics 11.12.1 and 11.12.3: Electric Potential, Field, and Force

24.2 A charged parallel-plate capacitor.

(a) Arrangement of the capacitor plates

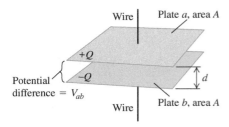

(b) Side view of the electric field $\vec{E}$

When the separation of the plates is small compared to their size, the fringing of the field is slight.

24.3 Inside a condenser microphone is a capacitor with one rigid plate and one flexible plate. The two plates are kept at a constant potential difference V_{ab}. Sound waves cause the flexible plate to move back and forth, varying the capacitance C and causing charge to flow to and from the capacitor in accordance with the relationship $C = Q/V_{ab}$. Thus a sound wave is converted to a charge flow that can be amplified and recorded digitally.

then using Eq. (24.1). For now we'll consider only *capacitors in vacuum;* that is, we'll assume that the conductors that make up the capacitor are separated by empty space.

The simplest form of capacitor consists of two parallel conducting plates, each with area A, separated by a distance d that is small in comparison with their dimensions (Fig. 24.2a). When the plates are charged, the electric field is almost completely localized in the region between the plates (Fig. 24.2b). As we discussed in Example 22.8 (Section 22.4), the field between such plates is essentially *uniform,* and the charges on the plates are uniformly distributed over their opposing surfaces. We call this arrangement a **parallel-plate capacitor.**

We worked out the electric-field magnitude E for this arrangement in Example 21.12 (Section 21.5) using the principle of superposition of electric fields and again in Example 22.8 (Section 22.4) using Gauss's law. It would be a good idea to review those examples. We found that $E = \sigma/\epsilon_0$, where σ is the magnitude (absolute value) of the surface charge density on each plate. This is equal to the magnitude of the total charge Q on each plate divided by the area A of the plate, or $\sigma = Q/A$, so the field magnitude E can be expressed as

$$E = \frac{\sigma}{\epsilon_0} = \frac{Q}{\epsilon_0 A}$$

The field is uniform and the distance between the plates is d, so the potential difference (voltage) between the two plates is

$$V_{ab} = Ed = \frac{1}{\epsilon_0}\frac{Qd}{A}$$

From this we see that the capacitance C of a parallel-plate capacitor in vacuum is

$$C = \frac{Q}{V_{ab}} = \epsilon_0\frac{A}{d} \qquad \text{(capacitance of a parallel-plate capacitor in vacuum)} \qquad (24.2)$$

The capacitance depends only on the geometry of the capacitor; it is directly proportional to the area A of each plate and inversely proportional to their separation d. The quantities A and d are constants for a given capacitor, and ϵ_0 is a universal constant. Thus in vacuum the capacitance C is a constant independent of the charge on the capacitor or the potential difference between the plates. If one of the capacitor plates is flexible, the capacitance C changes as the plate separation d changes. This is the operating principle of a condenser microphone (Fig. 24.3).

When matter is present between the plates, its properties affect the capacitance. We will return to this topic in Section 24.4. Meanwhile, we remark that if the space contains air at atmospheric pressure instead of vacuum, the capacitance differs from the prediction of Eq. (24.2) by less than 0.06%.

In Eq. (24.2), if A is in square meters and d in meters, C is in farads. The units of ϵ_0 are $C^2/N \cdot m^2$, so we see that

$$1\ F = 1\ C^2/N \cdot m = 1\ C^2/J$$

Because $1\ V = 1\ J/C$ (energy per unit charge), this is consistent with our definition $1\ F = 1\ C/V$. Finally, the units of ϵ_0 can be expressed as $1\ C^2/N \cdot m^2 = 1\ F/m$, so

$$\epsilon_0 = 8.85 \times 10^{-12}\ F/m$$

This relationship is useful in capacitance calculations, and it also helps us to verify that Eq. (24.2) is dimensionally consistent.

One farad is a very large capacitance, as the following example shows. In many applications the most convenient units of capacitance are the *microfarad*

($1 \ \mu\text{F} = 10^{-6} \text{ F}$) and the *picofarad* ($1 \text{ pF} = 10^{-12} \text{ F}$). For example, the flash unit in a point-and-shoot camera uses a capacitor of a few hundred microfarads (Fig. 24.4), while capacitances in a radio tuning circuit are typically from 10 to 100 picofarads.

For *any* capacitor in vacuum, the capacitance C depends only on the shapes, dimensions, and separation of the conductors that make up the capacitor. If the conductor shapes are more complex than those of the parallel-plate capacitor, the expression for capacitance is more complicated than in Eq. (24.2). In the following examples we show how to calculate C for two other conductor geometries.

24.4 A commercial capacitor is labeled with the value of its capacitance. For these capacitors, $C = 2200 \ \mu\text{F}$, $1000 \ \mu\text{F}$, and $470 \ \mu\text{F}$.

Example 24.1 **Size of a 1-F capacitor**

The parallel plates of a 1.0-F capacitor are 1.0 mm apart. What is their area?

SOLUTION

IDENTIFY and SET UP: This problem uses the relationship among the capacitance C, plate separation d, and plate area A (our target variable) for a parallel-plate capacitor. We solve Eq. (24.2) for A.

EXECUTE: From Eq. (24.2),

$$A = \frac{Cd}{\epsilon_0} = \frac{(1.0 \text{ F})(1.0 \times 10^{-3} \text{ m})}{8.85 \times 10^{-12} \text{ F/m}} = 1.1 \times 10^8 \text{ m}^2$$

EVALUATE: This corresponds to a square about 10 km (about 6 miles) on a side! The volume of such a capacitor would be at least $Ad = 1.1 \times 10^5 \text{ m}^3$, equivalent to that of a cube about 50 m on a side. In fact, it's possible to make 1-F capacitors a few *centimeters* on a side. The trick is to have an appropriate substance between the plates rather than a vacuum, so that (among other things) the plate separation d can greatly reduced. We'll explore this further in Section 24.4.

Example 24.2 **Properties of a parallel-plate capacitor**

The plates of a parallel-plate capacitor in vacuum are 5.00 mm apart and 2.00 m^2 in area. A 10.0-kV potential difference is applied across the capacitor. Compute (a) the capacitance; (b) the charge on each plate; and (c) the magnitude of the electric field between the plates.

SOLUTION

IDENTIFY and SET UP: We are given the plate area A, the plate spacing d, and the potential difference $V_{ab} = 1.00 \times 10^4$ V for this parallel-plate capacitor. Our target variables are the capacitance C, the charge Q on each plate, and the electric-field magnitude E. We use Eq. (24.2) to calculate C and then use Eq. (24.1) and V_{ab} to find Q. We use $E = Q/\epsilon_0 A$ to find E.

EXECUTE: (a) From Eq. (24.2),

$$C = \epsilon_0 \frac{A}{d} = (8.85 \times 10^{-12} \text{ F/m}) \frac{(2.00 \text{ m}^2)}{5.00 \times 10^{-3} \text{ m}}$$
$$= 3.54 \times 10^{-9} \text{ F} = 0.00354 \ \mu\text{F}$$

(b) The charge on the capacitor is

$$Q = CV_{ab} = (3.54 \times 10^{-9} \text{ C/V})(1.00 \times 10^4 \text{ V})$$
$$= 3.54 \times 10^{-5} \text{ C} = 35.4 \ \mu\text{C}$$

The plate at higher potential has charge $+35.4 \ \mu\text{C}$, and the other plate has charge $-35.4 \ \mu\text{C}$.

(c) The electric-field magnitude is

$$E = \frac{\sigma}{\epsilon_0} = \frac{Q}{\epsilon_0 A} = \frac{3.54 \times 10^{-5} \text{ C}}{(8.85 \times 10^{-12} \text{ C}^2/\text{N} \cdot \text{m}^2)(2.00 \text{ m}^2)}$$
$$= 2.00 \times 10^6 \text{ N/C}$$

EVALUATE: We can also find E by recalling that the electric field is equal in magnitude to the potential gradient [Eq. (23.22)]. The field between the plates is uniform, so

$$E = \frac{V_{ab}}{d} = \frac{1.00 \times 10^4 \text{ V}}{5.00 \times 10^{-3} \text{ m}} = 2.00 \times 10^6 \text{ V/m}$$

(Remember that 1 N/C $=$ 1 V/m.)

Example 24.3   A spherical capacitor

Two concentric spherical conducting shells are separated by vacuum (Fig. 24.5). The inner shell has total charge $+Q$ and outer radius r_a, and the outer shell has charge $-Q$ and inner radius r_b. Find the capacitance of this spherical capacitor.

SOLUTION

IDENTIFY and SET UP: By definition, the capacitance C is the magnitude Q of the charge on either sphere divided by the potential difference V_{ab} between the spheres. We first find V_{ab}, and then use Eq. (24.1) to find the capacitance $C = Q/V_{ab}$.

EXECUTE: Using a Gaussian surface such as that shown in Fig. 24.5, we found in Example 22.5 (Section 22.4) that the charge on a conducting sphere produces zero field *inside* the sphere, so the outer sphere makes no contribution to the field between the spheres. Therefore the electric field *and* the electric potential

24.5 A spherical capacitor.

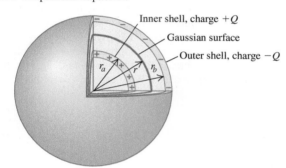

Inner shell, charge $+Q$
Gaussian surface
Outer shell, charge $-Q$

between the shells are the same as those outside a charged conducting sphere with charge $+Q$. We considered that problem in Example 23.8 (Section 23.3), so the same result applies here: The potential at any point between the spheres is $V = Q/4\pi\epsilon_0 r$. Hence the potential of the inner (positive) conductor at $r = r_a$ with respect to that of the outer (negative) conductor at $r = r_b$ is

$$V_{ab} = V_a - V_b = \frac{Q}{4\pi\epsilon_0 r_a} - \frac{Q}{4\pi\epsilon_0 r_b}$$

$$= \frac{Q}{4\pi\epsilon_0}\left(\frac{1}{r_a} - \frac{1}{r_b}\right) = \frac{Q}{4\pi\epsilon_0}\frac{r_b - r_a}{r_a r_b}$$

The capacitance is then

$$C = \frac{Q}{V_{ab}} = 4\pi\epsilon_0\frac{r_a r_b}{r_b - r_a}$$

As an example, if $r_a = 9.5$ cm and $r_b = 10.5$ cm,

$$C = 4\pi(8.85 \times 10^{-12} \text{ F/m})\frac{(0.095 \text{ m})(0.105 \text{ m})}{0.010 \text{ m}}$$

$$= 1.1 \times 10^{-10} \text{ F} = 110 \text{ pF}$$

EVALUATE: We can relate our expression for C to that for a parallel-plate capacitor. The quantity $4\pi r_a r_b$ is intermediate between the areas $4\pi r_a^2$ and $4\pi r_b^2$ of the two spheres; in fact, it's the *geometric mean* of these two areas, which we can denote by A_{gm}. The distance between spheres is $d = r_b - r_a$, so we can write $C = 4\pi\epsilon_0 r_a r_b/(r_b - r_a) = \epsilon_0 A_{gm}/d$. This has the same form as for parallel plates: $C = \epsilon_0 A/d$. If the distance between spheres is very small in comparison to their radii, their capacitance is the same as that of parallel plates with the same area and spacing.

Example 24.4   A cylindrical capacitor

Two long, coaxial cylindrical conductors are separated by vacuum (Fig. 24.6). The inner cylinder has radius r_a and linear charge density $+\lambda$. The outer cylinder has inner radius r_b and linear charge density $-\lambda$. Find the capacitance per unit length for this capacitor.

SOLUTION

IDENTIFY and SET UP: As in Example 24.3, we use the definition of capacitance, $C = Q/V_{ab}$. We use the result of Example 23.10

24.6 A long cylindrical capacitor. The linear charge density λ is assumed to be positive in this figure. The magnitude of charge in a length L of either cylinder is λL.

$-\lambda$
$+\lambda$
r_a
r_b
L

(Section 23.3) to find the potential difference V_{ab} between the cylinders, and find the charge Q on a length L of the cylinders from the linear charge density. We then find the corresponding capacitance C using Eq. (24.1). Our target variable is this capacitance divided by L.

EXECUTE: As in Example 24.3, the potential V between the cylinders is not affected by the presence of the charged outer cylinder. Hence our result in Example 23.10 for the potential outside a charged conducting cylinder also holds in this example for potential in the space between the cylinders:

$$V = \frac{\lambda}{2\pi\epsilon_0}\ln\frac{r_0}{r}$$

Here r_0 is the arbitrary, *finite* radius at which $V = 0$. We take $r_0 = r_b$, the radius of the inner surface of the outer cylinder. Then the potential at the outer surface of the inner cylinder (at which $r = r_a$) is just the potential V_{ab} of the inner (positive) cylinder a with respect to the outer (negative) cylinder b:

$$V_{ab} = \frac{\lambda}{2\pi\epsilon_0}\ln\frac{r_b}{r_a}$$

If λ is positive as in Fig. 24.6, then V_{ab} is positive as well: The inner cylinder is at higher potential than the outer.

The total charge Q in a length L is $Q = \lambda L$, so from Eq. (24.1) the capacitance C of a length L is

$$C = \frac{Q}{V_{ab}} = \frac{\lambda L}{\dfrac{\lambda}{2\pi\epsilon_0}\ln\dfrac{r_b}{r_a}} = \frac{2\pi\epsilon_0 L}{\ln(r_b/r_a)}$$

The capacitance per unit length is

$$\frac{C}{L} = \frac{2\pi\epsilon_0}{\ln(r_b/r_a)}$$

Substituting $\epsilon_0 = 8.85 \times 10^{-12}$ F/m $= 8.85$ pF/m, we get

$$\frac{C}{L} = \frac{55.6 \text{ pF/m}}{\ln(r_b/r_a)}$$

EVALUATE: The capacitance of coaxial cylinders is determined entirely by their dimensions, just as for parallel-plate and spherical capacitors. Ordinary coaxial cables are made like this but with an insulating material instead of vacuum between the conductors. A typical cable used for connecting a television to a cable TV feed has a capacitance per unit length of 69 pF/m.

Test Your Understanding of Section 24.1 A capacitor has vacuum in the space between the conductors. If you double the amount of charge on each conductor, what happens to the capacitance? (i) It increases; (ii) it decreases; (iii) it remains the same; (iv) the answer depends on the size or shape of the conductors.

24.2 Capacitors in Series and Parallel

Capacitors are manufactured with certain standard capacitances and working voltages (Fig. 24.7). However, these standard values may not be the ones you actually need in a particular application. You can obtain the values you need by combining capacitors; many combinations are possible, but the simplest combinations are a series connection and a parallel connection.

Capacitors in Series

Figure 24.8a is a schematic diagram of a **series connection.** Two capacitors are connected in series (one after the other) by conducting wires between points a and b. Both capacitors are initially uncharged. When a constant positive potential difference V_{ab} is applied between points a and b, the capacitors become charged; the figure shows that the charge on *all* conducting plates has the same magnitude. To see why, note first that the top plate of C_1 acquires a positive charge Q. The electric field of this positive charge pulls negative charge up to the bottom plate of C_1 until all of the field lines that begin on the top plate end on the bottom plate. This requires that the bottom plate have charge $-Q$. These negative charges had to come from the top plate of C_2, which becomes positively charged with charge $+Q$. This positive charge then pulls negative charge $-Q$ from the connection at point b onto the bottom plate of C_2. The total charge on the lower plate of C_1 and the upper plate of C_2 together must always be zero because these plates aren't connected to anything except each other. Thus *in a series connection the magnitude of charge on all plates is the same.*

Referring to Fig. 24.8a, we can write the potential differences between points a and c, c and b, and a and b as

$$V_{ac} = V_1 = \frac{Q}{C_1} \qquad V_{cb} = V_2 = \frac{Q}{C_2}$$

$$V_{ab} = V = V_1 + V_2 = Q\left(\frac{1}{C_1} + \frac{1}{C_2}\right)$$

and so

$$\frac{V}{Q} = \frac{1}{C_1} + \frac{1}{C_2} \tag{24.3}$$

Following a common convention, we use the symbols V_1, V_2, and V to denote the potential *differences* V_{ac} (across the first capacitor), V_{cb} (across the second capacitor), and V_{ab} (across the entire combination of capacitors), respectively.

24.7 An assortment of commercially available capacitors.

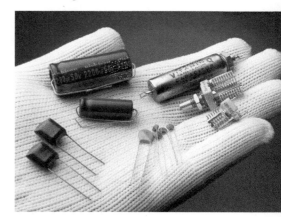

24.8 A series connection of two capacitors.

(a) Two capacitors in series

Capacitors in series:
• The capacitors have the same charge Q.
• Their potential differences add:
$V_{ac} + V_{cb} = V_{ab}.$

(b) The equivalent single capacitor

Equivalent capacitance is less than the individual capacitances:

Charge is the same as for the individual capacitors.

$$C_{eq} = \frac{Q}{V}$$

$$\frac{1}{C_{eq}} = \frac{1}{C_1} + \frac{1}{C_2}$$

Application Touch Screens and Capacitance

The touch screen on a mobile phone, an MP3 player, or (as shown here) a medical device uses the physics of capacitors. Behind the screen are two parallel layers, one behind the other, of thin strips of a transparent conductor such as indium tin oxide. A voltage is maintained between the two layers. The strips in one layer are oriented perpendicular to those in the other layer; the points where two strips overlap act as a grid of capacitors. When you bring your finger (a conductor) up to a point on the screen, your finger and the front conducting layer act like a second capacitor in series at that point. The circuitry attached to the conducting layers detects the location of the capacitance change, and so detects where you touched the screen.

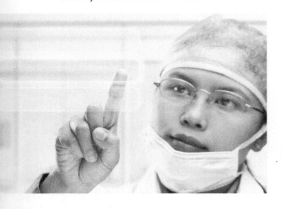

The **equivalent capacitance** C_{eq} of the series combination is defined as the capacitance of a *single* capacitor for which the charge Q is the same as for the combination, when the potential difference V is the same. In other words, the combination can be replaced by an *equivalent capacitor* of capacitance C_{eq}. For such a capacitor, shown in Fig. 24.8b,

$$C_{eq} = \frac{Q}{V} \quad \text{or} \quad \frac{1}{C_{eq}} = \frac{V}{Q} \tag{24.4}$$

Combining Eqs. (24.3) and (24.4), we find

$$\frac{1}{C_{eq}} = \frac{1}{C_1} + \frac{1}{C_2}$$

We can extend this analysis to any number of capacitors in series. We find the following result for the *reciprocal* of the equivalent capacitance:

$$\frac{1}{C_{eq}} = \frac{1}{C_1} + \frac{1}{C_2} + \frac{1}{C_3} + \cdots \quad \text{(capacitors in series)} \tag{24.5}$$

The reciprocal of the equivalent capacitance of a series combination equals the sum of the reciprocals of the individual capacitances. In a series connection the equivalent capacitance is always *less than* any individual capacitance.

CAUTION **Capacitors in series** The magnitude of charge is the same on all plates of all the capacitors in a series combination; however, the potential differences of the individual capacitors are *not* the same unless their individual capacitances are the same. The potential differences of the individual capacitors add to give the total potential difference across the series combination: $V_{total} = V_1 + V_2 + V_3 + \cdots$. ∎

Capacitors in Parallel

The arrangement shown in Fig. 24.9a is called a **parallel connection.** Two capacitors are connected in parallel between points a and b. In this case the upper plates of the two capacitors are connected by conducting wires to form an equipotential surface, and the lower plates form another. Hence *in a parallel connection the potential difference for all individual capacitors is the same* and is equal to $V_{ab} = V$. The charges Q_1 and Q_2 are not necessarily equal, however, since charges can reach each capacitor independently from the source (such as a battery) of the voltage V_{ab}. The charges are

$$Q_1 = C_1V \quad \text{and} \quad Q_2 = C_2V$$

The *total* charge Q of the combination, and thus the total charge on the equivalent capacitor, is

$$Q = Q_1 + Q_2 = (C_1 + C_2)V$$

so

$$\frac{Q}{V} = C_1 + C_2 \tag{24.6}$$

The parallel combination is equivalent to a single capacitor with the same total charge $Q = Q_1 + Q_2$ and potential difference V as the combination (Fig. 24.9b). The equivalent capacitance of the combination, C_{eq}, is the same as the capacitance Q/V of this single equivalent capacitor. So from Eq. (24.6),

$$C_{eq} = C_1 + C_2$$

24.9 A parallel connection of two capacitors.

(a) Two capacitors in parallel

Capacitors in parallel:
• The capacitors have the same potential V.
• The charge on each capacitor depends on its capacitance: $Q_1 = C_1V$, $Q_2 = C_2V$.

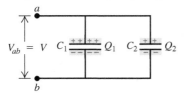

(b) The equivalent single capacitor

Charge is the sum of the individual charges:
$Q = Q_1 + Q_2$

Equivalent capacitance:
$C_{eq} = C_1 + C_2$

In the same way we can show that for any number of capacitors in parallel,

$$C_{eq} = C_1 + C_2 + C_3 + \cdots \qquad \text{(capacitors in parallel)} \qquad (24.7)$$

The equivalent capacitance of a parallel combination equals the *sum* of the individual capacitances. In a parallel connection the equivalent capacitance is always *greater than* any individual capacitance.

> **CAUTION** **Capacitors in parallel** The potential differences are the same for all the capacitors in a parallel combination; however, the charges on individual capacitors are *not* the same unless their individual capacitances are the same. The charges on the individual capacitors add to give the total charge on the parallel combination: $Q_{total} = Q_1 + Q_2 + Q_3 + \cdots$. [Compare these statements to those in the "Caution" paragraph following Eq. (24.5).]

Problem-Solving Strategy 24.1   Equivalent Capacitance

IDENTIFY *the relevant concepts:* The concept of equivalent capacitance is useful whenever two or more capacitors are connected.

SET UP *the problem* using the following steps:
1. Make a drawing of the capacitor arrangement.
2. Identify all groups of capacitors that are connected in series or in parallel.
3. Keep in mind that when we say a capacitor "has charge Q," we mean that the plate at higher potential has charge $+Q$ and the other plate has charge $-Q$.

EXECUTE *the solution* as follows:
1. Use Eq. (24.5) to find the equivalent capacitance of capacitors connected in series, as in Fig. 24.8. Such capacitors each have the *same charge* if they were uncharged before they were connected; that charge is the same as that on the equivalent capacitor. The potential difference across the combination is the sum of the potential differences across the individual capacitors.

2. Use Eq. (24.7) to find the equivalent capacitance of capacitors connected in parallel, as in Fig. 24.9. Such capacitors all have the *same potential difference* across them; that potential difference is the same as that across the equivalent capacitor. The total charge on the combination is the sum of the charges on the individual capacitors.

3. After replacing all the series or parallel groups you initially identified, you may find that more such groups reveal themselves. Replace those groups using the same procedure as above until no more replacements are possible. If you then need to find the charge or potential difference for an individual original capacitor, you may have to retrace your steps.

EVALUATE *your answer:* Check whether your result makes sense. If the capacitors are connected in series, the equivalent capacitance C_{eq} must be *smaller* than any of the individual capacitances. If the capacitors are connected in parallel, C_{eq} must be *greater* than any of the individual capacitances.

Example 24.5   Capacitors in series and in parallel

In Figs. 24.8 and 24.9, let $C_1 = 6.0 \ \mu F$, $C_2 = 3.0 \ \mu F$, and $V_{ab} = 18$ V. Find the equivalent capacitance and the charge and potential difference for each capacitor when the capacitors are connected (a) in series (see Fig. 24.8) and (b) in parallel (see Fig. 24.9).

SOLUTION

IDENTIFY and SET UP: In both parts of this example a target variable is the equivalent capacitance C_{eq}, which is given by Eq. (24.5) for the series combination in part (a) and by Eq. (24.7) for the parallel combination in part (b). In each part we find the charge and potential difference using the definition of capacitance, Eq. (24.1), and the rules outlined in Problem-Solving Strategy 24.1.

EXECUTE: (a) From Eq. (24.5) for a series combination,

$$\frac{1}{C_{eq}} = \frac{1}{C_1} + \frac{1}{C_2} = \frac{1}{6.0 \ \mu F} + \frac{1}{3.0 \ \mu F} \qquad C_{eq} = 2.0 \ \mu F$$

The charge Q on each capacitor in series is the same as that on the equivalent capacitor:

$$Q = C_{eq}V = (2.0 \ \mu F)(18 \ V) = 36 \ \mu C$$

The potential difference across each capacitor is inversely proportional to its capacitance:

$$V_{ac} = V_1 = \frac{Q}{C_1} = \frac{36 \ \mu C}{6.0 \ \mu F} = 6.0 \ V$$

$$V_{cb} = V_2 = \frac{Q}{C_2} = \frac{36 \ \mu C}{3.0 \ \mu F} = 12.0 \ V$$

(b) From Eq. (24.7) for a parallel combination,

$$C_{eq} = C_1 + C_2 = 6.0 \ \mu F + 3.0 \ \mu F = 9.0 \ \mu F$$

The potential difference across each of the capacitors is the same as that across the equivalent capacitor, 18 V. The charge on each capacitor is directly proportional to its capacitance:

$$Q_1 = C_1V = (6.0 \ \mu F)(18 \ V) = 108 \ \mu C$$
$$Q_2 = C_2V = (3.0 \ \mu F)(18 \ V) = 54 \ \mu C$$

EVALUATE: As expected, the equivalent capacitance C_{eq} for the series combination in part (a) is less than either C_1 or C_2, while

Continued

that for the parallel combination in part (b) is greater than either C_1 or C_2. For two capacitors in series, as in part (a), the charge is the same on either capacitor and the *larger* potential difference appears across the capacitor with the *smaller* capacitance. Furthermore, the sum of the potential differences across the individual capacitors in series equals the potential difference across the

equivalent capacitor: $V_{ac} + V_{cb} = V_{ab} = 18$ V. By contrast, for two capacitors in parallel, as in part (b), each capacitor has the same potential difference and the *larger* charge appears on the capacitor with the *larger* capacitance. Can you show that the total charge $Q_1 + Q_2$ on the parallel combination is equal to the charge $Q = C_{eq}V$ on the equivalent capacitor?

Example 24.6   A capacitor network

Find the equivalent capacitance of the five-capacitor network shown in Fig. 24.10a.

SOLUTION

IDENTIFY and SET UP: These capacitors are neither all in series nor all in parallel. We can, however, identify portions of the arrangement that *are* either in series or parallel. We combine these as described in Problem-Solving Strategy 24.1 to find the net equivalent capacitance, using Eq. (24.5) for series connections and Eq. (24.7) for parallel connections.

EXECUTE: The caption of Fig. 24.10 outlines our procedure. We first use Eq. (24.5) to replace the 12-μF and 6-μF series combination by its equivalent capacitance C':

$$\frac{1}{C'} = \frac{1}{12\ \mu\text{F}} + \frac{1}{6\ \mu\text{F}} \qquad C' = 4\ \mu\text{F}$$

This gives us the equivalent combination of Fig. 24.10b. Now we see three capacitors in parallel, and we use Eq. (24.7) to replace them with their equivalent capacitance C'':

$$C'' = 3\ \mu\text{F} + 11\ \mu\text{F} + 4\ \mu\text{F} = 18\ \mu\text{F}$$

This gives us the equivalent combination of Fig. 24.10c, which has two capacitors in series. We use Eq. (24.5) to replace them with their equivalent capacitance C_{eq}, which is our target variable (Fig. 24.10d):

$$\frac{1}{C_{eq}} = \frac{1}{18\ \mu\text{F}} + \frac{1}{9\ \mu\text{F}} \qquad C_{eq} = 6\ \mu\text{F}$$

EVALUATE: If the potential difference across the entire network in Fig. 24.10a is $V_{ab} = 9.0$ V, the net charge on the network is $Q = C_{eq}V_{ab} = (6\ \mu\text{F})(9.0\ \text{V}) = 54\ \mu\text{C}$. Can you find the charge on, and the voltage across, each of the five individual capacitors?

24.10 (a) A capacitor network between points a and b. (b) The 12-μF and 6-μF capacitors in series in (a) are replaced by an equivalent 4-μF capacitor. (c) The 3-μF, 11-μF, and 4-μF capacitors in parallel in (b) are replaced by an equivalent 18-μF capacitor. (d) Finally, the 18-μF and 9-μF capacitors in series in (c) are replaced by an equivalent 6-μF capacitor.

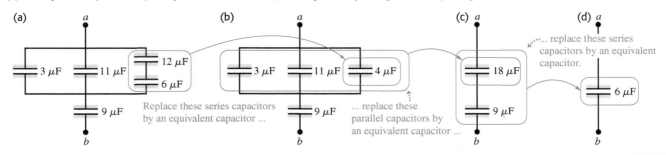

Test Your Understanding of Section 24.2   You want to connect a 4-μF capacitor and an 8-μF capacitor. (a) With which type of connection will the 4-μF capacitor have a greater potential difference across it than the 8-μF capacitor? (i) series; (ii) parallel; (iii) either series or parallel; (iv) neither series nor parallel. (b) With which type of connection will the 4-μF capacitor have a greater charge than the 8-μF capacitor? (i) series; (ii) parallel; (iii) either series or parallel; (iv) neither series nor parallel.

24.3 Energy Storage in Capacitors and Electric-Field Energy

Many of the most important applications of capacitors depend on their ability to store energy. The electric potential energy stored in a charged capacitor is just equal to the amount of work required to charge it—that is, to separate opposite charges and place them on different conductors. When the capacitor is discharged, this stored energy is recovered as work done by electrical forces.

We can calculate the potential energy U of a charged capacitor by calculating the work W required to charge it. Suppose that when we are done charging the capacitor, the final charge is Q and the final potential difference is V. From Eq. (24.1) these quantities are related by

$$V = \frac{Q}{C}$$

Let q and v be the charge and potential difference, respectively, at an intermediate stage during the charging process; then $v = q/C$. At this stage the work dW required to transfer an additional element of charge dq is

$$dW = v \, dq = \frac{q \, dq}{C}$$

The total work W needed to increase the capacitor charge q from zero to a final value Q is

$$W = \int_{0}^{W} dW = \frac{1}{C} \int_{0}^{Q} q \, dq = \frac{Q^2}{2C} \quad \text{(work to charge a capacitor)} \quad (24.8)$$

This is also equal to the total work done by the electric field on the charge when the capacitor discharges. Then q *decreases* from an initial value Q to zero as the elements of charge dq "fall" through potential differences v that vary from V down to zero.

If we define the potential energy of an *uncharged* capacitor to be zero, then W in Eq. (24.8) is equal to the potential energy U of the charged capacitor. The final stored charge is $Q = CV$, so we can express U (which is equal to W) as

$$U = \frac{Q^2}{2C} = \tfrac{1}{2}CV^2 = \tfrac{1}{2}QV \quad \begin{array}{l}\text{(potential energy stored} \\ \text{in a capacitor)}\end{array} \quad (24.9)$$

When Q is in coulombs, C in farads (coulombs per volt), and V in volts (joules per coulomb), U is in joules.

The last form of Eq. (24.9), $U = \tfrac{1}{2}QV$, shows that the total work W required to charge the capacitor is equal to the total charge Q multiplied by the *average* potential difference $\tfrac{1}{2}V$ during the charging process.

The expression $U = \tfrac{1}{2}(Q^2/C)$ in Eq. (24.9) shows that a charged capacitor is the electrical analog of a stretched spring with elastic potential energy $U = \tfrac{1}{2}kx^2$. The charge Q is analogous to the elongation x, and the *reciprocal* of the capacitance, $1/C$, is analogous to the force constant k. The energy supplied to a capacitor in the charging process is analogous to the work we do on a spring when we stretch it.

Equations (24.8) and (24.9) tell us that capacitance measures the ability of a capacitor to store both energy and charge. If a capacitor is charged by connecting it to a battery or other source that provides a fixed potential difference V, then increasing the value of C gives a greater charge $Q = CV$ and a greater amount of stored energy $U = \tfrac{1}{2}CV^2$. If instead the goal is to transfer a given quantity of charge Q from one conductor to another, Eq. (24.8) shows that the work W required is inversely proportional to C; the greater the capacitance, the easier it is to give a capacitor a fixed amount of charge.

Applications of Capacitors: Energy Storage

Most practical applications of capacitors take advantage of their ability to store and release energy. In electronic flash units used by photographers, the energy stored in a capacitor (see Fig. 24.4) is released by depressing the camera's shutter button. This provides a conducting path from one capacitor plate to the other through the flash tube. Once this path is established, the stored energy is rapidly converted into a brief but intense flash of light. An extreme example of the same principle is the Z machine at Sandia National Laboratories in New Mexico,

24.11 The Z machine uses a large number of capacitors in parallel to give a tremendous equivalent capacitance C (see Section 24.2). Hence a large amount of energy $U = \frac{1}{2}CV^2$ can be stored with even a modest potential difference V. The arcs shown here are produced when the capacitors discharge their energy into a target, which is no larger than a spool of thread. This heats the target to a temperature higher than 2×10^9 K.

which is used in experiments in controlled nuclear fusion (Fig. 24.11). A bank of charged capacitors releases more than a million joules of energy in just a few billionths of a second. For that brief space of time, the power output of the Z machine is 2.9×10^{14} W, or about 80 times the power output of all the electric power plants on earth combined!

In other applications, the energy is released more slowly. Springs in the suspension of an automobile help smooth out the ride by absorbing the energy from sudden jolts and releasing that energy gradually; in an analogous way, a capacitor in an electronic circuit can smooth out unwanted variations in voltage due to power surges. We'll discuss these circuits in detail in Chapter 26.

Electric-Field Energy

We can charge a capacitor by moving electrons directly from one plate to another. This requires doing work against the electric field between the plates. Thus we can think of the energy as being stored *in the field* in the region between the plates. To develop this relationship, let's find the energy *per unit volume* in the space between the plates of a parallel-plate capacitor with plate area A and separation d. We call this the **energy density,** denoted by u. From Eq. (24.9) the total stored potential energy is $\frac{1}{2}CV^2$ and the volume between the plates is just Ad; hence the energy density is

$$u = \text{Energy density} = \frac{\frac{1}{2}CV^2}{Ad} \qquad (24.10)$$

From Eq. (24.2) the capacitance C is given by $C = \epsilon_0 A/d$. The potential difference V is related to the electric-field magnitude E by $V = Ed$. If we use these expressions in Eq. (24.10), the geometric factors A and d cancel, and we find

$$u = \tfrac{1}{2}\epsilon_0 E^2 \qquad \text{(electric energy density in a vacuum)} \qquad (24.11)$$

Although we have derived this relationship only for a parallel-plate capacitor, it turns out to be valid for any capacitor in vacuum and indeed *for any electric field configuration in vacuum.* This result has an interesting implication. We think of vacuum as space with no matter in it, but vacuum can nevertheless have electric fields and therefore energy. Thus "empty" space need not be truly empty after all. We will use this idea and Eq. (24.11) in Chapter 32 in connection with the energy transported by electromagnetic waves.

CAUTION **Electric-field energy is electric potential energy** It's a common misconception that electric-field energy is a new kind of energy, different from the electric potential energy described before. This is *not* the case; it is simply a different way of interpreting electric potential energy. We can regard the energy of a given system of charges as being a shared property of all the charges, or we can think of the energy as being a property of the electric field that the charges create. Either interpretation leads to the same value of the potential energy.

Example 24.7 | **Transferring charge and energy between capacitors**

We connect a capacitor $C_1 = 8.0\ \mu\text{F}$ to a power supply, charge it to a potential difference $V_0 = 120$ V, and disconnect the power supply (Fig. 24.12). Switch S is open. (a) What is the charge Q_0 on C_1? (b) What is the energy stored in C_1? (c) Capacitor $C_2 = 4.0\ \mu\text{F}$ is initially uncharged. We close switch S. After charge no longer flows, what is the potential difference across each capacitor, and what is the charge on each capacitor? (d) What is the final energy of the system?

24.12 When the switch S is closed, the charged capacitor C_1 is connected to an uncharged capacitor C_2. The center part of the switch is an insulating handle; charge can flow only between the two upper terminals and between the two lower terminals.

IDENTIFY and SET UP: In parts (a) and (b) we find the charge Q_0 and stored energy $U_{initial}$ for the single charged capacitor C_1 using Eqs. (24.1) and (24.9), respectively. After we close switch S, one wire connects the upper plates of the two capacitors and another wire connects the lower plates; the capacitors are now connected in parallel. In part (c) we use the character of the parallel connection to determine how Q_0 is shared between the two capacitors. In part (d) we again use Eq. (24.9) to find the energy stored in capacitors C_1 and C_2; the energy of the system is the sum of these values.

EXECUTE: (a) The initial charge Q_0 on C_1 is

$$Q_0 = C_1 V_0 = (8.0\ \mu\text{F})(120\ \text{V}) = 960\ \mu\text{C}$$

(b) The energy initially stored in C_1 is

$$U_{initial} = \tfrac{1}{2} Q_0 V_0 = \tfrac{1}{2}(960 \times 10^{-6}\ \text{C})(120\ \text{V}) = 0.058\ \text{J}$$

(c) When we close the switch, the positive charge Q_0 is distributed over the upper plates of both capacitors and the negative charge $-Q_0$ is distributed over the lower plates. Let Q_1 and Q_2 be the magnitudes of the final charges on the capacitors. Conservation

of charge requires that $Q_1 + Q_2 = Q_0$. The potential difference V between the plates is the same for both capacitors because they are connected in parallel, so the charges are $Q_1 = C_1 V$ and $Q_2 = C_2 V$. We now have three independent equations relating the three unknowns Q_1, Q_2, and V. Solving these, we find

$$V = \frac{Q_0}{C_1 + C_2} = \frac{960\ \mu\text{C}}{8.0\ \mu\text{F} + 4.0\ \mu\text{F}} = 80\ \text{V}$$

$$Q_1 = 640\ \mu\text{C} \qquad Q_2 = 320\ \mu\text{C}$$

(d) The final energy of the system is

$$U_{final} = \tfrac{1}{2} Q_1 V + \tfrac{1}{2} Q_2 V = \tfrac{1}{2} Q_0 V$$

$$= \tfrac{1}{2}(960 \times 10^{-6}\ \text{C})(80\ \text{V}) = 0.038\ \text{J}$$

EVALUATE: The final energy is less than the initial energy; the difference was converted to energy of some other form. The conductors become a little warmer because of their resistance, and some energy is radiated as electromagnetic waves. We'll study the behavior of capacitors in more detail in Chapters 26 and 31.

Example 24.8 **Electric-field energy**

(a) What is the magnitude of the electric field required to store 1.00 J of electric potential energy in a volume of 1.00 m^3 in vacuum? (b) If the field magnitude is 10 times larger than that, how much energy is stored per cubic meter?

IDENTIFY and SET UP: We use the relationship between the electric-field magnitude E and the energy density u. In part (a) we use the given information to find u; then we use Eq. (24.11) to find the corresponding value of E. In part (b), Eq. (24.11) tells us how u varies with E.

EXECUTE: (a) The desired energy density is $u = 1.00\ \text{J/m}^3$. Then from Eq. (24.11),

$$E = \sqrt{\frac{2u}{\epsilon_0}} = \sqrt{\frac{2(1.00\ \text{J/m}^3)}{8.85 \times 10^{-12}\ \text{C}^2/\text{N} \cdot \text{m}^2}}$$

$$= 4.75 \times 10^5\ \text{N/C} = 4.75 \times 10^5\ \text{V/m}$$

(b) Equation (24.11) shows that u is proportional to E^2. If E increases by a factor of 10, u increases by a factor of $10^2 = 100$, so the energy density becomes $u = 100\ \text{J/m}^3$.

EVALUATE: Dry air can sustain an electric field of about 3×10^6 V/m without experiencing *dielectric breakdown*, which we will discuss in Section 24.4. There we will see that field magnitudes in practical insulators can be as great as this or even larger.

Example 24.9 **Two ways to calculate energy stored in a capacitor**

The spherical capacitor described in Example 24.3 (Section 24.1) has charges $+Q$ and $-Q$ on its inner and outer conductors. Find the electric potential energy stored in the capacitor (a) by using the capacitance C found in Example 24.3 and (b) by integrating the electric-field energy density u.

IDENTIFY and SET UP: We can determine the energy U stored in a capacitor in two ways: in terms of the work done to put the charges on the two conductors, and in terms of the energy in the electric field between the conductors. The descriptions are equivalent, so they must give us the same result. In Example 24.3 we found the capacitance C and the field magnitude E in the space between the conductors. (The electric field is zero inside the inner sphere and is also zero outside the inner surface of the outer sphere, because a Gaussian surface with radius $r < r_a$ or $r > r_b$ encloses zero net

charge. Hence the energy density is nonzero only in the space between the spheres, $r_a < r < r_b$.) In part (a) we use Eq. (24.9) to find U. In part (b) we use Eq. (24.11) to find u, which we integrate over the volume between the spheres to find U.

EXECUTE: (a) From Example 24.3, the spherical capacitor has capacitance

$$C = 4\pi\epsilon_0 \frac{r_a r_b}{r_b - r_a}$$

where r_a and r_b are the radii of the inner and outer conducting spheres, respectively. From Eq. (24.9) the energy stored in this capacitor is

$$U = \frac{Q^2}{2C} = \frac{Q^2}{8\pi\epsilon_0} \frac{r_b - r_a}{r_a r_b}$$

Continued

(b) The electric field in the region $r_a < r < r_b$ between the two conducting spheres has magnitude $E = Q/4\pi\epsilon_0 r^2$. The energy density in this region is

$$u = \tfrac{1}{2}\epsilon_0 E^2 = \tfrac{1}{2}\epsilon_0 \left(\frac{Q}{4\pi\epsilon_0 r^2}\right)^2 = \frac{Q^2}{32\pi^2\epsilon_0 r^4}$$

The energy density is *not* uniform; it decreases rapidly with increasing distance from the center of the capacitor. To find the total electric-field energy, we integrate u (the energy per unit volume) over the region $r_a < r < r_b$. We divide this region into spherical shells of radius r, surface area $4\pi r^2$, thickness dr, and volume $dV = 4\pi r^2\, dr$. Then

$$U = \int u\, dV = \int_{r_a}^{r_b} \left(\frac{Q^2}{32\pi^2\epsilon_0 r^4}\right) 4\pi r^2\, dr$$

$$= \frac{Q^2}{8\pi\epsilon_0} \int_{r_a}^{r_b} \frac{dr}{r^2} = \frac{Q^2}{8\pi\epsilon_0}\left(-\frac{1}{r_b} + \frac{1}{r_a}\right)$$

$$= \frac{Q^2}{8\pi\epsilon_0}\frac{r_b - r_a}{r_a r_b}$$

EVALUATE: Electric potential energy can be regarded as being associated with either the *charges,* as in part (a), or the *field,* as in part (b); the calculated amount of stored energy is the same in either case.

Test Your Understanding of Section 24.3 You want to connect a 4-μF capacitor and an 8-μF capacitor. With which type of connection will the 4-μF capacitor have a greater amount of *stored energy* than the 8-μF capacitor? (i) series; (ii) parallel; (iii) either series or parallel; (iv) neither series nor parallel.

24.4 Dielectrics

24.13 A common type of capacitor uses dielectric sheets to separate the conductors.

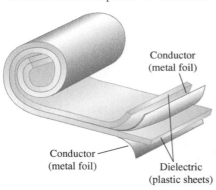

Conductor (metal foil)

Conductor (metal foil)

Dielectric (plastic sheets)

Most capacitors have a nonconducting material, or **dielectric,** between their conducting plates. A common type of capacitor uses long strips of metal foil for the plates, separated by strips of plastic sheet such as Mylar. A sandwich of these materials is rolled up, forming a unit that can provide a capacitance of several microfarads in a compact package (Fig. 24.13).

Placing a solid dielectric between the plates of a capacitor serves three functions. First, it solves the mechanical problem of maintaining two large metal sheets at a very small separation without actual contact.

Second, using a dielectric increases the maximum possible potential difference between the capacitor plates. As we described in Section 23.3, any insulating material, when subjected to a sufficiently large electric field, experiences a partial ionization that permits conduction through it. This is called **dielectric breakdown.** Many dielectric materials can tolerate stronger electric fields without breakdown than can air. Thus using a dielectric allows a capacitor to sustain a higher potential difference V and so store greater amounts of charge and energy.

Third, the capacitance of a capacitor of given dimensions is *greater* when there is a dielectric material between the plates than when there is vacuum. We can demonstrate this effect with the aid of a sensitive *electrometer,* a device that measures the potential difference between two conductors without letting any appreciable charge flow from one to the other. Figure 24.14a shows an electrometer connected across a charged capacitor, with magnitude of charge Q on each plate and potential difference V_0. When we insert an uncharged sheet of dielectric, such as glass, paraffin, or polystyrene, between the plates, experiment shows that the potential difference *decreases* to a smaller value V (Fig. 24.14b). When we remove the dielectric, the potential difference returns to its original value V_0, showing that the original charges on the plates have not changed.

The original capacitance C_0 is given by $C_0 = Q/V_0$, and the capacitance C with the dielectric present is $C = Q/V$. The charge Q is the same in both cases, and V is less than V_0, so we conclude that the capacitance C with the dielectric present is *greater* than C_0. When the space between plates is completely filled by the dielectric, the ratio of C to C_0 (equal to the ratio of V_0 to V) is called the **dielectric constant** of the material, K:

$$K = \frac{C}{C_0} \qquad \text{(definition of dielectric constant)} \qquad (24.12)$$

When the charge is constant, $Q = C_0 V_0 = CV$ and $C/C_0 = V_0/V$. In this case, Eq. (24.12) can be rewritten as

$$V = \frac{V_0}{K} \quad (\text{when } Q \text{ is constant}) \qquad (24.13)$$

With the dielectric present, the potential difference for a given charge Q is *reduced* by a factor K.

The dielectric constant K is a pure number. Because C is always greater than C_0, K is always greater than unity. Some representative values of K are given in Table 24.1. For vacuum, $K = 1$ by definition. For air at ordinary temperatures and pressures, K is about 1.0006; this is so nearly equal to 1 that for most purposes an air capacitor is equivalent to one in vacuum. Note that while water has a very large value of K, it is usually not a very practical dielectric for use in capacitors. The reason is that while pure water is a very poor conductor, it is also an excellent ionic solvent. Any ions that are dissolved in the water will cause charge to flow between the capacitor plates, so the capacitor discharges.

Table 24.1 Values of Dielectric Constant K at 20°C

Material	K	Material	K
Vacuum	1	Polyvinyl chloride	3.18
Air (1 atm)	1.00059	Plexiglas®	3.40
Air (100 atm)	1.0548	Glass	5–10
Teflon	2.1	Neoprene	6.70
Polyethylene	2.25	Germanium	16
Benzene	2.28	Glycerin	42.5
Mica	3–6	Water	80.4
Mylar	3.1	Strontium titanate	310

No real dielectric is a perfect insulator. Hence there is always some *leakage current* between the charged plates of a capacitor with a dielectric. We tacitly ignored this effect in Section 24.2 when we derived expressions for the equivalent capacitances of capacitors in series, Eq. (24.5), and in parallel, Eq. (24.7). But if a leakage current flows for a long enough time to substantially change the charges from the values we used to derive Eqs. (24.5) and (24.7), those equations may no longer be accurate.

Induced Charge and Polarization

When a dielectric material is inserted between the plates while the charge is kept constant, the potential difference between the plates decreases by a factor K. Therefore the electric field between the plates must decrease by the same factor. If E_0 is the vacuum value and E is the value with the dielectric, then

$$E = \frac{E_0}{K} \quad (\text{when } Q \text{ is constant}) \qquad (24.14)$$

Since the electric-field magnitude is smaller when the dielectric is present, the surface charge density (which causes the field) must be smaller as well. The surface charge on the conducting plates does not change, but an *induced* charge of the opposite sign appears on each surface of the dielectric (Fig. 24.15). The dielectric was originally electrically neutral and is still neutral; the induced surface charges arise as a result of *redistribution* of positive and negative charge within the dielectric material, a phenomenon called **polarization.** We first encountered polarization in Section 21.2, and we suggest that you reread the discussion of Fig. 21.8. We will assume that the induced surface charge is *directly proportional* to the electric-field magnitude E in the material; this is indeed the case for many common dielectrics. (This direct proportionality is analogous to

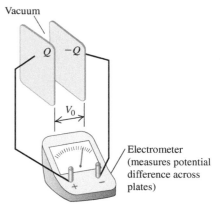

24.14 Effect of a dielectric between the plates of a parallel-plate capacitor. **(a)** With a given charge, the potential difference is V_0. **(b)** With the same charge but with a dielectric between the plates, the potential difference V is smaller than V_0.

(a)

Vacuum

Electrometer (measures potential difference across plates)

(b)

Dielectric

Adding the dielectric *reduces* the potential difference across the capacitor.

24.15 Electric field lines with **(a)** vacuum between the plates and **(b)** dielectric between the plates.

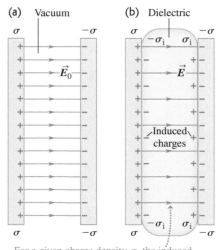

(a) Vacuum   **(b)** Dielectric

Induced charges

For a given charge density σ, the induced charges on the dielectric's surfaces reduce the electric field between the plates.

Hooke's law for a spring.) In that case, K is a constant for any particular material. When the electric field is very strong or if the dielectric is made of certain crystalline materials, the relationship between induced charge and the electric field can be more complex; we won't consider such cases here.

We can derive a relationship between this induced surface charge and the charge on the plates. Let's denote the magnitude of the charge per unit area induced on the surfaces of the dielectric (the induced surface charge density) by σ_i. The magnitude of the surface charge density on the capacitor plates is σ, as usual. Then the *net* surface charge on each side of the capacitor has magnitude $(\sigma - \sigma_i)$, as shown in Fig. 24.15b. As we found in Example 21.12 (Section 21.5) and in Example 22.8 (Section 22.4), the field between the plates is related to the net surface charge density by $E = \sigma_{net}/\epsilon_0$. Without and with the dielectric, respectively, we have

$$E_0 = \frac{\sigma}{\epsilon_0} \qquad E = \frac{\sigma - \sigma_i}{\epsilon_0} \tag{24.15}$$

Using these expressions in Eq. (24.14) and rearranging the result, we find

$$\sigma_i = \sigma\left(1 - \frac{1}{K}\right) \qquad \text{(induced surface charge density)} \tag{24.16}$$

This equation shows that when K is very large, σ_i is nearly as large as σ. In this case, σ_i nearly cancels σ, and the field and potential difference are much smaller than their values in vacuum.

The product $K\epsilon_0$ is called the **permittivity** of the dielectric, denoted by ϵ:

$$\epsilon = K\epsilon_0 \qquad \text{(definition of permittivity)} \tag{24.17}$$

In terms of ϵ we can express the electric field within the dielectric as

$$E = \frac{\sigma}{\epsilon} \tag{24.18}$$

The capacitance when the dielectric is present is given by

$$C = KC_0 = K\epsilon_0\frac{A}{d} = \epsilon\frac{A}{d} \qquad \begin{array}{l}\text{(parallel-plate capacitor,}\\ \text{dielectric between plates)}\end{array} \tag{24.19}$$

We can repeat the derivation of Eq. (24.11) for the energy density u in an electric field for the case in which a dielectric is present. The result is

$$u = \tfrac{1}{2}K\epsilon_0E^2 = \tfrac{1}{2}\epsilon E^2 \qquad \text{(electric energy density in a dielectric)} \tag{24.20}$$

In empty space, where $K = 1$, $\epsilon = \epsilon_0$ and Eqs. (24.19) and (24.20) reduce to Eqs. (24.2) and (24.11), respectively, for a parallel-plate capacitor in vacuum. For this reason, ϵ_0 is sometimes called the "permittivity of free space" or the "permittivity of vacuum." Because K is a pure number, ϵ and ϵ_0 have the same units, $C^2/N \cdot m^2$ or F/m.

Equation (24.19) shows that extremely high capacitances can be obtained with plates that have a large surface area A and are separated by a small distance d by a dielectric with a large value of K. In an *electrolytic double-layer capacitor,* tiny carbon granules adhere to each plate: The value of A is the combined surface area of the granules, which can be tremendous. The plates with granules attached are separated by a very thin dielectric sheet. A capacitor of this kind can have a capacitance of 5000 farads yet fit in the palm of your hand (compare Example 24.1 in Section 24.1).

Several practical devices make use of the way in which a capacitor responds to a change in dielectric constant. One example is an electric stud finder, used by home repair workers to locate metal studs hidden behind a wall's surface. It consists of a metal plate with associated circuitry. The plate acts as one half of a capacitor, with the wall acting as the other half. If the stud finder moves over a metal stud, the effective dielectric constant for the capacitor changes, changing the capacitance and triggering a signal.

Problem-Solving Strategy 24.2   Dielectrics

IDENTIFY *the relevant concepts:* The relationships in this section are useful whenever there is an electric field in a dielectric, such as a dielectric between charged capacitor plates. Typically you must relate the potential difference V_{ab} between the plates, the electric field magnitude E in the capacitor, the charge density σ on the capacitor plates, and the induced charge density σ_i on the surfaces of the capacitor.

SET UP *the problem* using the following steps:
1. Make a drawing of the situation.
2. Identify the target variables, and choose which equations from this section will help you solve for those variables.

EXECUTE *the solution* as follows:
1. In problems such as the next example, it is easy to get lost in a blizzard of formulas. Ask yourself at each step what kind of

quantity each symbol represents. For example, distinguish clearly between charges and charge densities, and between electric fields and electric potential differences.
2. Check for consistency of units. Distances must be in meters. A microfarad is 10^{-6} farad, and so on. Don't confuse the numerical value of ϵ_0 with the value of $1/4\pi\epsilon_0$. Electric-field magnitude can be expressed in both N/C and V/m. The units of ϵ_0 are $C^2/N \cdot m^2$ or F/m.

EVALUATE *your answer:* With a dielectric present, (a) the capacitance is greater than without a dielectric; (b) for a given charge on the capacitor, the electric field and potential difference are less than without a dielectric; and (c) the magnitude of the induced surface charge density σ_i on the dielectric is less than that of the charge density σ on the capacitor plates.

Example 24.10   A capacitor with and without a dielectric

Suppose the parallel plates in Fig. 24.15 each have an area of 2000 cm^2 (2.00×10^{-1} m^2) and are 1.00 cm (1.00×10^{-2} m) apart. We connect the capacitor to a power supply, charge it to a potential difference $V_0 = 3.00$ kV, and disconnect the power supply. We then insert a sheet of insulating plastic material between the plates, completely filling the space between them. We find that the potential difference decreases to 1.00 kV while the charge on each capacitor plate remains constant. Find (a) the original capacitance C_0; (b) the magnitude of charge Q on each plate; (c) the capacitance C after the dielectric is inserted; (d) the dielectric constant K of the dielectric; (e) the permittivity ϵ of the dielectric; (f) the magnitude of the induced charge Q_i on each face of the dielectric; (g) the original electric field E_0 between the plates; and (h) the electric field E after the dielectric is inserted.

SOLUTION

IDENTIFY and SET UP: This problem uses most of the relationships we have discussed for capacitors and dielectrics. (Energy relationships are treated in Example 24.11.) Most of the target variables can be obtained in several ways. The methods used below are a sample; we encourage you to think of others and compare your results.

EXECUTE: (a) With vacuum between the plates, we use Eq. (24.19) with $K = 1$:

$$C_0 = \epsilon_0 \frac{A}{d} = (8.85 \times 10^{-12} \text{ F/m}) \frac{2.00 \times 10^{-1} \text{ m}^2}{1.00 \times 10^{-2} \text{ m}}$$

$$= 1.77 \times 10^{-10} \text{ F} = 177 \text{ pF}$$

(b) From the definition of capacitance, Eq. (24.1),

$$Q = C_0 V_0 = (1.77 \times 10^{-10} \text{ F})(3.00 \times 10^3 \text{ V})$$

$$= 5.31 \times 10^{-7} \text{ C} = 0.531 \ \mu\text{C}$$

(c) When the dielectric is inserted, Q is unchanged but the potential difference decreases to $V = 1.00$ kV. Hence from Eq. (24.1), the new capacitance is

$$C = \frac{Q}{V} = \frac{5.31 \times 10^{-7} \text{ C}}{1.00 \times 10^3 \text{ V}} = 5.31 \times 10^{-10} \text{ F} = 531 \text{ pF}$$

(d) From Eq. (24.12), the dielectric constant is

$$K = \frac{C}{C_0} = \frac{5.31 \times 10^{-10} \text{ F}}{1.77 \times 10^{-10} \text{ F}} = \frac{531 \text{ pF}}{177 \text{ pF}} = 3.00$$

Alternatively, from Eq. (24.13),

$$K = \frac{V_0}{V} = \frac{3000 \text{ V}}{1000 \text{ V}} = 3.00$$

(e) Using K from part (d) in Eq. (24.17), the permittivity is

$$\epsilon = K\epsilon_0 = (3.00)(8.85 \times 10^{-12} \text{ C}^2/\text{N} \cdot \text{m}^2)$$

$$= 2.66 \times 10^{-11} \text{ C}^2/\text{N} \cdot \text{m}^2$$

(f) Multiplying both sides of Eq. (24.16) by the plate area A gives the induced charge $Q_i = \sigma_i A$ in terms of the charge $Q = \sigma A$ on each plate:

$$Q_i = Q\left(1 - \frac{1}{K}\right) = (5.31 \times 10^{-7} \text{ C})\left(1 - \frac{1}{3.00}\right)$$

$$= 3.54 \times 10^{-7} \text{ C}$$

Continued

(g) Since the electric field between the plates is uniform, its magnitude is the potential difference divided by the plate separation:

$$E_0 = \frac{V_0}{d} = \frac{3000 \text{ V}}{1.00 \times 10^{-2} \text{ m}} = 3.00 \times 10^5 \text{ V/m}$$

(h) After the dielectric is inserted,

$$E = \frac{V}{d} = \frac{1000 \text{ V}}{1.00 \times 10^{-2} \text{ m}} = 1.00 \times 10^5 \text{ V/m}$$

or, from Eq. (24.18),

$$E = \frac{\sigma}{\epsilon} = \frac{Q}{\epsilon A} = \frac{5.31 \times 10^{-7} \text{ C}}{(2.66 \times 10^{-11} \text{ C}^2/\text{N} \cdot \text{m}^2)(2.00 \times 10^{-1} \text{ m}^2)}$$

$$= 1.00 \times 10^5 \text{ V/m}$$

or, from Eq. (24.15),

$$E = \frac{\sigma - \sigma_i}{\epsilon_0} = \frac{Q - Q_i}{\epsilon_0 A}$$

$$= \frac{(5.31 - 3.54) \times 10^{-7} \text{ C}}{(8.85 \times 10^{-12} \text{ C}^2/\text{N} \cdot \text{m}^2)(2.00 \times 10^{-1} \text{ m}^2)}$$

$$= 1.00 \times 10^5 \text{ V/m}$$

or, from Eq. (24.14),

$$E = \frac{E_0}{K} = \frac{3.00 \times 10^5 \text{ V/m}}{3.00} = 1.00 \times 10^5 \text{ V/m}$$

EVALUATE: Inserting the dielectric increased the capacitance by a factor of $K = 3.00$ and reduced the electric field between the plates by a factor of $1/K = 1/3.00$. It did so by developing induced charges on the faces of the dielectric of magnitude $Q(1 - 1/K) = Q(1 - 1/3.00) = 0.667Q$.

Example 24.11   Energy storage with and without a dielectric

Find the energy stored in the electric field of the capacitor in Example 24.10 and the energy density, both before and after the dielectric sheet is inserted.

SOLUTION

IDENTIFY and SET UP: We now consider the ideas of energy stored in a capacitor and of electric-field energy density. We use Eq. (24.9) to find the stored energy and Eq. (24.20) to find the energy density.

EXECUTE: From Eq. (24.9), the stored energies U_0 and U without and with the dielectric in place are

$$U_0 = \tfrac{1}{2} C_0 V_0^2 = \tfrac{1}{2}(1.77 \times 10^{-10} \text{ F})(3000 \text{ V})^2 = 7.97 \times 10^{-4} \text{ J}$$

$$U = \tfrac{1}{2} C V^2 = \tfrac{1}{2}(5.31 \times 10^{-10} \text{ F})(1000 \text{ V})^2 = 2.66 \times 10^{-4} \text{ J}$$

The final energy is one-third of the original energy.

Equation (24.20) gives the energy densities without and with the dielectric:

$$u_0 = \tfrac{1}{2} \epsilon_0 E_0^2 = \tfrac{1}{2}(8.85 \times 10^{-12} \text{ C}^2/\text{N} \cdot \text{m}^2)(3.00 \times 10^5 \text{ N/C})^2$$

$$= 0.398 \text{ J/m}^3$$

$$u = \tfrac{1}{2} \epsilon E^2 = \tfrac{1}{2}(2.66 \times 10^{-11} \text{ C}^2/\text{N} \cdot \text{m}^2)(1.00 \times 10^5 \text{ N/C})^2$$

$$= 0.133 \text{ J/m}^3$$

The energy density with the dielectric is one-third of the original energy density.

EVALUATE: We can check our answer for u_0 by noting that the volume between the plates is $V = (0.200 \text{ m}^2)(0.0100 \text{ m}) = $ 0.00200 m³. Since the electric field between the plates is uniform, u_0 is uniform as well and the energy density is just the stored energy divided by the volume:

$$u_0 = \frac{U_0}{V} = \frac{7.97 \times 10^{-4} \text{ J}}{0.00200 \text{ m}^3} = 0.398 \text{ J/m}^3$$

This agrees with our earlier answer. You can use the same approach to check our result for u.

In general, when a dielectric is inserted into a capacitor while the charge on each plate remains the same, the permittivity ϵ increases by a factor of K (the dielectric constant), and the electric field E and the energy density $u = \tfrac{1}{2} \epsilon E^2$ decrease by a factor of $1/K$. Where does the energy go? The answer lies in the fringing field at the edges of a real parallel-plate capacitor. As Fig. 24.16 shows, that field tends to pull the dielectric into the space between the plates, doing work on it as it does so. We could attach a spring to the left end of the dielectric in Fig. 24.16 and use this force to stretch the spring. Because work is done by the field, the field energy density decreases.

24.16 The fringing field at the edges of the capacitor exerts forces $\vec{F}_{-i}$ and $\vec{F}_{+i}$ on the negative and positive induced surface charges of a dielectric, pulling the dielectric into the capacitor.

Dielectric Breakdown

We mentioned earlier that when a dielectric is subjected to a sufficiently strong electric field, *dielectric breakdown* takes place and the dielectric becomes a conductor. This occurs when the electric field is so strong that electrons are ripped loose from their molecules and crash into other molecules, liberating even more electrons. This avalanche of moving charge forms a spark or arc discharge. Lightning is a dramatic example of dielectric breakdown in air.

Because of dielectric breakdown, capacitors always have maximum voltage ratings. When a capacitor is subjected to excessive voltage, an arc may form through a layer of dielectric, burning or melting a hole in it. This arc creates a conducting path (a short circuit) between the conductors. If a conducting path remains after the arc is extinguished, the device is rendered permanently useless as a capacitor.

The maximum electric-field magnitude that a material can withstand without the occurrence of breakdown is called its **dielectric strength.** This quantity is affected significantly by temperature, trace impurities, small irregularities in the metal electrodes, and other factors that are difficult to control. For this reason we can give only approximate figures for dielectric strengths. The dielectric strength of dry air is about 3×10^6 V/m. Table 24.2 lists the dielectric strengths of a few common insulating materials. Note that the values are all substantially greater than the value for air. For example, a layer of polycarbonate 0.01 mm thick (about the smallest practical thickness) has 10 times the dielectric strength of air and can withstand a maximum voltage of about $(3 \times 10^7 \text{ V/m})(1 \times 10^{-5} \text{ m}) = 300$ V.

Table 24.2 Dielectric Constant and Dielectric Strength of Some Insulating Materials

Material	Dielectric Constant, K	Dielectric Strength, E_m (V/m)
Polycarbonate	2.8	3×10^7
Polyester	3.3	6×10^7
Polypropylene	2.2	7×10^7
Polystyrene	2.6	2×10^7
Pyrex glass	4.7	1×10^7

Test Your Understanding of Section 24.4 The space between the plates of an isolated parallel-plate capacitor is filled by a slab of dielectric with dielectric constant K. The two plates of the capacitor have charges Q and $-Q$. You pull out the dielectric slab. If the charges do not change, how does the energy in the capacitor change when you remove the slab? (i) It increases; (ii) it decreases; (iii) it remains the same.

24.5 Molecular Model of Induced Charge

In Section 24.4 we discussed induced surface charges on a dielectric in an electric field. Now let's look at how these surface charges can arise. If the material were a *conductor,* the answer would be simple. Conductors contain charge that is free to move, and when an electric field is present, some of the charge redistributes itself on the surface so that there is no electric field inside the conductor. But an ideal dielectric has *no* charges that are free to move, so how can a surface charge occur?

To understand this, we have to look again at rearrangement of charge at the *molecular* level. Some molecules, such as H_2O and N_2O, have equal amounts of positive and negative charges but a lopsided distribution, with excess positive charge concentrated on one side of the molecule and negative charge on the other. As we described in Section 21.7, such an arrangement is called an *electric dipole,* and the molecule is called a *polar molecule.* When no electric field is present in a gas or liquid with polar molecules, the molecules are oriented randomly (Fig. 24.17a). When they are placed in an electric field, however, they tend to orient themselves as in Fig. 24.17b, as a result of the electric-field torques described in Section 21.7. Because of thermal agitation, the alignment of the molecules with $\vec{E}$ is not perfect.

Application Dielectric Cell Membrane

The membrane of a living cell behaves like a dielectric between the plates of a capacitor. The membrane is made of two sheets of lipid molecules, with their water-insoluble ends in the middle and their water-soluble ends (shown in red) on the surfaces of the membrane. The conductive fluids on either side of the membrane (water with negative ions inside the cell, water with positive ions outside) act as charged capacitor plates, and the nonconducting membrane acts as a dielectric with K of about 10. The potential difference V across the membrane is about 0.07 V and the membrane thickness d is about 7×10^{-9} m, so the electric field $E = V/d$ in the membrane is about 10^7 V/m—close to the dielectric strength of the membrane. If the membrane were made of air, V and E would be larger by a factor of $K \approx 10$ and dielectric breakdown would occur.

24.17 Polar molecules (a) without and (b) with an applied electric field $\vec{E}$.

(a)

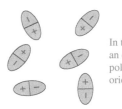

In the absence of an electric field, polar molecules orient randomly.

(b)

When an electric field is applied, the molecules tend to align with it.

24.18 Nonpolar molecules **(a)** without and **(b)** with an applied electric field $\vec{E}$.

(a)

(b)

In the absence of an electric field, nonpolar molecules are not electric dipoles.

An electric field causes the molecules' positive and negative charges to separate slightly, making the molecule effectively polar.

Even a molecule that is *not* ordinarily polar *becomes* a dipole when it is placed in an electric field because the field pushes the positive charges in the molecules in the direction of the field and pushes the negative charges in the opposite direction. This causes a redistribution of charge within the molecule (Fig. 24.18). Such dipoles are called *induced* dipoles.

With either polar or nonpolar molecules, the redistribution of charge caused by the field leads to the formation of a layer of charge on each surface of the dielectric material (Fig. 24.19). These layers are the surface charges described in Section 24.4; their surface charge density is denoted by σ_i. The charges are *not* free to move indefinitely, as they would be in a conductor, because each charge is bound to a molecule. They are in fact called **bound charges** to distinguish them from the **free charges** that are added to and removed from the conducting capacitor plates. In the interior of the material the net charge per unit volume remains zero. As we have seen, this redistribution of charge is called *polarization,* and we say that the material is *polarized.*

The four parts of Fig. 24.20 show the behavior of a slab of dielectric when it is inserted in the field between a pair of oppositely charged capacitor plates. Figure 24.20a shows the original field. Figure 24.20b is the situation after the dielectric has been inserted but before any rearrangement of charges has occurred. Figure 24.20c shows by thinner arrows the additional field set up in the dielectric by its induced surface charges. This field is *opposite* to the original field, but it is not great enough to cancel the original field completely because the charges in the dielectric are not free to move indefinitely. The resultant field

24.19 Polarization of a dielectric in an electric field $\vec{E}$ gives rise to thin layers of bound charges on the surfaces, creating surface charge densities σ_i and $-\sigma_i$. The sizes of the molecules are greatly exaggerated for clarity.

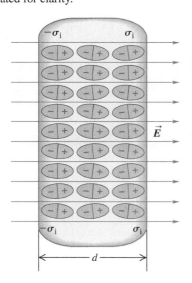

24.20 **(a)** Electric field of magnitude E_0 between two charged plates. **(b)** Introduction of a dielectric of dielectric constant K. **(c)** The induced surface charges and their field. **(d)** Resultant field of magnitude E_0/K.

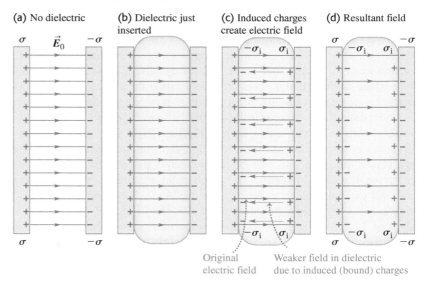

(a) No dielectric

(b) Dielectric just inserted

(c) Induced charges create electric field

(d) Resultant field

Original electric field

Weaker field in dielectric due to induced (bound) charges

in the dielectric, shown in Fig. 24.20d, is therefore decreased in magnitude. In the field-line representation, some of the field lines leaving the positive plate go through the dielectric, while others terminate on the induced charges on the faces of the dielectric.

As we discussed in Section 21.2, polarization is also the reason a charged body, such as an electrified plastic rod, can exert a force on an *uncharged* body such as a bit of paper or a pith ball. Figure 24.21 shows an uncharged dielectric sphere B in the radial field of a positively charged body A. The induced positive charges on B experience a force toward the right, while the force on the induced negative charges is toward the left. The negative charges are closer to A, and thus are in a stronger field, than are the positive charges. The force toward the left is stronger than that toward the right, and B is attracted toward A, even though its net charge is zero. The attraction occurs whether the sign of A's charge is positive or negative (see Fig. 21.8). Furthermore, the effect is not limited to dielectrics; an uncharged conducting body would be attracted in the same way.

Test Your Understanding of Section 24.5   A parallel-plate capacitor has charges Q and $-Q$ on its two plates. A dielectric slab with $K = 3$ is then inserted into the space between the plates as shown in Fig. 24.20. Rank the following electric-field magnitudes in order from largest to smallest. (i) the field before the slab is inserted; (ii) the resultant field after the slab is inserted; (iii) the field due to the bound charges.   ❚

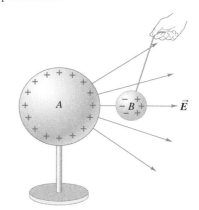

24.21 A neutral sphere B in the radial electric field of a positively charged sphere A is attracted to the charge because of polarization.

24.6 Gauss's Law in Dielectrics

We can extend the analysis of Section 24.4 to reformulate Gauss's law in a form that is particularly useful for dielectrics. Figure 24.22 is a close-up view of the left capacitor plate and left surface of the dielectric in Fig. 24.15b. Let's apply Gauss's law to the rectangular box shown in cross section by the purple line; the surface area of the left and right sides is A. The left side is embedded in the conductor that forms the left capacitor plate, and so the electric field everywhere on that surface is zero. The right side is embedded in the dielectric, where the electric field has magnitude E, and $E_\perp = 0$ everywhere on the other four sides. The total charge enclosed, including both the charge on the capacitor plate and the induced charge on the dielectric surface, is $Q_{encl} = (\sigma - \sigma_i)A$, so Gauss's law gives

$$EA = \frac{(\sigma - \sigma_i)A}{\epsilon_0} \qquad (24.21)$$

This equation is not very illuminating as it stands because it relates two unknown quantities: E inside the dielectric and the induced surface charge density σ_i. But now we can use Eq. (24.16), developed for this same situation, to simplify this equation by eliminating σ_i. Equation (24.16) is

$$\sigma_i = \sigma\left(1 - \frac{1}{K}\right) \quad \text{or} \quad \sigma - \sigma_i = \frac{\sigma}{K}$$

Combining this with Eq. (24.21), we get

$$EA = \frac{\sigma A}{K\epsilon_0} \quad \text{or} \quad KEA = \frac{\sigma A}{\epsilon_0} \qquad (24.22)$$

Equation (24.22) says that the flux of $K\vec{E}$, not $\vec{E}$, through the Gaussian surface in Fig. 24.22 is equal to the enclosed *free* charge σA divided by ϵ_0. It turns out that for *any* Gaussian surface, whenever the induced charge is proportional to the electric field in the material, we can rewrite Gauss's law as

$$\oint K\vec{E} \cdot d\vec{A} = \frac{Q_{encl\text{-}free}}{\epsilon_0} \qquad \text{(Gauss's law in a dielectric)} \qquad (24.23)$$

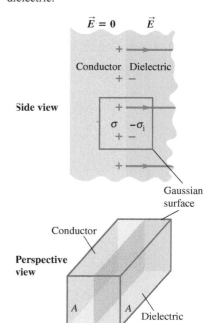

24.22 Gauss's law with a dielectric. This figure shows a close-up of the left-hand capacitor plate in Fig. 24.15b. The Gaussian surface is a rectangular box that lies half in the conductor and half in the dielectric.

where $Q_{\text{encl-free}}$ is the total *free* charge (not bound charge) enclosed by the Gaussian surface. The significance of these results is that the right sides contain only the *free* charge on the conductor, not the bound (induced) charge. In fact, although we have not proved it, Eq. (24.23) remains valid even when different parts of the Gaussian surface are embedded in dielectrics having different values of K, provided that the value of K in each dielectric is independent of the electric field (usually the case for electric fields that are not too strong) and that we use the appropriate value of K for each point on the Gaussian surface.

Example 24.12 **A spherical capacitor with dielectric**

Use Gauss's law to find the capacitance of the spherical capacitor of Example 24.3 (Section 24.1) if the volume between the shells is filled with an insulating oil with dielectric constant K.

SOLUTION

IDENTIFY and SET UP: The spherical symmetry of the problem is not changed by the presence of the dielectric, so as in Example 24.3, we use a concentric spherical Gaussian surface of radius r between the shells. Since a dielectric is present, we use Gauss's law in the form of Eq. (24.23).

EXECUTE: From Eq. (24.23),

$$\oint K\vec{E} \cdot d\vec{A} = \oint KE\, dA = KE \oint dA = (KE)(4\pi r^2) = \frac{Q}{\epsilon_0}$$

$$E = \frac{Q}{4\pi K\epsilon_0 r^2} = \frac{Q}{4\pi\epsilon r^2}$$

where $\epsilon = K\epsilon_0$. Compared to the case in which there is vacuum between the shells, the electric field is reduced by a factor of $1/K$. The potential difference V_{ab} between the shells is reduced by the same factor, and so the capacitance $C = Q/V_{ab}$ is *increased* by a factor of K, just as for a parallel-plate capacitor when a dielectric is inserted. Using the result of Example 24.3, we find that the capacitance with the dielectric is

$$C = \frac{4\pi K\epsilon_0 r_a r_b}{r_b - r_a} = \frac{4\pi\epsilon r_a r_b}{r_b - r_a}$$

EVALUATE: If the dielectric fills the volume between the two conductors, the capacitance is just K times the value with no dielectric. The result is more complicated if the dielectric only partially fills this volume (see Challenge Problem 24.78).

Test Your Understanding of Section 24.6 A single point charge q is imbedded in a dielectric of dielectric constant K. At a point inside the dielectric a distance r from the point charge, what is the magnitude of the electric field? (i) $q/4\pi\epsilon_0 r^2$; (ii) $Kq/4\pi\epsilon_0 r^2$; (iii) $q/4\pi K\epsilon_0 r^2$; (iv) none of these.

Capacitors and capacitance: A capacitor is any pair of conductors separated by an insulating material. When the capacitor is charged, there are charges of equal magnitude Q and opposite sign on the two conductors, and the potential V_{ab} of the positively charged conductor with respect to the negatively charged conductor is proportional to Q. The capacitance C is defined as the ratio of Q to V_{ab}. The SI unit of capacitance is the farad (F): $1\text{ F} = 1\text{ C/V}$.

A parallel-plate capacitor consists of two parallel conducting plates, each with area A, separated by a distance d. If they are separated by vacuum, the capacitance depends only on A and d. For other geometries, the capacitance can be found by using the definition $C = Q/V_{ab}$. (See Examples 24.1–24.4.)

$$C = \frac{Q}{V_{ab}} \tag{24.1}$$

$$C = \frac{Q}{V_{ab}} = \epsilon_0 \frac{A}{d} \tag{24.2}$$

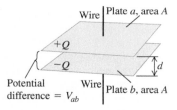

Capacitors in series and parallel: When capacitors with capacitances $C_1, C_2, C_3, \ldots$ are connected in series, the reciprocal of the equivalent capacitance C_{eq} equals the sum of the reciprocals of the individual capacitances. When capacitors are connected in parallel, the equivalent capacitance C_{eq} equals the sum of the individual capacitances. (See Examples 24.5 and 24.6.)

$$\frac{1}{C_{eq}} = \frac{1}{C_1} + \frac{1}{C_2} + \frac{1}{C_3} + \cdots \tag{24.5}$$
(capacitors in series)

$$C_{eq} = C_1 + C_2 + C_3 + \cdots \tag{24.7}$$
(capacitors in parallel)

Energy in a capacitor: The energy U required to charge a capacitor C to a potential difference V and a charge Q is equal to the energy stored in the capacitor. This energy can be thought of as residing in the electric field between the conductors; the energy density u (energy per unit volume) is proportional to the square of the electric-field magnitude. (See Examples 24.7–24.9.)

$$U = \frac{Q^2}{2C} = \tfrac{1}{2}CV^2 = \tfrac{1}{2}QV \tag{24.9}$$

$$u = \tfrac{1}{2}\epsilon_0 E^2 \tag{24.11}$$

Dielectrics: When the space between the conductors is filled with a dielectric material, the capacitance increases by a factor K, called the dielectric constant of the material. The quantity $\epsilon = K\epsilon_0$ is called the permittivity of the dielectric. For a fixed amount of charge on the capacitor plates, induced charges on the surface of the dielectric decrease the electric field and potential difference between the plates by the same factor K. The surface charge results from polarization, a microscopic rearrangement of charge in the dielectric. (See Example 24.10.)

Under sufficiently strong fields, dielectrics become conductors, a situation called dielectric breakdown. The maximum field that a material can withstand without breakdown is called its dielectric strength.

In a dielectric, the expression for the energy density is the same as in vacuum but with ϵ_0 replaced by $\epsilon = K\epsilon$. (See Example 24.11.)

Gauss's law in a dielectric has almost the same form as in vacuum, with two key differences: $\vec{E}$ is replaced by $K\vec{E}$ and Q_{encl} is replaced by $Q_{encl\text{-}free}$, which includes only the free charge (not bound charge) enclosed by the Gaussian surface. (See Example 24.12.)

$$C = KC_0 = K\epsilon_0 \frac{A}{d} = \epsilon \frac{A}{d} \tag{24.19}$$
(parallel-plate capacitor filled with dielectric)

$$u = \tfrac{1}{2}K\epsilon_0 E^2 = \tfrac{1}{2}\epsilon E^2 \tag{24.20}$$

$$\oint K\vec{E} \cdot d\vec{A} = \frac{Q_{encl\text{-}free}}{\epsilon_0} \tag{24.23}$$

Dielectric between plates

BRIDGING PROBLEM **Electric-Field Energy and Capacitance of a Conducting Sphere**

A solid conducting sphere of radius R carries a charge Q. Calculate the electric-field energy density at a point a distance r from the center of the sphere for (a) $r < R$ and (b) $r > R$. (c) Calculate the total electric-field energy associated with the charged sphere. (d) How much work is required to assemble the charge Q on the sphere? (e) Use the result of part (c) to find the capacitance of the sphere. (You can think of the second conductor as a hollow conducting shell of infinite radius.)

SOLUTION GUIDE

See MasteringPhysics® study area for a Video Tutor solution

IDENTIFY and SET UP

1. You know the electric field for this situation at all values of r from Example 22.5 (Section 22.4). You'll use this to find the electric-field energy density u and the *total* electric-field energy U. You can then find the capacitance from the relationship $U = Q^2/2C$.

2. To find U, consider a spherical shell of radius r and thickness dr that has volume $dV = 4\pi r^2 dr$. The energy stored in this volume

is $u\, dV$, and the total energy is the integral of $u\, dV$ from $r = 0$ to $r \to \infty$. Set up this integral.

EXECUTE

3. Find u for $r < R$ and for $r > R$.

4. Substitute your results from step 3 into the expression from step 2. Then calculate the integral to find the total electric-field energy U.

5. Use your understanding of the energy stored in a charge distribution to find the work required to assemble the charge Q.

6. Find the capacitance of the sphere.

EVALUATE

7. Where is the electric-field energy density greatest? Where is it least?

8. How would the results be affected if the solid sphere were replaced by a hollow conducting sphere of the same radius R?

9. You can find the potential difference between the sphere and infinity from $C = Q/V$. Does this agree with the result of Example 23.8 (Section 23.3)?

Problems

For instructor-assigned homework, go to www.masteringphysics.com

•, ••, •••: Problems of increasing difficulty. **CP**: Cumulative problems incorporating material from earlier chapters. **CALC**: Problems requiring calculus. **BIO**: Biosciences problems.

DISCUSSION QUESTIONS

Q24.1 Equation (24.2) shows that the capacitance of a parallel-plate capacitor becomes larger as the plate separation d decreases. However, there is a practical limit to how small d can be made, which places limits on how large C can be. Explain what sets the limit on d. (*Hint:* What happens to the magnitude of the electric field as $d \to 0$?)

Q24.2 Suppose several different parallel-plate capacitors are charged up by a constant-voltage source. Thinking of the actual movement and position of the charges on an atomic level, why does it make sense that the capacitances are proportional to the surface areas of the plates? Why does it make sense that the capacitances are *inversely* proportional to the distance between the plates?

Q24.3 Suppose the two plates of a capacitor have different areas. When the capacitor is charged by connecting it to a battery, do the charges on the two plates have equal magnitude, or may they be different? Explain your reasoning.

Q24.4 At the Fermi National Accelerator Laboratory (Fermilab) in Illinois, protons are accelerated around a ring 2 km in radius to speeds that approach that of light. The energy for this is stored in capacitors the size of a house. When these capacitors are being charged, they make a very loud creaking sound. What is the origin of this sound?

Q24.5 In the parallel-plate capacitor of Fig. 24.2, suppose the plates are pulled apart so that the separation d is much larger than the size of the plates. (a) Is it still accurate to say that the electric field between the plates is uniform? Why or why not? (b) In the sit-

uation shown in Fig. 24.2, the potential difference between the plates is $V_{ab} = Qd/\epsilon_0 A$. If the plates are pulled apart as described above, is V_{ab} more or less than this formula would indicate? Explain your reasoning. (c) With the plates pulled apart as described above, is the capacitance more than, less than, or the same as that given by Eq. (24.2)? Explain your reasoning.

Q24.6 A parallel-plate capacitor is charged by being connected to a battery and is kept connected to the battery. The separation between the plates is then doubled. How does the electric field change? The charge on the plates? The total energy? Explain your reasoning.

Q24.7 A parallel-plate capacitor is charged by being connected to a battery and is then disconnected from the battery. The separation between the plates is then doubled. How does the electric field change? The potential difference? The total energy? Explain your reasoning.

Q24.8 Two parallel-plate capacitors, identical except that one has twice the plate separation of the other, are charged by the same voltage source. Which capacitor has a stronger electric field between the plates? Which capacitor has a greater charge? Which has greater energy density? Explain your reasoning.

Q24.9 The charged plates of a capacitor attract each other, so to pull the plates farther apart requires work by some external force. What becomes of the energy added by this work? Explain your reasoning.

Q24.10 The two plates of a capacitor are given charges $\pm Q$. The capacitor is then disconnected from the charging device so that the charges on the plates can't change, and the capacitor is immersed in a tank of oil. Does the electric field between the plates increase, decrease, or stay the same? Explain your reasoning. How can this field be measured?

Q24.11 As shown in Table 24.1, water has a very large dielectric constant $K = 80.4$. Why do you think water is not commonly used as a dielectric in capacitors?

Q24.12 Is dielectric strength the same thing as dielectric constant? Explain any differences between the two quantities. Is there a simple relationship between dielectric strength and dielectric constant (see Table 24.2)?

Q24.13 A capacitor made of aluminum foil strips separated by Mylar film was subjected to excessive voltage, and the resulting dielectric breakdown melted holes in the Mylar. After this, the capacitance was found to be about the same as before, but the breakdown voltage was much less. Why?

Q24.14 Suppose you bring a slab of dielectric close to the gap between the plates of a charged capacitor, preparing to slide it between the plates. What force will you feel? What does this force tell you about the energy stored between the plates once the dielectric is in place, compared to before the dielectric is in place?

Q24.15 The freshness of fish can be measured by placing a fish between the plates of a capacitor and measuring the capacitance. How does this work? (*Hint:* As time passes, the fish dries out. See Table 24.1.)

Q24.16 *Electrolytic* capacitors use as their dielectric an extremely thin layer of nonconducting oxide between a metal plate and a conducting solution. Discuss the advantage of such a capacitor over one constructed using a solid dielectric between the metal plates.

Q24.17 In terms of the dielectric constant K, what happens to the electric flux through the Gaussian surface shown in Fig. 24.22 when the dielectric is inserted into the previously empty space between the plates? Explain.

Q24.18 A parallel-plate capacitor is connected to a power supply that maintains a fixed potential difference between the plates. (a) If a sheet of dielectric is then slid between the plates, what happens to (i) the electric field between the plates, (ii) the magnitude of charge on each plate, and (iii) the energy stored in the capacitor? (b) Now suppose that before the dielectric is inserted, the charged capacitor is disconnected from the power supply. In this case, what happens to (i) the electric field between the plates, (ii) the magnitude of charge on each plate, and (iii) the energy stored in the capacitor? Explain any differences between the two situations.

Q24.19 Liquid dielectrics that have polar molecules (such as water) always have dielectric constants that decrease with increasing temperature. Why?

Q24.20 A conductor is an extreme case of a dielectric, since if an electric field is applied to a conductor, charges are free to move within the conductor to set up "induced charges." What is the dielectric constant of a perfect conductor? Is it $K = 0$, $K \rightarrow \infty$, or something in between? Explain your reasoning.

EXERCISES

Section 24.1 Capacitors and Capacitance

24.1 • The plates of a parallel-plate capacitor are 2.50 mm apart, and each carries a charge of magnitude 80.0 nC. The plates are in vacuum. The electric field between the plates has a magnitude of 4.00×10^6 V/m. (a) What is the potential difference between the plates? (b) What is the area of each plate? (c) What is the capacitance?

24.2 • The plates of a parallel-plate capacitor are 3.28 mm apart, and each has an area of 12.2 cm². Each plate carries a charge of magnitude 4.35×10^{-8} C. The plates are in vacuum. (a) What is the capacitance? (b) What is the potential difference between the plates? (c) What is the magnitude of the electric field between the plates?

24.3 • A parallel-plate air capacitor of capacitance 245 pF has a charge of magnitude 0.148 μC on each plate. The plates are 0.328 mm apart. (a) What is the potential difference between the plates? (b) What is the area of each plate? (c) What is the electric-field magnitude between the plates? (d) What is the surface charge density on each plate?

24.4 •• **Capacitance of an Oscilloscope.** Oscilloscopes have parallel metal plates inside them to deflect the electron beam. These plates are called the *deflecting plates*. Typically, they are squares 3.0 cm on a side and separated by 5.0 mm, with vacuum in between. What is the capacitance of these deflecting plates and hence of the oscilloscope? (*Note:* This capacitance can sometimes have an effect on the circuit you are trying to study and must be taken into consideration in your calculations.)

24.5 • A 10.0-μF parallel-plate capacitor with circular plates is connected to a 12.0-V battery. (a) What is the charge on each plate? (b) How much charge would be on the plates if their separation were doubled while the capacitor remained connected to the battery? (c) How much charge would be on the plates if the capacitor were connected to the 12.0-V battery after the radius of each plate was doubled without changing their separation?

24.6 • A 10.0-μF parallel-plate capacitor is connected to a 12.0-V battery. After the capacitor is fully charged, the battery is disconnected without loss of any of the charge on the plates. (a) A voltmeter is connected across the two plates without discharging them. What does it read? (b) What would the voltmeter read if (i) the plate separation were doubled; (ii) the radius of each plate were doubled but their separation was unchanged?

24.7 •• How far apart would parallel pennies have to be to make a 1.00-pF capacitor? Does your answer suggest that you are justified in treating these pennies as infinite sheets? Explain.

24.8 • A 5.00-pF, parallel-plate, air-filled capacitor with circular plates is to be used in a circuit in which it will be subjected to potentials of up to 1.00×10^2 V. The electric field between the plates is to be no greater than 1.00×10^4 N/C. As a budding electrical engineer for Live-Wire Electronics, your tasks are to (a) design the capacitor by finding what its physical dimensions and separation must be; (b) find the maximum charge these plates can hold.

24.9 • A parallel-plate air capacitor is to store charge of magnitude 240.0 pC on each plate when the potential difference between the plates is 42.0 V. (a) If the area of each plate is 6.80 cm², what is the separation between the plates? (b) If the separation between the two plates is double the value calculated in part (a), what potential difference is required for the capacitor to store charge of magnitude 240.0 pC on each plate?

24.10 • A cylindrical capacitor consists of a solid inner conducting core with radius 0.250 cm, surrounded by an outer hollow conducting tube. The two conductors are separated by air, and the length of the cylinder is 12.0 cm. The capacitance is 36.7 pF. (a) Calculate the inner radius of the hollow tube. (b) When the capacitor is charged to 125 V, what is the charge per unit length λ on the capacitor?

24.11 • A capacitor is made from two hollow, coaxial, iron cylinders, one inside the other. The inner cylinder is negatively charged and the outer is positively charged; the magnitude of the charge on each is 10.0 pC. The inner cylinder has radius 0.50 mm, the outer one has radius 5.00 mm, and the length of each cylinder is 18.0 cm. (a) What is the capacitance? (b) What applied potential difference is necessary to produce these charges on the cylinders?

24.12 •• A cylindrical capacitor has an inner conductor of radius 1.5 mm and an outer conductor of radius 3.5 mm. The two conductors are separated by vacuum, and the entire capacitor is 2.8 m long. (a) What is the capacitance per unit length? (b) The potential of the inner conductor is 350 mV higher than that of the outer conductor. Find the charge (magnitude and sign) on both conductors.

24.13 •• A spherical capacitor contains a charge of 3.30 nC when connected to a potential difference of 220 V. If its plates are separated by vacuum and the inner radius of the outer shell is 4.00 cm, calculate: (a) the capacitance; (b) the radius of the inner sphere; (c) the electric field just outside the surface of the inner sphere.

24.14 • A spherical capacitor is formed from two concentric, spherical, conducting shells separated by vacuum. The inner sphere has radius 15.0 cm and the capacitance is 116 pF. (a) What is the radius of the outer sphere? (b) If the potential difference between the two spheres is 220 V, what is the magnitude of charge on each sphere?

Section 24.2 Capacitors in Series and Parallel

24.15 • BIO **Electric Eels.** Electric eels and electric fish generate large potential differences that are used to stun enemies and prey. These potentials are produced by cells that each can generate 0.10 V. We can plausibly model such cells as charged capacitors. (a) How should these cells be connected (in series or in parallel) to produce a total potential of more than 0.10 V? (b) Using the connection in part (a), how many cells must be connected together to produce the 500-V surge of the electric eel?

24.16 • For the system of capacitors shown in Fig. E24.16, find the equivalent capacitance (a) between b and c, and (b) between a and c.

Figure **E24.16**

24.17 • In Fig. E24.17, each capacitor has $C = 4.00 \ \mu F$ and $V_{ab} = +28.0$ V. Calculate (a) the charge on each capacitor; (b) the potential difference across each capacitor; (c) the potential difference between points a and d.

24.18 • In Fig. 24.8a, let $C_1 = 3.00 \ \mu F$, $C_2 = 5.00 \ \mu F$, and $V_{ab} = +52.0$ V. Calculate (a) the charge on each capacitor and (b) the potential difference across each capacitor.

24.19 • In Fig. 24.9a, let $C_1 = 3.00 \ \mu F$, $C_2 = 5.00 \ \mu F$, and $V_{ab} = +52.0$ V. Calculate (a) the charge on each capacitor and (b) the potential difference across each capacitor.

Figure **E24.17**

24.20 • In Fig. E24.20, $C_1 = 6.00 \ \mu F$, $C_2 = 3.00 \ \mu F$, and $C_3 = 5.00 \ \mu F$. The capacitor network is connected to an applied potential V_{ab}. After the charges on the capacitors have reached their final values, the charge on C_2 is 40.0 μC. (a) What are the charges on capacitors C_1 and C_3? (b) What is the applied voltage V_{ab}?

24.21 •• For the system of capacitors shown in Fig. E24.21, a potential difference of 25 V is maintained across ab. (a) What is the equivalent capacitance of this system between a and b? (b) How much charge is stored by this system? (c) How much charge does the 6.5-nF capacitor store? (d) What is the potential difference across the 7.5-nF capacitor?

24.22 • Figure E24.22 shows a system of four capacitors, where the potential difference across ab is 50.0 V. (a) Find the equivalent capacitance of this system between a and b. (b) How much charge is stored by this combination of capacitors? (c) How much charge is stored in each of the 10.0-μF and the 9.0-μF capacitors?

24.23 •• Suppose the 3-μF capacitor in Fig. 24.10a were removed and replaced by a different one, and that this changed the equivalent capacitance between points a and b to 8 μF. What would be the capacitance of the replacement capacitor?

Figure **E24.20**

Figure **E24.21**

Figure **E24.22**

Section 24.3 Energy Storage in Capacitors and Electric-Field Energy

24.24 • A parallel-plate air capacitor has a capacitance of 920 pF. The charge on each plate is 2.55 μC. (a) What is the potential difference between the plates? (b) If the charge is kept constant, what will be the potential difference between the plates if the separation is doubled? (c) How much work is required to double the separation?

24.25 • A 5.80-μF, parallel-plate, air capacitor has a plate separation of 5.00 mm and is charged to a potential difference of 400 V. Calculate the energy density in the region between the plates, in units of J/m³.

24.26 • An air capacitor is made from two flat parallel plates 1.50 mm apart. The magnitude of charge on each plate is 0.0180 μC when the potential difference is 200 V. (a) What is the capacitance? (b) What is the area of each plate? (c) What maximum voltage can be applied without dielectric breakdown? (Dielectric breakdown for air occurs at an electric-field strength of 3.0×10^6 V/m.) (d) When the charge is 0.0180 μC, what total energy is stored?

24.27 • A parallel-plate vacuum capacitor with plate area A and separation x has charges $+Q$ and $-Q$ on its plates. The capacitor is disconnected from the source of charge, so the charge on each plate remains fixed. (a) What is the total energy stored in the capacitor? (b) The plates are pulled apart an additional distance dx. What is the change in the stored energy? (c) If F is the force with which the plates attract each other, then the change in the stored energy must equal the work $dW = Fdx$ done in pulling the plates apart. Find an expression for F. (d) Explain why F is *not* equal to QE, where E is the electric field between the plates.

24.28 •• A parallel-plate vacuum capacitor has 8.38 J of energy stored in it. The separation between the plates is 2.30 mm. If the separation is decreased to 1.15 mm, what is the energy stored (a) if the capacitor is disconnected from the potential source so the charge on the plates remains constant, and (b) if the capacitor remains connected to the potential source so the potential difference between the plates remains constant?

24.29 • You have two identical capacitors and an external potential source. (a) Compare the total energy stored in the capacitors when they are connected to the applied potential in series and in parallel. (b) Compare the maximum amount of charge stored in each case. (c) Energy storage in a capacitor can be limited by the maximum electric field between the plates. What is the ratio of the electric field for the series and parallel combinations?

24.30 • For the capacitor network shown in Fig. E24.30, the potential difference across ab is 36 V. Find (a) the total charge stored in this network; (b) the charge on each capacitor; (c) the total energy stored in the network; (d) the energy stored in each capacitor; (e) the potential differences across each capacitor.

Figure **E24.30**

150 nF   120 nF
a —| |—| |— b

24.31 • For the capacitor network shown in Fig. E24.31, the potential difference across ab is 220 V. Find (a) the total charge stored in this network; (b) the charge on each capacitor; (c) the total energy stored in the network; (d) the energy stored in each capacitor; (e) the potential difference across each capacitor.

Figure **E24.31**

35 nF
a b
75 nF

24.32 • A 0.350-m-long cylindrical capacitor consists of a solid conducting core with a radius of 1.20 mm and an outer hollow conducting tube with an inner radius of 2.00 mm. The two conductors are separated by air and charged to a potential difference of 6.00 V. Calculate (a) the charge per length for the capacitor; (b) the total charge on the capacitor; (c) the capacitance; (d) the energy stored in the capacitor when fully charged.

24.33 • A cylindrical air capacitor of length 15.0 m stores 3.20×10^{-9} J of energy when the potential difference between the two conductors is 4.00 V. (a) Calculate the magnitude of the charge on each conductor. (b) Calculate the ratio of the radii of the inner and outer conductors.

24.34 •• A capacitor is formed from two concentric spherical conducting shells separated by vacuum. The inner sphere has radius 12.5 cm, and the outer sphere has radius 14.8 cm. A potential difference of 120 V is applied to the capacitor. (a) What is the energy density at $r = 12.6$ cm, just outside the inner sphere? (b) What is the energy density at $r = 14.7$ cm, just inside the outer sphere? (c) For a parallel-plate capacitor the energy density is uniform in the region between the plates, except near the edges of the plates. Is this also true for a spherical capacitor?

Section 24.4 Dielectrics

24.35 • A 12.5-μF capacitor is connected to a power supply that keeps a constant potential difference of 24.0 V across the plates. A piece of material having a dielectric constant of 3.75 is placed

between the plates, completely filling the space between them. (a) How much energy is stored in the capacitor before and after the dielectric is inserted? (b) By how much did the energy change during the insertion? Did it increase or decrease?

24.36 • A parallel-plate capacitor has capacitance $C_0 = 5.00$ pF when there is air between the plates. The separation between the plates is 1.50 mm. (a) What is the maximum magnitude of charge Q that can be placed on each plate if the electric field in the region between the plates is not to exceed 3.00×10^4 V/m? (b) A dielectric with $K = 2.70$ is inserted between the plates of the capacitor, completely filling the volume between the plates. Now what is the maximum magnitude of charge on each plate if the electric field between the plates is not to exceed 3.00×10^4 V/m?

24.37 • Two parallel plates have equal and opposite charges. When the space between the plates is evacuated, the electric field is $E = 3.20 \times 10^5$ V/m. When the space is filled with dielectric, the electric field is $E = 2.50 \times 10^5$ V/m. (a) What is the charge density on each surface of the dielectric? (b) What is the dielectric constant?

24.38 • A budding electronics hobbyist wants to make a simple 1.0-nF capacitor for tuning her crystal radio, using two sheets of aluminum foil as plates, with a few sheets of paper between them as a dielectric. The paper has a dielectric constant of 3.0, and the thickness of one sheet of it is 0.20 mm. (a) If the sheets of paper measure 22 × 28 cm and she cuts the aluminum foil to the same dimensions, how many sheets of paper should she use between her plates to get the proper capacitance? (b) Suppose for convenience she wants to use a single sheet of posterboard, with the same dielectric constant but a thickness of 12.0 mm, instead of the paper. What area of aluminum foil will she need for her plates to get her 1.0 nF of capacitance? (c) Suppose she goes high-tech and finds a sheet of Teflon of the same thickness as the posterboard to use as a dielectric. Will she need a larger or smaller area of Teflon than of posterboard? Explain.

24.39 • The dielectric to be used in a parallel-plate capacitor has a dielectric constant of 3.60 and a dielectric strength of 1.60×10^7 V/m. The capacitor is to have a capacitance of 1.25×10^{-9} F and must be able to withstand a maximum potential difference of 5500 V. What is the minimum area the plates of the capacitor may have?

24.40 •• **BIO Potential in Human Cells.** Some cell walls in the human body have a layer of negative charge on the inside surface and a layer of positive charge of equal magnitude on the outside surface. Suppose that the charge density on either surface is $\pm 0.50 \times 10^{-3}$ C/m^2, the cell wall is 5.0 nm thick, and the cell-wall material is air. (a) Find the magnitude of $\vec{E}$ in the wall between the two layers of charge. (b) Find the potential difference between the inside and the outside of the cell. Which is at the higher potential? (c) A typical cell in the human body has a volume of 10^{-16} m^3. Estimate the total electric-field energy stored in the wall of a cell of this size. (*Hint:* Assume that the cell is spherical, and calculate the volume of the cell wall.) (d) In reality, the cell wall is made up, not of air, but of tissue with a dielectric constant of 5.4. Repeat parts (a) and (b) in this case.

24.41 • A capacitor has parallel plates of area 12 cm^2 separated by 2.0 mm. The space between the plates is filled with polystyrene (see Table 24.2). (a) Find the permittivity of polystyrene. (b) Find the maximum permissible voltage across the capacitor to avoid dielectric breakdown. (c) When the voltage equals the value found in part (b), find the surface charge density on each plate and the induced surface charge density on the surface of the dielectric.

24.42 • A constant potential difference of 12 V is maintained between the terminals of a 0.25-μF, parallel-plate, air capacitor. (a) A sheet of Mylar is inserted between the plates of the capacitor, completely filling the space between the plates. When this is done, how much additional charge flows onto the positive plate of the capacitor (see Table 24.1)? (b) What is the total induced charge on either face of the Mylar sheet? (c) What effect does the Mylar sheet have on the electric field between the plates? Explain how you can reconcile this with the increase in charge on the plates, which acts to *increase* the electric field.

24.43 • When a 360-nF air capacitor (1 nF $= 10^{-9}$ F) is connected to a power supply, the energy stored in the capacitor is 1.85×10^{-5} J. While the capacitor is kept connected to the power supply, a slab of dielectric is inserted that completely fills the space between the plates. This increases the stored energy by 2.32×10^{-5} J. (a) What is the potential difference between the capacitor plates? (b) What is the dielectric constant of the slab?

24.44 • A parallel-plate capacitor has capacitance $C = 12.5$ pF when the volume between the plates is filled with air. The plates are circular, with radius 3.00 cm. The capacitor is connected to a battery, and a charge of magnitude 25.0 pC goes onto each plate. With the capacitor still connected to the battery, a slab of dielectric is inserted between the plates, completely filling the space between the plates. After the dielectric has been inserted, the charge on each plate has magnitude 45.0 pC. (a) What is the dielectric constant K of the dielectric? (b) What is the potential difference between the plates before and after the dielectric has been inserted? (c) What is the electric field at a point midway between the plates before and after the dielectric has been inserted?

Section 24.6 Gauss's Law in Dielectrics

24.45 • A parallel-plate capacitor has the volume between its plates filled with plastic with dielectric constant K. The magnitude of the charge on each plate is Q. Each plate has area A, and the distance between the plates is d. (a) Use Gauss's law as stated in Eq. (24.23) to calculate the magnitude of the electric field in the dielectric. (b) Use the electric field determined in part (a) to calculate the potential difference between the two plates. (c) Use the result of part (b) to determine the capacitance of the capacitor. Compare your result to Eq. (24.12).

24.46 • A parallel-plate capacitor has plates with area 0.0225 m^2 separated by 1.00 mm of Teflon. (a) Calculate the charge on the plates when they are charged to a potential difference of 12.0 V. (b) Use Gauss's law (Eq. 24.23) to calculate the electric field inside the Teflon. (c) Use Gauss's law to calculate the electric field if the voltage source is disconnected and the Teflon is removed.

PROBLEMS

24.47 • Electronic flash units for cameras contain a capacitor for storing the energy used to produce the flash. In one such unit, the flash lasts for $\frac{1}{675}$ s with an average light power output of 2.70×10^5 W. (a) If the conversion of electrical energy to light is 95% efficient (the rest of the energy goes to thermal energy), how much energy must be stored in the capacitor for one flash? (b) The capacitor has a potential difference between its plates of 125 V when the stored energy equals the value calculated in part (a). What is the capacitance?

24.48 • A parallel-plate air capacitor is made by using two plates 16 cm square, spaced 3.7 mm apart. It is connected to a 12-V battery. (a) What is the capacitance? (b) What is the charge on each plate? (c) What is the electric field between the plates? (d) What is the energy stored in the capacitor? (e) If the battery is disconnected and then the plates are pulled apart to a separation of 7.4 mm, what are the answers to parts (a)–(d)?

24.49 •• Suppose the battery in Problem 24.48 remains connected while the plates are pulled apart. What are the answers then to parts (a)–(d) after the plates have been pulled apart?

24.50 ••• **BIO Cell Membranes.** Cell membranes (the walled enclosure around a cell) are typically about 7.5 nm thick. They are partially permeable to allow charged material to pass in and out, as needed. Equal but opposite charge densities build up on the inside and outside faces of such a membrane, and these charges prevent additional charges from passing through the cell wall. We can model a cell membrane as a parallel-plate capacitor, with the membrane itself containing proteins embedded in an organic material to give the membrane a dielectric constant of about 10. (See Fig. P24.50.) (a) What is the capacitance per square centimeter of such a cell wall? (b) In its normal resting state, a cell has a potential difference of 85 mV across its membrane. What is the electric field inside this membrane?

Figure **P24.50**

24.51 • A capacitor is made from two hollow, coaxial copper cylinders, one inside the other. There is air in the space between the cylinders. The inner cylinder has net positive charge and the outer cylinder has net negative charge. The inner cylinder has radius 2.50 mm, the outer cylinder has radius 3.10 mm, and the length of each cylinder is 36.0 cm. If the potential difference between the surfaces of the two cylinders is 80.0 V, what is the magnitude of the electric field at a point between the two cylinders that is a distance of 2.80 mm from their common axis and midway between the ends of the cylinders?

24.52 ••• In one type of computer keyboard, each key holds a small metal plate that serves as one plate of a parallel-plate, air-filled capacitor. When the key is depressed, the plate separation decreases and the capacitance increases. Electronic circuitry detects the change in capacitance and thus detects that the key has been pressed. In one particular keyboard, the area of each metal plate is 42.0 mm^2, and the separation between the plates is 0.700 mm before the key is depressed. (a) Calculate the capacitance before the key is depressed. (b) If the circuitry can detect a change in capacitance of 0.250 pF, how far must the key be depressed before the circuitry detects its depression?

24.53 •• A 20.0-μF capacitor is charged to a potential difference of 800 V. The terminals of the charged capacitor are then connected to those of an uncharged 10.0-μF capacitor. Compute (a) the original charge of the system, (b) the final potential difference across each capacitor, (c) the final energy of the system, and (d) the decrease in energy when the capacitors are connected.

24.54 •• In Fig. 24.9a, let $C_1 = 9.0 \mu$F, $C_2 = 4.0 \mu$F, and $V_{ab} = 36$ V. Suppose the charged capacitors are disconnected from the source and from each other, and then reconnected to each other with plates of *opposite* sign together. By how much does the energy of the system decrease?

24.55 • For the capacitor network shown in Fig. P24.55, the potential difference across ab is 12.0 V. Find (a) the total energy stored in this network and (b) the energy stored in the 4.80-μF capacitor.

Figure **P24.55**

24.56 •• Several 0.25-μF capacitors are available. The voltage across each is not to exceed 600 V. You need to make a capacitor with capacitance 0.25 μF to be connected across a potential differ-ence of 960 V. (a) Show in a diagram how an equivalent capacitor with the desired properties can be obtained. (b) No dielectric is a perfect insulator that would not permit the flow of any charge through its volume. Suppose that the dielectric in one of the capac-itors in your diagram is a moderately good conductor. What will happen in this case when your combination of capacitors is con-nected across the 960-V potential difference?

24.57 • In Fig. P24.57, $C_1 =$ $C_5 = 8.4$ μF and $C_2 = C_3 = $ $C_4 = 4.2$ μF. The applied poten-tial is $V_{ab} = 220$ V. (a) What is the equivalent capacitance of the network between points a and b? (b) Calculate the charge on each capacitor and the potential difference across each capacitor.

Figure **P24.57**

24.58 •• You are working on an electronics project requiring a variety of capacitors, but you have only a large supply of 100-nF capacitors available. Show how you can connect these capacitors to produce each of the following equivalent capacitances: (a) 50 nF; (b) 450 nF; (c) 25 nF; (d) 75 nF.

24.59 •• In Fig. E24.20, $C_1 = 3.00$ μF and $V_{ab} = 150$ V. The charge on capacitor C_1 is 150 μC and the charge on C_3 is 450 μC. What are the values of the capacitances of C_2 and C_3?

24.60 • The capacitors in Fig. P24.60 are initially uncharged and are connected, as in the dia-gram, with switch S open. The applied potential difference is $V_{ab} = +210$ V. (a) What is the potential difference V_{cd}? (b) What is the potential difference across each capacitor after switch S is closed? (c) How much charge flowed through the switch when it was closed?

Figure **P24.60**

24.61 •• Three capacitors having capacitances of 8.4, 8.4, and 4.2 μF are connected in series across a 36-V potential difference. (a) What is the charge on the 4.2-μF capacitor? (b) What is the total energy stored in all three capacitors? (c) The capacitors are disconnected from the potential difference without allowing them to discharge. They are then reconnected in parallel with each other, with the positively charged plates connected together. What is the voltage across each capacitor in the parallel combination? (d) What is the total energy now stored in the capacitors?

24.62 • **Capacitance of a Thundercloud.** The charge center of a thundercloud, drifting 3.0 km above the earth's surface, contains 20 C of negative charge. Assuming the charge center has a radius of 1.0 km, and modeling the charge center and the earth's surface as parallel plates, calculate: (a) the capacitance of the system; (b)

the potential difference between charge center and ground; (c) the average strength of the electric field between cloud and ground; (d) the electrical energy stored in the system.

24.63 •• In Fig. P24.63, each capacitance C_1 is 6.9 μF, and each capacitance C_2 is 4.6 μF. (a) Com-pute the equivalent capacitance of the network between points a and b. (b) Compute the charge on each of the three capacitors near-est a and b when $V_{ab} = 420$ V. (c) With 420 V across a and b, compute V_{cd}.

Figure **P24.63**

24.64 • Each combination of capacitors between points a and b in Fig. P24.64 is first connected across a 120-V bat-tery, charging the combination to 120 V. These combinations are then connected to make the circuits shown. When the switch S is thrown, a surge of charge for the discharging capacitors flows to trigger the signal device. How much charge flows through the signal device in each case?

Figure **P24.64**

(a)

(b)

24.65 • A parallel-plate capac-itor with only air between the plates is charged by connecting it to a battery. The capacitor is then disconnected from the bat-tery, without any of the charge leaving the plates. (a) A voltmeter reads 45.0 V when placed across the capacitor. When a dielectric is inserted between the plates, com-pletely filling the space, the voltmeter reads 11.5 V. What is the dielectric constant of this material? (b) What will the voltmeter read if the dielectric is now pulled partway out so it fills only one-third of the space between the plates?

24.66 •• An air capacitor is made by using two flat plates, each with area A, separated by a distance d. Then a metal slab having thickness a (less than d) and the same shape and size as the plates is inserted between them, parallel to the plates and not touching either plate (Fig. P24.66). (a) What is the capacitance of this arrangement? (b) Express the capacitance as a multiple of the capacitance C_0 when the metal slab is not present. (c) Discuss what happens to the capacitance in the limits $a \rightarrow 0$ and $a \rightarrow d$.

Figure **P24.66**

24.67 •• **Capacitance of the Earth.** Consider a spherical capacitor with one conductor being a solid conducting sphere of radius R and the other conductor being at infinity. (a) Use Eq. (24.1) and what you know about the potential at the surface of a conducting sphere with charge Q to derive an expression for the capacitance of the charged sphere. (b) Use your result in part (a) to calculate the capacitance of the earth. The earth is a good conduc-tor and has a radius of 6380 km. Compare your results to the capacitance of typical capacitors used in electronic circuits, which ranges from 10 pF to 100 pF.

24.68 •• A potential difference $V_{ab} = 48.0$ V is applied across the capacitor network of Fig. E24.17. If $C_1 = C_2 = 4.00$ μF and

$C_4 = 8.00 \ \mu\text{F}$, what must the capacitance C_3 be if the network is to store 2.90×10^{-3} J of electrical energy?

24.69 • **Earth-Ionosphere Capacitance.** The earth can be considered as a single-conductor capacitor (see Problem 24.67). It can also be considered in combination with a charged layer of the atmosphere, the ionosphere, as a spherical capacitor with two plates, the surface of the earth being the negative plate. The ionosphere is at a level of about 70 km, and the potential difference between earth and ionosphere is about 350,000 V. Calculate: (a) the capacitance of this system; (b) the total charge on the capacitor; (c) the energy stored in the system.

24.70 • **CALC** The inner cylinder of a long, cylindrical capacitor has radius r_a and linear charge density $+\lambda$. It is surrounded by a coaxial cylindrical conducting shell with inner radius r_b and linear charge density $-\lambda$ (see Fig. 24.6). (a) What is the energy density in the region between the conductors at a distance r from the axis? (b) Integrate the energy density calculated in part (a) over the volume between the conductors in a length L of the capacitor to obtain the total electric-field energy per unit length. (c) Use Eq. (24.9) and the capacitance per unit length calculated in Example 24.4 (Section 24.1) to calculate U/L. Does your result agree with that obtained in part (b)?

24.71 •• **CP** A capacitor has a potential difference of 2.25×10^3 V between its plates. A short aluminum wire with initial temperature 23.0°C is connected between the plates of the capacitor and all the energy stored in the wire goes into heating the wire. The wire has mass 12.0 g. If no heat is lost to the surroundings and the final temperature of the wire is 34.2°C, what is the capacitance of the capacitor?

24.72 •• A parallel-plate capacitor is made from two plates 12.0 cm on each side and 4.50 mm apart. Half of the space between these plates contains only air, but the other half is filled with Plexiglas® of dielectric constant 3.40 (Fig.

Figure **P24.72**

P24.72). An 18.0-V battery is connected across the plates. (a) What is the capacitance of this combination? (*Hint:* Can you think of this capacitor as equivalent to two capacitors in parallel?) (b) How much energy is stored in the capacitor? (c) If we remove the Plexiglas® but change nothing else, how much energy will be stored in the capacitor?

24.73 •• A parallel-plate capacitor has square plates that are 8.00 cm on each side and 3.80 mm apart. The space between the plates is completely filled with two square slabs of dielectric, each 8.00 cm on a side and 1.90 mm thick. One slab is pyrex glass and the other is polystyrene. If the potential difference between the plates is 86.0 V, how much electrical energy is stored in the capacitor?

24.74 •• A fuel gauge uses a capacitor to determine the height of the fuel in a tank. The effective dielectric constant K_{eff} changes from a value of 1 when the tank is empty to a value of K, the dielectric constant of the fuel, when the tank is full. The appropriate electronic circuitry can determine the effective dielectric constant of the combined air and fuel between the capacitor plates. Each of the two rectangular plates has a width

Figure **P24.74**

w and a length L (Fig. P24.74). The height of the fuel between the plates is h. You can ignore any fringing effects. (a) Derive an expression for K_{eff} as a function of h. (b) What is the effective dielectric constant for a tank $\frac{1}{4}$ full, $\frac{1}{2}$ full, and $\frac{3}{4}$ full if the fuel is gasoline ($K = 1.95$)? (c) Repeat part (b) for methanol ($K = 33.0$). (d) For which fuel is this fuel gauge more practical?

24.75 •• Three square metal plates A, B, and C, each 12.0 cm on a side and 1.50 mm thick, are arranged as in Fig. P24.75. The plates are separated by sheets of paper 0.45 mm thick and with dielectric constant 4.2. The outer plates are connected together and connected to point b. The inner plate is connected to point a.

Figure **P24.75**

(a) Copy the diagram and show by plus and minus signs the charge distribution on the plates when point a is maintained at a positive potential relative to point b. (b) What is the capacitance between points a and b?

CHALLENGE PROBLEMS

24.76 ••• **CP** The parallel-plate air capacitor in Fig. P24.76 consists of two horizontal conducting plates of equal area A. The bottom plate rests on a fixed support, and the top plate is suspended by four springs with spring constant k, positioned at each of the four corners of the top plate as shown in the figure. When uncharged, the plates are separated by a distance z_0. A battery is connected to the plates and produces a potential difference V between them. This causes the plate separation to decrease to z. Neglect any fringing effects. (a) Show that the electrostatic force between the charged plates has a magnitude $\epsilon_0 A V^2 / 2z^2$. (*Hint:* See Exercise 24.27.) (b) Obtain an expression that relates the plate separation z to the potential difference V. The resulting equation will be cubic in z. (c) Given the values $A = 0.300 \text{ m}^2$, $z_0 = 1.20 \text{ mm}$, $k = 25.0 \text{ N/m}$, and $V = 120 \text{ V}$, find the two values of z for which the top plate will be in equilibrium. (*Hint:* You can solve the cubic equation by plugging a trial value of z into the equation and then adjusting your guess until the equation is satisfied to three significant figures. Locating the roots of the cubic equation graphically can help you pick starting values of z for this trial-and-error procedure. One root of the cubic equation has a nonphysical negative value.) (d) For each of the two values of z found in part (c), is the equilibrium stable or unstable? For stable equilibrium a small displacement of the object will give rise to a net force tending to return the object to the equilibrium position. For unstable equilibrium a small displacement gives rise to a net force that takes the object farther away from equilibrium.

Figure **P24.76**

24.77 ••• Two square conducting plates with sides of length L are separated by a distance D. A dielectric slab with constant K with dimensions $L \times L \times D$ is inserted a distance x into the space between the plates, as shown in Fig. P24.77. (a) Find the capacitance

C of this system. (b) Suppose that the capacitor is connected to a battery that maintains a constant potential difference *V* between the plates. If the dielectric slab is inserted an additional distance *dx* into the space between the plates, show that the change in stored energy is

$$dU = +\frac{(K-1)\epsilon_0 V^2 L}{2D}dx$$

(c) Suppose that before the slab is moved by *dx*, the plates are disconnected from the battery, so that the charges on the plates remain constant. Determine the magnitude of the charge on each plate, and then show that when the slab is moved *dx* farther into the space between the plates, the stored energy changes by an amount that is the *negative* of the expression for *dU* given in part (b). (d) If *F* is the force exerted on the slab by the charges on the plates, then *dU* should equal the work done *against* this force to move the slab a distance *dx*. Thus *dU* = −*F dx*. Show that applying this expression to the result of part (b) suggests that the electric force on the slab pushes it *out* of the capacitor, while the result of part (c) suggests that the force

Figure **P24.77**

pulls the slab *into* the capacitor. (e) Figure 24.16 shows that the force in fact pulls the slab into the capacitor. Explain why the result of part (b) gives an incorrect answer for the direction of this force, and calculate the magnitude of the force. (This method does not require knowledge of the nature of the fringing field.)

24.78 ••• An isolated spherical capacitor has charge +*Q* on its inner conductor (radius r_a) and charge −*Q* on its outer conductor (radius r_b). Half of the volume between the two conductors is then filled with a liquid dielectric of constant *K*, as shown in cross section in Fig. P24.78. (a) Find the capacitance of the half-filled capacitor. (b) Find the magnitude of $\vec{E}$ in the volume between the two conductors as a function of the distance *r* from the center of the capacitor. Give answers for both the upper and lower halves of this volume. (c) Find the surface density of free charge on the upper and lower halves of the inner and outer conductors. (d) Find the surface density of bound charge on the inner ($r = r_a$) and outer ($r = r_b$) surfaces of the dielectric. (e) What is the surface density of bound charge on the flat surface of the dielectric? Explain.

Figure **P24.78**

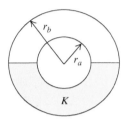

Answers

Chapter Opening Question ?

Equation (24.9) shows that the energy stored in a capacitor with capacitance *C* and charge *Q* is $U = Q^2/2C$. If the charge *Q* is doubled, the stored energy increases by a factor of $2^2 = 4$. Note that if the value of *Q* is too great, the electric-field magnitude inside the capacitor will exceed the dielectric strength of the material between the plates and dielectric breakdown will occur (see Section 24.4). This puts a practical limit on the amount of energy that can be stored.

Test Your Understanding Questions

24.1 Answer: (iii) The capacitance does not depend on the value of the charge *Q*. Doubling the value of *Q* causes the potential difference V_{ab} to double, so the capacitance $C = Q/V_{ab}$ remains the same. These statements are true no matter what the geometry of the capacitor.

24.2 Answers: (a) (i), (b) (iv) In a series connection the two capacitors carry the same charge *Q* but have different potential differences $V_{ab} = Q/C$; the capacitor with the smaller capacitance *C* has the greater potential difference. In a parallel connection the two capacitors have the same potential difference V_{ab} but carry different charges $Q = CV_{ab}$; the capacitor with the larger capacitance *C* has the greater charge. Hence a 4-μF capacitor will have a greater potential difference than an 8-μF capacitor if the two are connected in series. The 4-μF capacitor cannot carry more charge than the 8-μF capacitor no matter how they are connected: In a series connection they will carry the same charge, and in a parallel connection the 8-μF capacitor will carry more charge.

24.3 Answer: (i) Capacitors connected in series carry the same charge *Q*. To compare the amount of energy stored, we use the expression $U = Q^2/2C$ from Eq. (24.9); it shows that the capacitor with the *smaller* capacitance ($C = 4$ μF) has more stored

energy in a series combination. By contrast, capacitors in parallel have the same potential difference *V*, so to compare them we use $U = \frac{1}{2}CV^2$ from Eq. (24.9). It shows that in a parallel combination, the capacitor with the *larger* capacitance ($C = 8$ μF) has more stored energy. (If we had instead used $U = \frac{1}{2}CV^2$ to analyze the series combination, we would have to account for the different potential differences across the two capacitors. Likewise, using $U = Q^2/2C$ to study the parallel combination would require us to account for the different charges on the capacitors.)

24.4 Answer: (i) Here *Q* remains the same, so we use $U = Q^2/2C$ from Eq. (24.9) for the stored energy. Removing the dielectric lowers the capacitance by a factor of $1/K$; since *U* is inversely proportional to *C*, the stored energy *increases* by a factor of *K*. It takes work to pull the dielectric slab out of the capacitor because the fringing field tries to pull the slab back in (Fig. 24.16). The work that you do goes into the energy stored in the capacitor.

24.5 Answer: (i), (iii), (ii) Equation (24.14) says that if E_0 is the initial electric-field magnitude (before the dielectric slab is inserted), then the resultant field magnitude after the slab is inserted is $E_0/K = E_0/3$. The magnitude of the resultant field equals the difference between the initial field magnitude and the magnitude E_i of the field due to the bound charges (see Fig. 24.20). Hence $E_0 - E_i = E_0/3$ and $E_i = 2E_0/3$.

24.6 Answer: (iii) Equation (24.23) shows that this situation is the same as an isolated point charge in vacuum but with $\vec{E}$ replaced by $K\vec{E}$. Hence *KE* at the point of interest is equal to $q/4\pi\epsilon_0 r^2$, and so $E = q/4\pi K\epsilon_0 r^2$. As in Example 24.12, filling the space with a dielectric reduces the electric field by a factor of $1/K$.

Bridging Problem

Answers: (a) 0 **(b)** $Q^2/32\pi^2\epsilon_0 r^4$ **(c)** $Q^2/8\pi\epsilon_0 R$
  (d) $Q^2/8\pi\epsilon_0 R$ **(e)** $C = 4\pi\epsilon_0 R$

25 CURRENT, RESISTANCE, AND ELECTROMOTIVE FORCE

LEARNING GOALS

By studying this chapter, you will learn:

- The meaning of electric current, and how charges move in a conductor.

- What is meant by the resistivity and conductivity of a substance.

- How to calculate the resistance of a conductor from its dimensions and its resistivity.

- How an electromotive force (emf) makes it possible for current to flow in a circuit.

- How to do calculations involving energy and power in circuits.

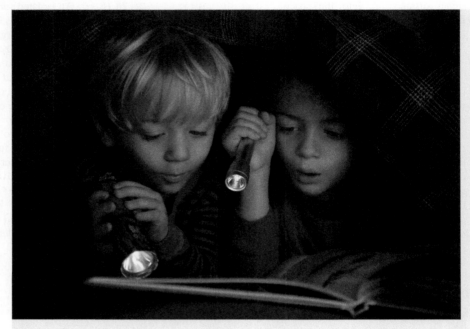

? In a flashlight, is the amount of current that flows out of the bulb less than, greater than, or equal to the amount of current that flows into the bulb?

In the past four chapters we studied the interactions of electric charges *at rest;* now we're ready to study charges *in motion.* An *electric current* consists of charges in motion from one region to another. If the charges follow a conducting path that forms a closed loop, the path is called an *electric circuit.*

Fundamentally, electric circuits are a means for conveying *energy* from one place to another. As charged particles move within a circuit, electric potential energy is transferred from a source (such as a battery or generator) to a device in which that energy is either stored or converted to another form: into sound in a stereo system or into heat and light in a toaster or light bulb. Electric circuits are useful because they allow energy to be transported without any moving parts (other than the moving charged particles themselves). They are at the heart of flashlights, computers, radio and television transmitters and receivers, and household and industrial power distribution systems. Your nervous system is a specialized electric circuit that carries vital signals from one part of your body to another.

In Chapter 26 we will see how to analyze electric circuits and will examine some practical applications of circuits. Before we can do so, however, you must understand the basic properties of electric currents. These properties are the subject of this chapter. We'll begin by describing the nature of electric conductors and considering how they are affected by temperature. We'll learn why a short, fat, cold copper wire is a better conductor than a long, skinny, hot steel wire. We'll study the properties of batteries and see how they cause current and energy transfer in a circuit. In this analysis we will use the concepts of current, potential difference (or voltage), resistance, and electromotive force. Finally, we'll look at electric current in a material from a microscopic viewpoint.

25.1 Current

A **current** is any motion of charge from one region to another. In this section we'll discuss currents in conducting materials. The vast majority of technological applications of charges in motion involve currents of this kind.

In electrostatic situations (discussed in Chapters 21 through 24) the electric field is zero everywhere within the conductor, and there is *no* current. However, this does not mean that all charges within the conductor are at rest. In an ordinary metal such as copper or alumium, some of the electrons are free to move within the conducting material. These free electrons move randomly in all directions, somewhat like the molecules of a gas but with much greater speeds, of the order of 10^6 m/s. The electrons nonetheless do not escape from the conducting material, because they are attracted to the positive ions of the material. The motion of the electrons is random, so there is no *net* flow of charge in any direction and hence no current.

Now consider what happens if a constant, steady electric field $\vec{E}$ is established inside a conductor. (We'll see later how this can be done.) A charged particle (such as a free electron) inside the conducting material is then subjected to a steady force $\vec{F} = q\vec{E}$. If the charged particle were moving in *vacuum,* this steady force would cause a steady acceleration in the direction of $\vec{F}$, and after a time the charged particle would be moving in that direction at high speed. But a charged particle moving in a *conductor* undergoes frequent collisions with the massive, nearly stationary ions of the material. In each such collision the particle's direction of motion undergoes a random change. The net effect of the electric field $\vec{E}$ is that in addition to the random motion of the charged particles within the conductor, there is also a very slow net motion or *drift* of the moving charged particles as a group in the direction of the electric force $\vec{F} = q\vec{E}$ (Fig. 25.1). This motion is described in terms of the **drift velocity** $\vec{v}_d$ of the particles. As a result, there is a net current in the conductor.

While the random motion of the electrons has a very fast average speed of about 10^6 m/s, the drift speed is very slow, often on the order of 10^{-4} m/s. Given that the electrons move so slowly, you may wonder why the light comes on immediately when you turn on the switch of a flashlight. The reason is that the electric field is set up in the wire with a speed approaching the speed of light, and electrons start to move all along the wire at very nearly the same time. The time that it takes any individual electron to get from the switch to the light bulb isn't really relevant. A good analogy is a group of soldiers standing at attention when the sergeant orders them to start marching; the order reaches the soldiers' ears at the speed of sound, which is much faster than their marching speed, so all the soldiers start to march essentially in unison.

The Direction of Current Flow

The drift of moving charges through a conductor can be interpreted in terms of work and energy. The electric field $\vec{E}$ does work on the moving charges. The resulting kinetic energy is transferred to the material of the conductor by means of collisions with the ions, which vibrate about their equilibrium positions in the crystalline structure of the conductor. This energy transfer increases the average vibrational energy of the ions and therefore the temperature of the material. Thus much of the work done by the electric field goes into heating the conductor, *not* into making the moving charges move ever faster and faster. This heating is sometimes useful, as in an electric toaster, but in many situations is simply an unavoidable by-product of current flow.

In different current-carrying materials, the charges of the moving particles may be positive or negative. In metals the moving charges are always (negative) electrons, while in an ionized gas (plasma) or an ionic solution the moving charges may include both electrons and positively charged ions. In a semiconductor

25.1 If there is no electric field inside a conductor, an electron moves randomly from point P_1 to point P_2 in a time Δt. If an electric field $\vec{E}$ is present, the electric force $\vec{F} = q\vec{E}$ imposes a small drift (greatly exaggerated here) that takes the electron to point P_2', a distance $v_d \Delta t$ from P_2 in the direction of the force.

Conductor without internal $\vec{E}$ field

Path of electron without $\vec{E}$ field. Electron moves randomly.

Path of electron with $\vec{E}$ field. The motion is mostly random, but ...

P_1

P_2 P_2'

$v_d \Delta t$

...the $\vec{E}$ field results in a net displacement along the wire.

Conductor with internal $\vec{E}$ field

$\vec{E}$ $\vec{F} = q\vec{E}$ $\vec{E}$

An electron has a negative charge q, so the force on it due to the $\vec{E}$ field is in the direction opposite to $\vec{E}$.

25.2 The same current can be produced by (a) positive charges moving in the direction of the electric field $\vec{E}$ or (b) the same number of negative charges moving at the same speed in the direction opposite to $\vec{E}$.

(a)

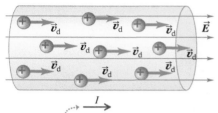

A **conventional current** is treated as a flow of positive charges, regardless of whether the free charges in the conductor are positive, negative, or both.

(b)

In a metallic conductor, the moving charges are electrons — but the *current* still points in the direction positive charges would flow.

25.3 The current I is the time rate of charge transfer through the cross-sectional area A. The random component of each moving charged particle's motion averages to zero, and the current is in the same direction as $\vec{E}$ whether the moving charges are positive (as shown here) or negative (see Fig. 25.2b).

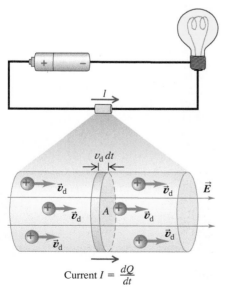

Current $I = \dfrac{dQ}{dt}$

material such as germanium or silicon, conduction is partly by electrons and partly by motion of *vacancies,* also known as *holes;* these are sites of missing electrons and act like positive charges.

Figure 25.2 shows segments of two different current-carrying materials. In Fig. 25.2a the moving charges are positive, the electric force is in the same direction as $\vec{E}$, and the drift velocity $\vec{v}_d$ is from left to right. In Fig. 25.2b the charges are negative, the electric force is opposite to $\vec{E}$, and the drift velocity $\vec{v}_d$ is from right to left. In both cases there is a net flow of positive charge from left to right, and positive charges end up to the right of negative ones. We *define* the current, denoted by I, to be in the direction in which there is a flow of *positive* charge. Thus we describe currents as though they consisted entirely of positive charge flow, even in cases in which we know that the actual current is due to electrons. Hence the current is to the right in both Figs. 25.2a and 25.2b. This choice or convention for the direction of current flow is called **conventional current.** While the direction of the conventional current is *not* necessarily the same as the direction in which charged particles are actually moving, we'll find that the sign of the moving charges is of little importance in analyzing electric circuits.

Figure 25.3 shows a segment of a conductor in which a current is flowing. We consider the moving charges to be *positive,* so they are moving in the same direction as the current. We define the current through the cross-sectional area A to be *the net charge flowing through the area per unit time.* Thus, if a net charge dQ flows through an area in a time dt, the current I through the area is

$$I = \frac{dQ}{dt} \qquad \text{(definition of current)} \qquad (25.1)$$

CAUTION **Current is not a vector** Although we refer to the *direction* of a current, current as defined by Eq. (25.1) is *not* a vector quantity. In a current-carrying wire, the current is always along the length of the wire, regardless of whether the wire is straight or curved. No single vector could describe motion along a curved path, which is why current is not a vector. We'll usually describe the direction of current either in words (as in "the current flows clockwise around the circuit") or by choosing a current to be positive if it flows in one direction along a conductor and negative if it flows in the other direction.

The SI unit of current is the **ampere;** one ampere is defined to be *one coulomb per second* (1 A = 1 C/s). This unit is named in honor of the French scientist André Marie Ampère (1775–1836). When an ordinary flashlight (D-cell size) is turned on, the current in the flashlight is about 0.5 to 1 A; the current in the wires of a car engine's starter motor is around 200 A. Currents in radio and television circuits are usually expressed in *milliamperes* (1 mA = 10^{-3} A) or *microamperes* (1 μA = 10^{-6} A), and currents in computer circuits are expressed in *nanoamperes* (1 nA = 10^{-9} A) or *picoamperes* (1 pA = 10^{-12} A).

Current, Drift Velocity, and Current Density

We can express current in terms of the drift velocity of the moving charges. Let's consider again the situation of Fig. 25.3 of a conductor with cross-sectional area A and an electric field $\vec{E}$ directed from left to right. To begin with, we'll assume that the free charges in the conductor are positive; then the drift velocity is in the same direction as the field.

Suppose there are n moving charged particles per unit volume. We call n the **concentration** of particles; its SI unit is m^{-3}. Assume that all the particles move with the same drift velocity with magnitude v_d. In a time interval dt, each particle moves a distance $v_d \, dt$. The particles that flow out of the right end of the shaded cylinder with length $v_d \, dt$ during dt are the particles that were within this cylinder at the beginning of the interval dt. The volume of the cylinder is $Av_d \, dt$, and the number of particles within it is $nAv_d \, dt$. If each particle has a charge q, the charge dQ that flows out of the end of the cylinder during time dt is

$$dQ = q(nAv_d \, dt) = nqv_d A \, dt$$

and the current is

$$I = \frac{dQ}{dt} = nqv_d A$$

The current *per unit cross-sectional area* is called the **current density** J:

$$J = \frac{I}{A} = nqv_d$$

The units of current density are amperes per square meter (A/m^2).

If the moving charges are negative rather than positive, as in Fig. 25.2b, the drift velocity is opposite to $\vec{E}$. But the *current* is still in the same direction as $\vec{E}$ at each point in the conductor. Hence the current I and current density J don't depend on the sign of the charge, and so in the above expressions for I and J we replace the charge q by its absolute value $|q|$:

$$I = \frac{dQ}{dt} = n|q|v_d A \qquad \text{(general expression for current)} \qquad (25.2)$$

$$J = \frac{I}{A} = n|q|v_d \qquad \text{(general expression for current density)} \qquad (25.3)$$

The current in a conductor is the product of the concentration of moving charged particles, the magnitude of charge of each such particle, the magnitude of the drift velocity, and the cross-sectional area of the conductor.

We can also define a *vector* current density $\vec{J}$ that includes the direction of the drift velocity:

$$\vec{J} = nq\vec{v}_d \qquad \text{(vector current density)} \qquad (25.4)$$

There are *no* absolute value signs in Eq. (25.4). If q is positive, $\vec{v}_d$ is in the same direction as $\vec{E}$; if q is negative, $\vec{v}_d$ is opposite to $\vec{E}$. In either case, $\vec{J}$ is in the same direction as $\vec{E}$. Equation (25.3) gives the *magnitude* J of the vector current density $\vec{J}$.

CAUTION **Current density vs. current** Note that current density $\vec{J}$ is a vector, but current I is not. The difference is that the current density $\vec{J}$ describes how charges flow at a certain point, and the vector's direction tells you about the direction of the flow at that point. By contrast, the current I describes how charges flow through an extended object such as a wire. For example, I has the same value at all points in the circuit of Fig. 25.3, but $\vec{J}$ does not: The current density is directed downward in the left-hand side of the loop and upward in the right-hand side. The magnitude of $\vec{J}$ can also vary around a circuit. In Fig. 25.3 the current density magnitude $J = I/A$ is less in the battery (which has a large cross-sectional area A) than in the wires (which have a small cross-sectional area). |

In general, a conductor may contain several different kinds of moving charged particles having charges $q_1, q_2, \ldots$, concentrations $n_1, n_2, \ldots$, and drift velocities with magnitudes $v_{d1}, v_{d2}, \ldots$. An example is current flow in an ionic solution (Fig. 25.4). In a sodium chloride solution, current can be carried by both positive sodium ions and negative chlorine ions; the total current I is found by adding up the currents due to each kind of charged particle, using Eq. (25.2). Likewise, the total vector current density $\vec{J}$ is found by using Eq. (25.4) for each kind of charged particle and adding the results.

We will see in Section 25.4 that it is possible to have a current that is *steady* (that is, one that is constant in time) only if the conducting material forms a

25.4 Part of the electric circuit that includes this light bulb passes through a beaker with a solution of sodium chloride. The current in the solution is carried by both positive charges (Na^+ ions) and negative charges (Cl^- ions).

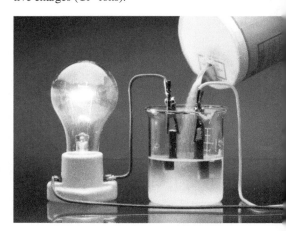

closed loop, called a *complete circuit*. In such a steady situation, the total charge in every segment of the conductor is constant. Hence the rate of flow of charge *out* at one end of a segment at any instant equals the rate of flow of charge *in* at the other end of the segment, and *the current is the same at all cross sections of the circuit*. We'll make use of this observation when we analyze electric circuits later in this chapter.

In many simple circuits, such as flashlights or cordless electric drills, the direction of the current is always the same; this is called *direct current*. But home appliances such as toasters, refrigerators, and televisions use *alternating current*, in which the current continuously changes direction. In this chapter we'll consider direct current only. Alternating current has many special features worthy of detailed study, which we'll examine in Chapter 31.

Example 25.1 Current density and drift velocity in a wire

An 18-gauge copper wire (the size usually used for lamp cords), with a diameter of 1.02 mm, carries a constant current of 1.67 A to a 200-W lamp. The free-electron density in the wire is 8.5×10^{28} per cubic meter. Find (a) the current density and (b) the drift speed.

SOLUTION

IDENTIFY and SET UP: This problem uses the relationships among current I, current density J, and drift speed v_d. We are given I and the wire diameter d, so we use Eq. (25.3) to find J. We use Eq. (25.3) again to find v_d from J and the known electron density n.

EXECUTE: (a) The cross-sectional area is

$$A = \frac{\pi d^2}{4} = \frac{\pi (1.02 \times 10^{-3} \text{ m})^2}{4} = 8.17 \times 10^{-7} \text{ m}^2$$

The magnitude of the current density is then

$$J = \frac{I}{A} = \frac{1.67 \text{ A}}{8.17 \times 10^{-7} \text{ m}^2} = 2.04 \times 10^6 \text{ A/m}^2$$

(b) From Eq. (25.3) for the drift velocity magnitude v_d, we find

$$v_d = \frac{J}{n|q|} = \frac{2.04 \times 10^6 \text{ A/m}^2}{(8.5 \times 10^{28} \text{ m}^{-3})|-1.60 \times 10^{-19} \text{ C}|}$$

$$= 1.5 \times 10^{-4} \text{ m/s} = 0.15 \text{ mm/s}$$

EVALUATE: At this speed an electron would require 6700 s (almost 2 h) to travel 1 m along this wire. The speeds of random motion of the electrons are roughly 10^6 m/s, around 10^{10} times the drift speed. Picture the electrons as bouncing around frantically, with a very slow drift!

Test Your Understanding of Section 25.1   Suppose we replaced the wire in Example 25.1 with 12-gauge copper wire, which has twice the diameter of 18-gauge wire. If the current remains the same, what effect would this have on the magnitude of the drift velocity v_d? (i) none—v_d would be unchanged; (ii) v_d would be twice as great; (iii) v_d would be four times greater; (iv) v_d would be half as great; (v) v_d would be one-fourth as great.

25.2 Resistivity

The current density $\vec{J}$ in a conductor depends on the electric field $\vec{E}$ and on the properties of the material. In general, this dependence can be quite complex. But for some materials, especially metals, at a given temperature, $\vec{J}$ is nearly *directly proportional* to $\vec{E}$, and the ratio of the magnitudes of E and J is constant. This relationship, called Ohm's law, was discovered in 1826 by the German physicist Georg Simon Ohm (1787–1854). The word "law" should actually be in quotation marks, since **Ohm's law,** like the ideal-gas equation and Hooke's law, is an *idealized model* that describes the behavior of some materials quite well but is not a general description of *all* matter. In the following discussion we'll assume that Ohm's law is valid, even though there are many situations in which it is not. The situation is comparable to our representation of the behavior of the static and kinetic friction forces; we treated these friction forces as being directly proportional to the normal force, even though we knew that this was at best an approximate description.

Table 25.1 Resistivities at Room Temperature (20°C)

	Substance	ρ ($\Omega \cdot$m)		Substance	ρ ($\Omega \cdot$m)
Conductors				**Semiconductors**	
Metals	Silver	1.47×10^{-8}		Pure carbon (graphite)	3.5×10^{-5}
	Copper	1.72×10^{-8}		Pure germanium	0.60
	Gold	2.44×10^{-8}		Pure silicon	2300
	Aluminum	2.75×10^{-8}	**Insulators**		
	Tungsten	5.25×10^{-8}		Amber	5×10^{14}
	Steel	20×10^{-8}		Glass	10^{10}–10^{14}
	Lead	22×10^{-8}		Lucite	$>10^{13}$
	Mercury	95×10^{-8}		Mica	10^{11}–10^{15}
Alloys	Manganin (Cu 84%, Mn 12%, Ni 4%)	44×10^{-8}		Quartz (fused)	75×10^{16}
	Constantan (Cu 60%, Ni 40%)	49×10^{-8}		Sulfur	10^{15}
	Nichrome	100×10^{-8}		Teflon	$>10^{13}$
				Wood	10^{8}–10^{11}

We define the **resistivity** ρ of a material as the ratio of the magnitudes of electric field and current density:

$$\rho = \frac{E}{J} \quad \text{(definition of resistivity)} \quad (25.5)$$

The greater the resistivity, the greater the field needed to cause a given current density, or the smaller the current density caused by a given field. From Eq. (25.5) the units of ρ are $(\text{V/m})/(\text{A/m}^2) = \text{V} \cdot \text{m/A}$. As we will discuss in the next section, 1 V/A is called one *ohm* (1 Ω; we use the Greek letter Ω, or omega, which is alliterative with "ohm"). So the SI units for ρ are $\Omega \cdot$ m (ohm-meters). Table 25.1 lists some representative values of resistivity. A perfect conductor would have zero resistivity, and a perfect insulator would have an infinite resistivity. Metals and alloys have the smallest resistivities and are the best conductors. The resistivities of insulators are greater than those of the metals by an enormous factor, on the order of 10^{22}.

The reciprocal of resistivity is **conductivity.** Its units are $(\Omega \cdot \text{m})^{-1}$. Good conductors of electricity have larger conductivity than insulators. Conductivity is the direct electrical analog of thermal conductivity. Comparing Table 25.1 with Table 17.5 (Thermal Conductivities), we note that good electrical conductors, such as metals, are usually also good conductors of heat. Poor electrical conductors, such as ceramic and plastic materials, are also poor thermal conductors. In a metal the free electrons that carry charge in electrical conduction also provide the principal mechanism for heat conduction, so we should expect a correlation between electrical and thermal conductivity. Because of the enormous difference in conductivity between electrical conductors and insulators, it is easy to confine electric currents to well-defined paths or circuits (Fig. 25.5). The variation in *thermal* conductivity is much less, only a factor of 10^3 or so, and it is usually impossible to confine heat currents to that extent.

Semiconductors have resistivities intermediate between those of metals and those of insulators. These materials are important because of the way their resistivities are affected by temperature and by small amounts of impurities.

A material that obeys Ohm's law reasonably well is called an *ohmic* conductor or a *linear* conductor. For such materials, at a given temperature, ρ is a *constant* that does not depend on the value of E. Many materials show substantial departures from Ohm's-law behavior; they are *nonohmic,* or *nonlinear.* In these materials, J depends on E in a more complicated manner.

Analogies with fluid flow can be a big help in developing intuition about electric current and circuits. For example, in the making of wine or maple syrup, the product is sometimes filtered to remove sediments. A pump forces the fluid through the filter under pressure; if the flow rate (analogous to J) is proportional to the pressure difference between the upstream and downstream sides (analogous to E), the behavior is analogous to Ohm's law.

25.5 The copper "wires," or traces, on this circuit board are printed directly onto the surface of the dark-colored insulating board. Even though the traces are very close to each other (only about a millimeter apart), the board has such a high resistivity (and low conductivity) that no current can flow between the traces.

Conducting paths
(traces)

25.6 Variation of resistivity ρ with absolute temperature T for **(a)** a normal metal, **(b)** a semiconductor, and **(c)** a superconductor. In **(a)** the linear approximation to ρ as a function of T is shown as a green line; the approximation agrees exactly at $T = T_0$, where $\rho = \rho_0$.

(a)

(b)

(c)

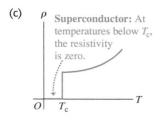

Resistivity and Temperature

The resistivity of a *metallic* conductor nearly always increases with increasing temperature, as shown in Fig. 25.6a. As temperature increases, the ions of the conductor vibrate with greater amplitude, making it more likely that a moving electron will collide with an ion as in Fig. 25.1; this impedes the drift of electrons through the conductor and hence reduces the current. Over a small temperature range (up to 100 C° or so), the resistivity of a metal can be represented approximately by the equation

$$\rho(T) = \rho_0[1 + \alpha(T - T_0)] \qquad \text{(temperature dependence of resistivity)} \qquad (25.6)$$

where ρ_0 is the resistivity at a reference temperature T_0 (often taken as 0°C or 20°C) and $\rho(T)$ is the resistivity at temperature T, which may be higher or lower than T_0. The factor α is called the **temperature coefficient of resistivity.** Some representative values are given in Table 25.2. The resistivity of the alloy manganin is practically independent of temperature.

Table 25.2 **Temperature Coefficients of Resistivity (Approximate Values Near Room Temperature)**

Material	$\alpha\,[(°C)^{-1}]$	Material	$\alpha\,[(°C)^{-1}]$
Aluminum	0.0039	Lead	0.0043
Brass	0.0020	Manganin	0.00000
Carbon (graphite)	−0.0005	Mercury	0.00088
Constantan	0.00001	Nichrome	0.0004
Copper	0.00393	Silver	0.0038
Iron	0.0050	Tungsten	0.0045

The resistivity of graphite (a nonmetal) *decreases* with increasing temperature, since at higher temperatures, more electrons are "shaken loose" from the atoms and become mobile; hence the temperature coefficient of resistivity of graphite is negative. This same behavior occurs for semiconductors (Fig. 25.6b). Measuring the resistivity of a small semiconductor crystal is therefore a sensitive measure of temperature; this is the principle of a type of thermometer called a *thermistor.*

Some materials, including several metallic alloys and oxides, show a phenomenon called *superconductivity.* As the temperature decreases, the resistivity at first decreases smoothly, like that of any metal. But then at a certain critical temperature T_c a phase transition occurs and the resistivity suddenly drops to zero, as shown in Fig. 25.6c. Once a current has been established in a superconducting ring, it continues indefinitely without the presence of any driving field.

Superconductivity was discovered in 1911 by the Dutch physicist Heike Kamerlingh Onnes (1853–1926). He discovered that at very low temperatures, below 4.2 K, the resistivity of mercury suddenly dropped to zero. For the next 75 years, the highest T_c attained was about 20 K. This meant that superconductivity occurred only when the material was cooled using expensive liquid helium, with a boiling-point temperature of 4.2 K, or explosive liquid hydrogen, with a boiling point of 20.3 K. But in 1986 Karl Müller and Johannes Bednorz discovered an oxide of barium, lanthanum, and copper with a T_c of nearly 40 K, and the race was on to develop "high-temperature" superconducting materials.

By 1987 a complex oxide of yttrium, copper, and barium had been found that has a value of T_c well above the 77 K boiling temperature of liquid nitrogen, a refrigerant that is both inexpensive and safe. The current (2010) record for T_c at atmospheric pressure is 138 K, and materials that are superconductors at room temperature may become a reality. The implications of these discoveries for power-distribution systems, computer design, and transportation are enormous. Meanwhile, superconducting electromagnets cooled by liquid helium are used in particle accelerators and some experimental magnetic-levitation railroads.

Superconductors have other exotic properties that require an understanding of magnetism to explore; we will discuss these further in Chapter 29.

Test Your Understanding of Section 25.2 You maintain a constant electric field inside a piece of semiconductor while lowering the semiconductor's temperature. What happens to the current density in the semiconductor? (i) It increases; (ii) it decreases; (iii) it remains the same.

25.3 Resistance

Mastering**PHYSICS**

PhET: Resistance in a Wire

For a conductor with resistivity ρ, the current density $\vec{J}$ at a point where the electric field is $\vec{E}$ is given by Eq. (25.5), which we can write as

$$\vec{E} = \rho\vec{J} \tag{25.7}$$

When Ohm's law is obeyed, ρ is constant and independent of the magnitude of the electric field, so $\vec{E}$ is directly proportional to $\vec{J}$. Often, however, we are more interested in the total current in a conductor than in $\vec{J}$ and more interested in the potential difference between the ends of the conductor than in $\vec{E}$. This is so largely because current and potential difference are much easier to measure than are $\vec{J}$ and $\vec{E}$.

Suppose our conductor is a wire with uniform cross-sectional area A and length L, as shown in Fig. 25.7. Let V be the potential difference between the higher-potential and lower-potential ends of the conductor, so that V is positive. The *direction* of the current is always from the higher-potential end to the lower-potential end. That's because current in a conductor flows in the direction of $\vec{E}$, no matter what the sign of the moving charges (Fig. 25.2), and because $\vec{E}$ points in the direction of *decreasing* electric potential (see Section 23.2). As the current flows through the potential difference, electric potential energy is lost; this energy is transferred to the ions of the conducting material during collisions.

We can also relate the *value* of the current I to the potential difference between the ends of the conductor. If the magnitudes of the current density $\vec{J}$ and the electric field $\vec{E}$ are uniform throughout the conductor, the total current I is given by $I = JA$, and the potential difference V between the ends is $V = EL$. When we solve these equations for J and E, respectively, and substitute the results in Eq. (25.7), we obtain

$$\frac{V}{L} = \frac{\rho I}{A} \quad \text{or} \quad V = \frac{\rho L}{A}I \tag{25.8}$$

This shows that when ρ is constant, the total current I is proportional to the potential difference V.

The ratio of V to I for a particular conductor is called its **resistance** R:

$$R = \frac{V}{I} \tag{25.9}$$

Comparing this definition of R to Eq. (25.8), we see that the resistance R of a particular conductor is related to the resistivity ρ of its material by

$$R = \frac{\rho L}{A} \quad \begin{array}{l}\text{(relationship between} \\ \text{resistance and resistivity)}\end{array} \tag{25.10}$$

If ρ is constant, as is the case for ohmic materials, then so is R.

The equation

$$V = IR \quad \begin{array}{l}\text{(relationship among voltage,} \\ \text{current, and resistance)}\end{array} \tag{25.11}$$

is often called Ohm's law, but it is important to understand that the real content of Ohm's law is the direct proportionality (for some materials) of V to I or of J to E.

25.7 A conductor with uniform cross section. The current density is uniform over any cross section, and the electric field is constant along the length.

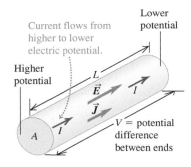

Current flows from higher to lower electric potential.

Higher potential

Lower potential

L

$\vec{E}$

$\vec{J}$

I

A

I

V = potential difference between ends

Equation (25.9) or (25.11) *defines* resistance R for *any* conductor, whether or not it obeys Ohm's law, but only when R is constant can we correctly call this relationship Ohm's law.

Interpreting Resistance

Equation (25.10) shows that the resistance of a wire or other conductor of uniform cross section is directly proportional to its length and inversely proportional to its cross-sectional area. It is also proportional to the resistivity of the material of which the conductor is made.

The flowing-fluid analogy is again useful. In analogy to Eq. (25.10), a narrow water hose offers more resistance to flow than a fat one, and a long hose has more resistance than a short one (Fig. 25.8). We can increase the resistance to flow by stuffing the hose with cotton or sand; this corresponds to increasing the resistivity. The flow rate is approximately proportional to the pressure difference between the ends. Flow rate is analogous to current, and pressure difference is analogous to potential difference ("voltage"). Let's not stretch this analogy too far, though; the water flow rate in a pipe is usually *not* proportional to its cross-sectional area (see Section 14.6).

The SI unit of resistance is the **ohm,** equal to one volt per ampere ($1 \, \Omega = 1 \, \text{V/A}$). The *kilohm* ($1 \, \text{k}\Omega = 10^3 \, \Omega$) and the *megohm* ($1 \, \text{M}\Omega = 10^6 \, \Omega$) are also in common use. A 100-m length of 12-gauge copper wire, the size usually used in household wiring, has a resistance at room temperature of about 0.5 Ω. A 100-W, 120-V light bulb has a resistance (at operating temperature) of 140 Ω. If the same current I flows in both the copper wire and the light bulb, the potential difference $V = IR$ is much greater across the light bulb, and much more potential energy is lost per charge in the light bulb. This lost energy is converted by the light bulb filament into light and heat. You don't want your household wiring to glow white-hot, so its resistance is kept low by using wire of low resistivity and large cross-sectional area.

Because the resistivity of a material varies with temperature, the resistance of a specific conductor also varies with temperature. For temperature ranges that are not too great, this variation is approximately a linear relationship, analogous to Eq. (25.6):

$$R(T) = R_0[1 + \alpha(T - T_0)] \qquad (25.12)$$

In this equation, $R(T)$ is the resistance at temperature T and R_0 is the resistance at temperature T_0, often taken to be 0°C or 20°C. The *temperature coefficient of resistance* α is the same constant that appears in Eq. (25.6) if the dimensions L and A in Eq. (25.10) do not change appreciably with temperature; this is indeed the case for most conducting materials (see Problem 25.67). Within the limits of validity of Eq. (25.12), the *change* in resistance resulting from a temperature change $T - T_0$ is given by $R_0\alpha(T - T_0)$.

A circuit device made to have a specific value of resistance between its ends is called a **resistor.** Resistors in the range 0.01 to $10^7 \, \Omega$ can be bought off the shelf. Individual resistors used in electronic circuitry are often cylindrical, a few millimeters in diameter and length, with wires coming out of the ends. The resistance may be marked with a standard code using three or four color bands near one end (Fig. 25.9), according to the scheme shown in Table 25.3. The first two bands (starting with the band nearest an end) are digits, and the third is a power-of-10 multiplier, as shown in Fig. 25.9. For example, green–violet–red means $57 \times 10^2 \, \Omega$, or 5.7 kΩ. The fourth band, if present, indicates the precision (tolerance) of the value; no band means ±20%, a silver band ±10%, and a gold band ±5%. Another important characteristic of a resistor is the maximum *power* it can dissipate without damage. We'll return to this point in Section 25.5.

25.8 A long fire hose offers substantial resistance to water flow. To make water pass through the hose rapidly, the upstream end of the hose must be at much higher pressure than the end where the water emerges. In an analogous way, there must be a large potential difference between the ends of a long wire in order to cause a substantial electric current through the wire.

25.9 This resistor has a resistance of 5.7 kΩ with a precision (tolerance) of ±10%.

Second digit Multiplier

First digit Tolerance

Table 25.3 Color Codes for Resistors

Color	Value as Digit	Value as Multiplier
Black	0	1
Brown	1	10
Red	2	10^2
Orange	3	10^3
Yellow	4	10^4
Green	5	10^5
Blue	6	10^6
Violet	7	10^7
Gray	8	10^8
White	9	10^9

25.10 Current–voltage relationships for two devices. Only for a resistor that obeys Ohm's law as in **(a)** is current I proportional to voltage V.

(a)

Ohmic resistor (e.g., typical metal wire): At a given temperature, current is proportional to voltage.

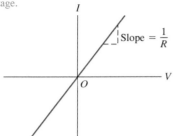

(b)

Semiconductor diode: a nonohmic resistor

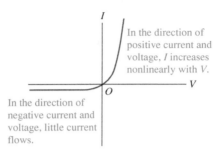

In the direction of positive current and voltage, I increases nonlinearly with V.

In the direction of negative current and voltage, little current flows.

For a resistor that obeys Ohm's law, a graph of current as a function of potential difference (voltage) is a straight line (Fig. 25.10a). The slope of the line is $1/R$. If the sign of the potential difference changes, so does the sign of the current produced; in Fig. 25.7 this corresponds to interchanging the higher- and lower-potential ends of the conductor, so the electric field, current density, and current all reverse direction. In devices that do not obey Ohm's law, the relationship of voltage to current may not be a direct proportion, and it may be different for the two directions of current. Figure 25.10b shows the behavior of a semiconductor *diode*, a device used to convert alternating current to direct current and to perform a wide variety of logic functions in computer circuitry. For positive potentials V of the anode (one of two terminals of the diode) with respect to the cathode (the other terminal), I increases exponentially with increasing V; for negative potentials the current is extremely small. Thus a positive V causes a current to flow in the positive direction, but a potential difference of the other sign causes little or no current. Hence a diode acts like a one-way valve in a circuit.

Example 25.2 **Electric field, potential difference, and resistance in a wire**

The 18-gauge copper wire of Example 25.1 has a cross-sectional area of 8.20×10^{-7} m². It carries a current of 1.67 A. Find (a) the electric-field magnitude in the wire; (b) the potential difference between two points in the wire 50.0 m apart; (c) the resistance of a 50.0-m length of this wire.

SOLUTION

IDENTIFY and SET UP: We are given the cross-sectional area A and current I. Our target variables are the electric-field magnitude E, potential difference V, and resistance R. The current density is $J = I/A$. We find E from Eq. (25.5), $E = \rho J$ (Table 25.1 gives the resistivity ρ for copper). The potential difference is then the product of E and the length of the wire. We can use either Eq. (25.10) or Eq. (25.11) to find R.

EXECUTE: (a) From Table 25.1, $\rho = 1.72 \times 10^{-8}$ Ω·m. Hence, using Eq. (25.5),

$$E = \rho J = \frac{\rho I}{A} = \frac{(1.72 \times 10^{-8} \ \Omega \cdot m)(1.67 \ A)}{8.20 \times 10^{-7} \ m^2}$$

$$= 0.0350 \ V/m$$

(b) The potential difference is

$$V = EL = (0.0350 \ V/m)(50.0 \ m) = 1.75 \ V$$

(c) From Eq. (25.10) the resistance of 50.0 m of this wire is

$$R = \frac{\rho L}{A} = \frac{(1.72 \times 10^{-8} \ \Omega \cdot m)(50.0 \ m)}{8.20 \times 10^{-7} \ m^2} = 1.05 \ \Omega$$

Alternatively, we can find R using Eq. (25.11):

$$R = \frac{V}{I} = \frac{1.75 \ V}{1.67 \ A} = 1.05 \ \Omega$$

EVALUATE: We emphasize that the resistance of the wire is *defined* to be the ratio of voltage to current. If the wire is made of nonohmic material, then R is different for different values of V but is always given by $R = V/I$. Resistance is also always given by $R = \rho L/A$; if the material is nonohmic, ρ is not constant but depends on E (or, equivalently, on $V = EL$).

Example 25.3 | Temperature dependence of resistance

Suppose the resistance of a copper wire is 1.05 Ω at 20°C. Find the resistance at 0°C and 100°C.

SOLUTION

IDENTIFY and SET UP: We are given the resistance $R_0 = 1.05$ Ω at a reference temperature $T_0 = 20°C$. We use Eq. (25.12) to find the resistances at $T = 0°C$ and $T = 100°C$ (our target variables), taking the temperature coefficient of resistivity from Table 25.2.

EXECUTE: From Table 25.2, $\alpha = 0.00393$ (C°)$^{-1}$ for copper. Then from Eq. (25.12),

$$R = R_0[1 + \alpha(T - T_0)]$$
$$= (1.05 \text{ Ω})\{1 + [0.00393 \text{ (C°)}^{-1}][0°C - 20°C]\}$$
$$= 0.97 \text{ Ω at } T = 0°C$$

$$R = (1.05 \text{ Ω})\{1 + [0.00393 \text{ (C°)}^{-1}][100°C - 20°C]\}$$
$$= 1.38 \text{ Ω at } T = 100°C$$

EVALUATE: The resistance at 100°C is greater than that at 0°C by a factor of (1.38 Ω)/(0.97 Ω) = 1.42: Raising the temperature of copper wire from 0°C to 100°C increases its resistance by 42%. From Eq. (25.11), $V = IR$, this means that 42% more voltage is required to produce the same current at 100°C than at 0°C. Designers of electric circuits that must operate over a wide temperature range must take this substantial effect into account.

Test Your Understanding of Section 25.3 Suppose you increase the voltage across the copper wire in Examples 25.2 and 25.3. The increased voltage causes more current to flow, which makes the temperature of the wire increase. (The same thing happens to the coils of an electric oven or a toaster when a voltage is applied to them. We'll explore this issue in more depth in Section 25.5.) If you double the voltage across the wire, the current in the wire increases. By what factor does it increase? (i) 2; (ii) greater than 2; (iii) less than 2. ❙

25.4 Electromotive Force and Circuits

25.11 If an electric field is produced inside a conductor that is *not* part of a complete circuit, current flows for only a very short time.

(a) An electric field E_1 produced inside an isolated conductor causes a current.

(b) The current causes charge to build up at the ends.

The charge buildup produces an opposing field $\vec{E}_2$, thus reducing the current.

(c) After a very short time $\vec{E}_2$ has the same magnitude as $\vec{E}_1$; then the total field is $\vec{E}_{\text{total}} = 0$ and the current stops completely.

For a conductor to have a steady current, it must be part of a path that forms a closed loop or **complete circuit.** Here's why. If you establish an electric field $\vec{E}_1$ inside an isolated conductor with resistivity ρ that is *not* part of a complete circuit, a current begins to flow with current density $\vec{J} = \vec{E}_1/\rho$ (Fig. 25.11a). As a result a net positive charge quickly accumulates at one end of the conductor and a net negative charge accumulates at the other end (Fig. 25.11b). These charges themselves produce an electric field $\vec{E}_2$ in the direction opposite to $\vec{E}_1$, causing the total electric field and hence the current to decrease. Within a very small fraction of a second, enough charge builds up on the conductor ends that the total electric field $\vec{E} = \vec{E}_1 + \vec{E}_2 = 0$ inside the conductor. Then $\vec{J} = 0$ as well, and the current stops altogether (Fig. 25.11c). So there can be no steady motion of charge in such an *incomplete* circuit.

To see how to maintain a steady current in a *complete* circuit, we recall a basic fact about electric potential energy: If a charge q goes around a complete circuit and returns to its starting point, the potential energy must be the same at the end of the round trip as at the beginning. As described in Section 25.3, there is always a *decrease* in potential energy when charges move through an ordinary conducting material with resistance. So there must be some part of the circuit in which the potential energy *increases.*

The problem is analogous to an ornamental water fountain that recycles its water. The water pours out of openings at the top, cascades down over the terraces and spouts (moving in the direction of decreasing gravitational potential energy), and collects in a basin in the bottom. A pump then lifts it back to the top (increasing the potential energy) for another trip. Without the pump, the water would just fall to the bottom and stay there.

Electromotive Force

In an electric circuit there must be a device somewhere in the loop that acts like the water pump in a water fountain (Fig. 25.12). In this device a charge travels "uphill," from lower to higher potential energy, even though the electrostatic force is trying to push it from higher to lower potential energy. The direction of current in such a device is from lower to higher potential, just the opposite of what happens in an ordinary conductor. The influence that makes current flow from lower to higher potential is called **electromotive force** (abbreviated **emf** and pronounced "ee-em-eff"). This is a poor term because emf is *not* a force but an energy-per-unit-charge quantity, like potential. The SI unit of emf is the same as that for potential, the volt ($1\ \text{V} = 1\ \text{J/C}$). A typical flashlight battery has an emf of 1.5 V; this means that the battery does 1.5 J of work on every coulomb of charge that passes through it. We'll use the symbol $\mathcal{E}$ (a script capital E) for emf.

Every complete circuit with a steady current must include some device that provides emf. Such a device is called a **source of emf.** Batteries, electric genera-tors, solar cells, thermocouples, and fuel cells are all examples of sources of emf. All such devices convert energy of some form (mechanical, chemical, thermal, and so on) into electric potential energy and transfer it into the circuit to which the device is connected. An *ideal* source of emf maintains a constant potential difference between its terminals, independent of the current through it. We define electromotive force quantitatively as the magnitude of this potential difference. As we will see, such an ideal source is a mythical beast, like the frictionless plane and the massless rope. We will discuss later how real-life sources of emf differ in their behavior from this idealized model.

Figure 25.13 is a schematic diagram of an ideal source of emf that maintains a potential difference between conductors a and b, called the *terminals* of the device. Terminal a, marked $+$, is maintained at *higher* potential than terminal b, marked $-$. Associated with this potential difference is an electric field $\vec{E}$ in the region around the terminals, both inside and outside the source. The electric field inside the device is directed from a to b, as shown. A charge q within the source experiences an electric force $\vec{F}_e = q\vec{E}$. But the source also provides an additional influence, which we represent as a nonelectrostatic force $\vec{F}_n$. This force, oper-ating inside the device, pushes charge from b to a in an "uphill" direction against the electric force $\vec{F}_e$. Thus $\vec{F}_n$ maintains the potential difference between the ter-minals. If $\vec{F}_n$ were not present, charge would flow between the terminals until the potential difference was zero. The origin of the additional influence $\vec{F}_n$ depends on the kind of source. In a generator it results from magnetic-field forces on mov-ing charges. In a battery or fuel cell it is associated with diffusion processes and varying electrolyte concentrations resulting from chemical reactions. In an elec-trostatic machine such as a Van de Graaff generator (see Fig. 22.26), an actual mechanical force is applied by a moving belt or wheel.

If a positive charge q is moved from b to a inside the source, the nonelectro-static force $\vec{F}_n$ does a positive amount of work $W_n = q\mathcal{E}$ on the charge. This dis-placement is *opposite* to the electrostatic force $\vec{F}_e$, so the potential energy associated with the charge *increases* by an amount equal to qV_{ab}, where $V_{ab} = V_a - V_b$ is the (positive) potential of point a with respect to point b. For the ideal source of emf that we've described, $\vec{F}_e$ and $\vec{F}_n$ are equal in magnitude but opposite in direction, so the total work done on the charge q is zero; there is an increase in potential energy but *no* change in the kinetic energy of the charge. It's like lifting a book from the floor to a high shelf at constant speed. The increase in potential energy is just equal to the nonelectrostatic work W_n, so $q\mathcal{E} = qV_{ab}$, or

$$V_{ab} = \mathcal{E} \qquad \text{(ideal source of emf)} \qquad (25.13)$$

Now let's make a complete circuit by connecting a wire with resistance R to the terminals of a source (Fig. 25.14). The potential difference between terminals a and b sets up an electric field within the wire; this causes current to flow around the loop from a toward b, from higher to lower potential. Where the wire bends, equal amounts of positive and negative charge persist on the "inside" and "outside"

25.12 Just as a water fountain requires a pump, an electric circuit requires a source of electromotive force to sustain a steady current.

25.13 Schematic diagram of a source of emf in an "open-circuit" situation. The electric-field force $\vec{F}_e = q\vec{E}$ and the nonelectrostatic force $\vec{F}_n$ are shown for a positive charge q.

When the emf source is not part of a closed circuit, $F_n = F_e$ and there is no net motion of charge between the terminals.

25.14 Schematic diagram of an ideal source of emf in a complete circuit. The electric-field force $\vec{F}_e = q\vec{E}$ and the non-electrostatic force $\vec{F}_n$ are shown for a positive charge q. The current is in the direction from a to b in the external circuit and from b to a within the source.

Potential across terminals creates electric field in circuit, causing charges to move.

Ideal emf source

V_a

$+ \, a$

$\vec{E}$

I

$V_{ab} = \mathcal{E}$ $\vec{E}$

$\vec{F}_n$

$\vec{F}_e$

$\vec{E}$ I

V_b

$- \, b$

$\vec{E}$

I

When a real (as opposed to ideal) emf source is connected to a circuit, V_{ab} and thus $\vec{F}_e$ fall, so that $F_n > F_e$ and $\vec{F}_n$ does work on the charges.

Application Danger: Electric Ray!
Electric rays deliver electric shocks to stun their prey and to discourage predators. (In ancient Rome, physicians practiced a primitive form of electroconvulsive therapy by placing electric rays on their patients to cure headaches and gout.) The shocks are produced by specialized flattened cells called electroplaques. Such a cell moves ions across membranes to produce an emf of about 0.05 V. Thousands of electroplaques are stacked on top of each other, so their emfs add to a total of as much as 200 V. These stacks make up more than half of an electric ray's body mass. A ray can use these to deliver an impressive current of up to 30 A for a few milliseconds.

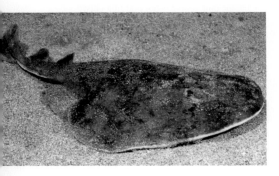

of the bend. These charges exert the forces that cause the current to follow the bends in the wire.

From Eq. (25.11) the potential difference between the ends of the wire in Fig. 25.14 is given by $V_{ab} = IR$. Combining with Eq. (25.13), we have

$$\mathcal{E} = V_{ab} = IR \qquad \text{(ideal source of emf)} \qquad (25.14)$$

That is, when a positive charge q flows around the circuit, the potential *rise* $\mathcal{E}$ as it passes through the ideal source is numerically equal to the potential *drop* $V_{ab} = IR$ as it passes through the remainder of the circuit. Once $\mathcal{E}$ and R are known, this relationship determines the current in the circuit.

CAUTION **Current is not "used up" in a circuit** It's a common misconception that in a closed circuit, current is something that squirts out of the positive terminal of a battery and is consumed or "used up" by the time it reaches the negative terminal. In fact the current is the *same* at every point in a simple loop circuit like that in Fig. 25.14, even if the thickness of the wires is different at different points in the circuit. This happens because charge is conserved (that is, it can be neither created nor destroyed) and because charge cannot accumulate in the circuit devices we have described. If charge did accumulate, the potential differences would change with time. It's like the flow of water in an ornamental fountain; water flows out of the top of the fountain at the same rate at which it reaches the bottom, no matter what the dimensions of the fountain. None of the water is "used up" along the way!

Internal Resistance

Real sources of emf in a circuit don't behave in exactly the way we have described; the potential difference across a real source in a circuit is *not* equal to the emf as in Eq. (25.14). The reason is that charge moving through the material of any real source encounters *resistance*. We call this the **internal resistance** of the source, denoted by r. If this resistance behaves according to Ohm's law, r is constant and independent of the current I. As the current moves through r, it experiences an associated drop in potential equal to Ir. Thus, when a current is flowing through a source from the negative terminal b to the positive terminal a, the potential difference V_{ab} between the terminals is

$$V_{ab} = \mathcal{E} - Ir \qquad \begin{array}{l}\text{(terminal voltage, source} \\ \text{with internal resistance)}\end{array} \qquad (25.15)$$

The potential V_{ab}, called the **terminal voltage,** is less than the emf $\mathcal{E}$ because of the term Ir representing the potential drop across the internal resistance r. Expressed another way, the increase in potential energy qV_{ab} as a charge q moves from b to a within the source is now less than the work $q\mathcal{E}$ done by the nonelectrostatic force $\vec{F}_n$, since some potential energy is lost in traversing the internal resistance.

A 1.5-V battery has an emf of 1.5 V, but the terminal voltage V_{ab} of the battery is equal to 1.5 V only if no current is flowing through it so that $I = 0$ in Eq. (25.15). If the battery is part of a complete circuit through which current is flowing, the terminal voltage will be less than 1.5 V. *For a real source of emf, the terminal voltage equals the emf only if no current is flowing through the source* (Fig. 25.15). Thus we can describe the behavior of a source in terms of two properties: an emf $\mathcal{E}$, which supplies a constant potential difference independent of current, in series with an internal resistance r.

The current in the external circuit connected to the source terminals a and b is still determined by $V_{ab} = IR$. Combining this with Eq. (25.15), we find

$$\mathcal{E} - Ir = IR \quad \text{or} \quad I = \frac{\mathcal{E}}{R + r} \qquad \begin{array}{l}\text{(current, source with} \\ \text{internal resistance)}\end{array} \qquad (25.16)$$

That is, the current equals the source emf divided by the *total* circuit resistance $(R + r)$.

> **CAUTION** **A battery is not a "current source"** You might have thought that a battery or other source of emf always produces the same current, no matter what circuit it's used in. Equation (25.16) shows that this isn't so! The greater the resistance R of the external circuit, the less current the source will produce. It's analogous to pushing an object through a thick, viscous liquid such as oil or molasses; if you exert a certain steady push (emf), you can move a small object at high speed (small R, large I) or a large object at low speed (large R, small I).

Symbols for Circuit Diagrams

An important part of analyzing any electric circuit is drawing a schematic *circuit diagram.* Table 25.4 shows the usual symbols used in circuit diagrams. We will use these symbols extensively in this chapter and the next. We usually assume that the wires that connect the various elements of the circuit have negligible resistance; from Eq. (25.11), $V = IR$, the potential difference between the ends of such a wire is zero.

Table 25.4 includes two *meters* that are used to measure the properties of circuits. Idealized meters do not disturb the circuit in which they are connected. A **voltmeter,** introduced in Section 23.2, measures the potential difference between its terminals; an idealized voltmeter has infinitely large resistance and measures potential difference without having any current diverted through it. An ammeter measures the current passing through it; an idealized **ammeter** has zero resistance and has no potential difference between its terminals. Because meters act as part of the circuit in which they are connected, these properties are important to remember.

25.15 The emf of this battery—that is, the terminal voltage when it's not connected to anything—is 12 V. But because the battery has internal resistance, the terminal voltage of the battery is less than 12 V when it is supplying current to a light bulb.

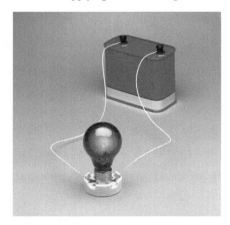

Table 25.4 Symbols for Circuit Diagrams

	Conductor with negligible resistance
R (resistor symbol)	Resistor
$+$ ǁ $\mathcal{E}$	Source of emf (longer vertical line always represents the positive terminal, usually the terminal with higher potential)
$\mathcal{E}$ $+$ / or $+$ $\mathcal{E}$	Source of emf with internal resistance r (r can be placed on either side)
V	Voltmeter (measures potential difference between its terminals)
A	Ammeter (measures current through it)

Conceptual Example 25.4 **A source in an open circuit**

Figure 25.16 shows a source (a battery) with emf $\mathcal{E} = 12$ V and internal resistance $r = 2\ \Omega$. (For comparison, the internal resistance of a commercial 12-V lead storage battery is only a few thousandths of an ohm.) The wires to the left of a and to the right of the ammeter A are not connected to anything. Determine the respective readings V_{ab} and I of the idealized voltmeter V and the idealized ammeter A.

25.16 A source of emf in an open circuit.

$r = 2\ \Omega, \mathcal{E} = 12$ V

Continued

There is *zero* current because there is no complete circuit. (Our idealized voltmeter has an infinitely large resistance, so no current flows through it.) Hence the ammeter reads $I = 0$. Because there is no current through the battery, there is no potential difference across

its internal resistance. From Eq. (25.15) with $I = 0$, the potential difference V_{ab} across the battery terminals is equal to the emf. So the voltmeter reads $V_{ab} = \mathcal{E} = 12$ V. The terminal voltage of a real, nonideal source equals the emf *only* if there is no current flowing through the source, as in this example.

Example 25.5 A source in a complete circuit

We add a 4-Ω resistor to the battery in Conceptual Example 25.4, forming a complete circuit (Fig. 25.17). What are the voltmeter and ammeter readings V_{ab} and I now?

SOLUTION

IDENTIFY and SET UP: Our target variables are the current I through the circuit $aa'b'b$ and the potential difference V_{ab}. We first find I using Eq. (25.16). To find V_{ab}, we can use either Eq. (25.11) or Eq. (25.15).

25.17 A source of emf in a complete circuit.

EXECUTE: The ideal ammeter has zero resistance, so the total resistance external to the source is $R = 4 \ \Omega$. From Eq. (25.16), the current through the circuit $aa'b'b$ is then

$$I = \frac{\mathcal{E}}{R + r} = \frac{12 \ \text{V}}{4 \ \Omega + 2 \ \Omega} = 2 \ \text{A}$$

Our idealized conducting wires and the idealized ammeter have zero resistance, so there is no potential difference between points a and a' or between points b and b'; that is, $V_{ab} = V_{a'b'}$. We find V_{ab} by considering a and b as the terminals of the resistor: From Ohm's law, Eq. (25.11), we then have

$$V_{a'b'} = IR = (2 \ \text{A})(4 \ \Omega) = 8 \ \text{V}$$

Alternatively, we can consider a and b as the terminals of the source. Then, from Eq. (25.15),

$$V_{ab} = \mathcal{E} - Ir = 12 \ \text{V} - (2 \ \text{A})(2 \ \Omega) = 8 \ \text{V}$$

Either way, we see that the voltmeter reading is 8 V.

EVALUATE: With current flowing through the source, the terminal voltage V_{ab} is less than the emf $\mathcal{E}$. The smaller the internal resistance r, the less the difference between V_{ab} and $\mathcal{E}$.

Conceptual Example 25.6 Using voltmeters and ammeters

We move the voltmeter and ammeter in Example 25.5 to different positions in the circuit. What are the readings of the ideal voltmeter and ammeter in the situations shown in (a) Fig. 25.18a and (b) Fig. 25.18b?

SOLUTION

(a) The voltmeter now measures the potential difference between points a' and b'. As in Example 25.5, $V_{ab} = V_{a'b'}$, so the voltmeter reads the same as in Example 25.5: $V_{a'b'} = 8$ V.

25.18 Different placements of a voltmeter and an ammeter in a complete circuit.

(a)   (b)

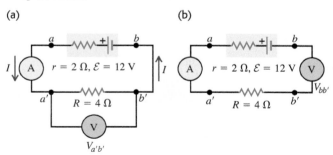

CAUTION **Current in a simple loop** As charges move through a resistor, there is a decrease in electric potential energy, but there is *no* change in the current. *The current in a simple loop is the same at every point;* it is not "used up" as it moves through a resistor. Hence the ammeter in Fig. 25.17 ("downstream" of the 4-Ω resistor) and the ammeter in Fig. 25.18b ("upstream" of the resistor) both read $I = 2$ A.

(b) There is no current through the ideal voltmeter because it has infinitely large resistance. Since the voltmeter is now part of the circuit, there is no current at all in the circuit, and the ammeter reads $I = 0$.

The voltmeter measures the potential difference $V_{bb'}$ between points b and b'. Since $I = 0$, the potential difference across the resistor is $V_{a'b'} = IR = 0$, and the potential difference between the ends a and a' of the idealized ammeter is also zero. So $V_{bb'}$ is equal to V_{ab}, the terminal voltage of the source. As in Conceptual Example 25.4, there is no current, so the terminal voltage equals the emf, and the voltmeter reading is $V_{ab} = \mathcal{E} = 12$ V.

This example shows that ammeters and voltmeters are circuit elements, too. Moving the voltmeter from the position in Fig. 25.18a to that in Fig. 25.18b makes large changes in the current and potential differences in the circuit. If you want to measure the potential difference between two points in a circuit without disturbing the circuit, use a voltmeter as in Fig. 25.17 or 25.18a, *not* as in Fig. 25.18b.

Example 25.7   **A source with a short circuit**

In the circuit of Example 25.5 we replace the 4-Ω resistor with a zero-resistance conductor. What are the meter readings now?

SOLUTION

IDENTIFY and SET UP: Figure 25.19 shows the new circuit. Our target variables are again I and V_{ab}. There is now a zero-resistance path between points a and b, through the lower loop, so the potential difference between these points must be zero.

25.19 Our sketch for this problem.

EXECUTE: We must have $V_{ab} = IR = I(0) = 0$, no matter what the current. We can therefore find the current I from Eq. (25.15):

$$V_{ab} = \mathcal{E} - Ir = 0$$

$$I = \frac{\mathcal{E}}{r} = \frac{12 \text{ V}}{2 \text{ }\Omega} = 6 \text{ A}$$

EVALUATE: The current has a different value than in Example 25.5, even though the same battery is used; the current depends on both the internal resistance r and the resistance of the external circuit.

The situation here is called a *short circuit*. The external-circuit resistance is zero, because terminals of the battery are connected directly to each other. The short-circuit current is equal to the emf $\mathcal{E}$ divided by the internal resistance r. *Warning:* Short circuits can be dangerous! An automobile battery or a household power line has very small internal resistance (much less than in these examples), and the short-circuit current can be great enough to melt a small wire or cause a storage battery to explode.

Potential Changes Around a Circuit

The net change in potential energy for a charge q making a round trip around a complete circuit must be zero. Hence the net change in *potential* around the circuit must also be zero; in other words, the algebraic sum of the potential differences and emfs around the loop is zero. We can see this by rewriting Eq. (25.16) in the form

$$\mathcal{E} - Ir - IR = 0$$

A potential gain of $\mathcal{E}$ is associated with the emf, and potential drops of Ir and IR are associated with the internal resistance of the source and the external circuit, respectively. Figure 25.20 is a graph showing how the potential varies as we go around the complete circuit of Fig. 25.17. The horizontal axis doesn't necessarily represent actual distances, but rather various points in the loop. If we take the potential to be zero at the negative terminal of the battery, then we have a rise $\mathcal{E}$ and a drop Ir in the battery and an additional drop IR in the external resistor, and as we finish our trip around the loop, the potential is back where it started.

In this section we have considered only situations in which the resistances are ohmic. If the circuit includes a nonlinear device such as a diode (see Fig. 25.10b), Eq. (25.16) is still valid but cannot be solved algebraically because R is not a constant. In such a situation, the current I can be found by using numerical techniques.

Finally, we remark that Eq. (25.15) is not always an adequate representation of the behavior of a source. The emf may not be constant, and what we have described as an internal resistance may actually be a more complex voltage–current relationship that doesn't obey Ohm's law. Nevertheless, the concept of internal resistance frequently provides an adequate description of batteries, generators, and other energy converters. The principal difference between a fresh flashlight battery and an old one is not in the emf, which decreases only slightly with use, but in the internal resistance, which may increase from less than an ohm when the battery is fresh to as much as 1000 Ω or more after long use. Similarly, a car battery can deliver less current to the starter motor on a cold morning than when the battery is warm, not because the emf is appreciably less but because the internal resistance increases with decreasing temperature.

25.20 Potential rises and drops in a circuit.

25.5 Energy and Power in Electric Circuits

25.21 The power input to the circuit element between a and b is $P = (V_a - V_b)I = V_{ab}I$.

MasteringPHYSICS

PhET: Battery-Resistor Circuit
PhET: Circuit Construction Kit (AC+DC)
PhET: Circuit Construction Kit (DC Only)
PhET: Ohm's Law

Let's now look at some energy and power relationships in electric circuits. The box in Fig. 25.21 represents a circuit element with potential difference $V_a - V_b = V_{ab}$ between its terminals and current I passing through it in the direction from a toward b. This element might be a resistor, a battery, or something else; the details don't matter. As charge passes through the circuit element, the electric field does work on the charge. In a source of emf, additional work is done by the force $\vec{F}_n$ that we mentioned in Section 25.4.

As an amount of charge q passes through the circuit element, there is a change in potential energy equal to qV_{ab}. For example, if $q > 0$ and $V_{ab} = V_a - V_b$ is positive, potential energy decreases as the charge "falls" from potential V_a to lower potential V_b. The moving charges don't gain *kinetic* energy, because the current (the rate of charge flow) out of the circuit element must be the same as the current into the element. Instead, the quantity qV_{ab} represents energy transferred into the circuit element. This situation occurs in the coils of a toaster or electric oven, in which electrical energy is converted to thermal energy.

If the potential at a is lower than at b, then V_{ab} is negative and there is a net transfer of energy *out* of the circuit element. The element then acts as a source, delivering electrical energy into the circuit to which it is attached. This is the usual situation for a battery, which converts chemical energy into electrical energy and delivers it to the external circuit. Thus qV_{ab} can denote either a quantity of energy delivered to a circuit element or a quantity of energy extracted from that element.

In electric circuits we are most often interested in the *rate* at which energy is either delivered to or extracted from a circuit element. If the current through the element is I, then in a time interval dt an amount of charge $dQ = I\, dt$ passes through the element. The potential energy change for this amount of charge is $V_{ab}\, dQ = V_{ab}I\, dt$. Dividing this expression by dt, we obtain the *rate* at which energy is transferred either into or out of the circuit element. The time rate of energy transfer is *power*, denoted by P, so we write

$$P = V_{ab}I \qquad \begin{array}{l}\text{(rate at which energy is delivered to}\\ \text{or extracted from a circuit element)}\end{array} \qquad (25.17)$$

The unit of V_{ab} is one volt, or one joule per coulomb, and the unit of I is one ampere, or one coulomb per second. Hence the unit of $P = V_{ab}I$ is one watt, as it should be:

$$(1 \text{ J/C})(1 \text{ C/s}) = 1 \text{ J/s} = 1 \text{ W}$$

Let's consider a few special cases.

Power Input to a Pure Resistance

If the circuit element in Fig. 25.21 is a resistor, the potential difference is $V_{ab} = IR$. From Eq. (25.17) the electrical power delivered to the resistor by the circuit is

$$P = V_{ab}I = I^2R = \frac{V_{ab}^2}{R} \qquad \text{(power delivered to a resistor)} \qquad (25.18)$$

In this case the potential at *a* (where the current enters the resistor) is always higher than that at *b* (where the current exits). Current enters the higher-potential terminal of the device, and Eq. (25.18) represents the rate of transfer of electric potential energy *into* the circuit element.

What becomes of this energy? The moving charges collide with atoms in the resistor and transfer some of their energy to these atoms, increasing the internal energy of the material. Either the temperature of the resistor increases or there is a flow of heat out of it, or both. In any of these cases we say that energy is *dissipated* in the resistor at a rate I^2R. Every resistor has a *power rating,* the maximum power the device can dissipate without becoming overheated and damaged. Some devices, such as electric heaters, are designed to get hot and transfer heat to their surroundings. But if the power rating is exceeded, even such a device may melt or even explode.

Power Output of a Source

The upper rectangle in Fig. 25.22a represents a source with emf $\mathcal{E}$ and internal resistance *r*, connected by ideal (resistanceless) conductors to an external circuit represented by the lower box. This could describe a car battery connected to one of the car's headlights (Fig. 25.22b). Point *a* is at higher potential than point *b*, so $V_a > V_b$ and V_{ab} is positive. Note that the current *I* is *leaving* the source at the higher-potential terminal (rather than entering there). Energy is being delivered to the external circuit, at a rate given by Eq. (25.17):

$$P = V_{ab}I$$

For a source that can be described by an emf $\mathcal{E}$ and an internal resistance *r*, we may use Eq. (25.15):

$$V_{ab} = \mathcal{E} - Ir$$

Multiplying this equation by *I*, we find

$$P = V_{ab}I = \mathcal{E}I - I^2r \qquad (25.19)$$

What do the terms $\mathcal{E}I$ and I^2r mean? In Section 25.4 we defined the emf $\mathcal{E}$ as the work per unit charge performed on the charges by the nonelectrostatic force as the charges are pushed "uphill" from *b* to *a* in the source. In a time *dt*, a charge $dQ = I\,dt$ flows through the source; the work done on it by this nonelectrostatic force is $\mathcal{E}\,dQ = \mathcal{E}I\,dt$. Thus $\mathcal{E}I$ is the *rate* at which work is done on the circulating charges by whatever agency causes the nonelectrostatic force in the source. This term represents the rate of conversion of nonelectrical energy to electrical energy within the source. The term I^2r is the rate at which electrical energy is *dissipated* in the internal resistance of the source. The difference $\mathcal{E}I - I^2r$ is the *net* electrical power output of the source—that is, the rate at which the source delivers electrical energy to the remainder of the circuit.

Power Input to a Source

Suppose that the lower rectangle in Fig. 25.22a is itself a source, with an emf *larger* than that of the upper source and with its emf opposite to that of the upper source. Figure 25.23 shows a practical example, an automobile battery (the upper circuit element) being charged by the car's alternator (the lower element). The current *I* in the circuit is then *opposite* to that shown in Fig. 25.22; the lower source is pushing current backward through the upper source. Because of this reversal of current, instead of Eq. (25.15) we have for the upper source

$$V_{ab} = \mathcal{E} + Ir$$

and instead of Eq. (25.19), we have

$$P = V_{ab}I = \mathcal{E}I + I^2r \qquad (25.20)$$

25.22 Energy conversion in a simple circuit.

(a) Diagrammatic circuit

- The emf source converts nonelectrical to electrical energy at a rate $\mathcal{E}I$.
- Its internal resistance *dissipates* energy at a rate I^2r.
- The difference $\mathcal{E}I - I^2r$ is its power output.

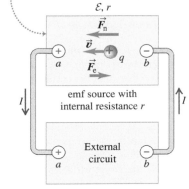

(b) A real circuit of the type shown in (a)

25.23 When two sources are connected in a simple loop circuit, the source with the larger emf delivers energy to the other source.

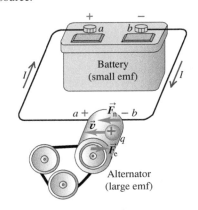

Work is being done *on,* rather than *by,* the agent that causes the nonelectrostatic force in the upper source. There is a conversion of electrical energy into nonelectrical energy in the upper source at a rate $\mathcal{E}I$. The term I^2r in Eq. (25.20) is again the rate of dissipation of energy in the internal resistance of the upper source, and the sum $\mathcal{E}I + I^2r$ is the total electrical power *input* to the upper source. This is what happens when a rechargeable battery (a storage battery) is connected to a charger. The charger supplies electrical energy to the battery; part of it is converted to chemical energy, to be reconverted later, and the remainder is dissipated (wasted) in the battery's internal resistance, warming the battery and causing a heat flow out of it. If you have a power tool or laptop computer with a rechargeable battery, you may have noticed that it gets warm while it is charging.

| **Problem-Solving Strategy 25.1** | **Power and Energy in Circuits** | |

IDENTIFY *the relevant concepts:* The ideas of electric power input and output can be applied to any electric circuit. Many problems will ask you to explicitly consider power or energy.

SET UP *the problem* using the following steps:
1. Make a drawing of the circuit.
2. Identify the circuit elements, including sources of emf and resistors. We will introduce other circuit elements later, including capacitors (Chapter 26) and inductors (Chapter 30).
3. Identify the target variables. Typically they will be the power input or output for each circuit element, or the total amount of energy put into or taken out of a circuit element in a given time.

EXECUTE *the solution* as follows:
1. A source of emf $\mathcal{E}$ delivers power $\mathcal{E}I$ into a circuit when current I flows through the source in the direction from − to +. (For example, energy is converted from chemical energy in a battery, or from mechanical energy in a generator.) In this case there is a *positive* power output to the circuit or, equivalently, a *negative* power input to the source.
2. A source of emf takes power $\mathcal{E}I$ from a circuit when current passes through the source from + to −. (This occurs in charging a storage battery, when electrical energy is converted to chemical energy.) In this case there is a *negative* power output

to the circuit or, equivalently, a *positive* power input to the source.
3. There is always a *positive* power input to a resistor through which current flows, irrespective of the direction of current flow. This process removes energy from the circuit, converting it to heat at the rate $VI = I^2R = V^2/R$, where V is the potential difference across the resistor.
4. Just as in item 3, there always is a positive power input to the internal resistance r of a source through which current flows, irrespective of the direction of current flow. This process likewise removes energy from the circuit, converting it into heat at the rate I^2r.
5. If the power into or out of a circuit element is constant, the energy delivered to or extracted from that element is the product of power and elapsed time. (In Chapter 26 we will encounter situations in which the power is not constant. In such cases, calculating the total energy requires an integral over the relevant time interval.)

EVALUATE *your answer:* Check your results; in particular, check that energy is conserved. This conservation can be expressed in either of two forms: "net power input = net power output" or "the algebraic sum of the power inputs to the circuit elements is zero."

Example 25.8 Power input and output in a complete circuit

For the circuit that we analyzed in Example 25.5, find the rates of energy conversion (chemical to electrical) and energy dissipation in the battery, the rate of energy dissipation in the 4-Ω resistor, and the battery's net power output.

25.24 Our sketch for this problem.

SOLUTION

IDENTIFY and SET UP: Figure 25.24 shows the circuit, gives values of quantities known from Example 25.5, and indicates how we find the target variables. We use Eq. (25.19) to find the battery's net power output, the rate of chemical-to-electrical energy conversion, and the rate of energy dissipation in the battery's internal resistance. We use Eq. (25.18) to find the power delivered to (and dissipated in) the 4-Ω resistor.

EXECUTE: From the first term in Eq. (25.19), the rate of energy conversion in the battery is

$$\mathcal{E}I = (12 \text{ V})(2 \text{ A}) = 24 \text{ W}$$

From the second term in Eq. (25.19), the rate of dissipation of energy in the battery is

$$I^2r = (2 \text{ A})^2(2 \text{ }\Omega) = 8 \text{ W}$$

The *net* electrical power output of the battery is the difference between these: $\mathcal{E}I - I^2r = 16$ W. From Eq. (25.18), the electrical power input to, and the equal rate of dissipation of electrical energy in, the 4-Ω resistor are

$$V_{a'b'}I = (8 \text{ V})(2 \text{ A}) = 16 \text{ W} \quad \text{and}$$
$$I^2R = (2 \text{ A})^2(4 \text{ } \Omega) = 16 \text{ W}$$

Example 25.9 Increasing the resistance

Suppose we replace the external 4-Ω resistor in Fig. 25.24 with an 8-Ω resistor. How does this affect the electrical power dissipated in this resistor?

SOLUTION

IDENTIFY and SET UP: Our target variable is the power dissipated in the resistor to which the battery is connected. The situation is the same as in Example 25.8, but with a higher external resistance R.

EXECUTE: According to Eq. (25.18), the power dissipated in the resistor is $P = I^2R$. You might conclude that making the resistance R twice as great as in Example 25.8 should also make the power twice as great, or $2(16 \text{ W}) = 32$ W. If instead you used the formula $P = V_{ab}^2/R$, you might conclude that the power should be one-half as great as in the preceding example, or $(16 \text{ W})/2 = 8$ W. Which answer is correct?

In fact, *both* of these answers are *incorrect*. The first is wrong because changing the resistance R also changes the current in the circuit (remember, a source of emf does *not* generate the same current in all situations). The second answer is wrong because the potential difference V_{ab} across the resistor changes when the current changes. To get the correct answer, we first find the current just as we did in Example 25.5:

$$I = \frac{\mathcal{E}}{R + r} = \frac{12 \text{ V}}{8 \text{ } \Omega + 2 \text{ } \Omega} = 1.2 \text{ A}$$

EVALUATE: The rate $V_{a'b'}I$ at which energy is supplied to the 4-Ω resistor equals the rate I^2R at which energy is dissipated there. This is also equal to the battery's net power output: $P = V_{ab}I = (8 \text{ V})(2 \text{ A}) = 16$ W. In summary, the rate at which the source of emf supplies energy is $\mathcal{E}I = 24$ W, of which $I^2r = 8$ W is dissipated in the battery's internal resistor and $I^2R = 16$ W is dissipated in the external resistor.

The greater resistance causes the current to decrease. The potential difference across the resistor is

$$V_{ab} = IR = (1.2 \text{ A})(8 \text{ } \Omega) = 9.6 \text{ V}$$

which is greater than that with the 4-Ω resistor. We can then find the power dissipated in the resistor in either of two ways:

$$P = I^2R = (1.2 \text{ A})^2(8 \text{ } \Omega) = 12 \text{ W} \quad \text{or}$$
$$P = \frac{V_{ab}^2}{R} = \frac{(9.6 \text{ V})^2}{8 \text{ } \Omega} = 12 \text{ W}$$

EVALUATE: Increasing the resistance R causes a *reduction* in the power input to the resistor. In the expression $P = I^2R$ the decrease in current is more important than the increase in resistance; in the expression $P = V_{ab}^2/R$ the increase in resistance is more important than the increase in V_{ab}. This same principle applies to ordinary light bulbs; a 50-W light bulb has a greater resistance than does a 100-W light bulb.

Can you show that replacing the 4-Ω resistor with an 8-Ω resistor decreases both the rate of energy conversion (chemical to electrical) in the battery and the rate of energy dissipation in the battery?

Example 25.10 Power in a short circuit

For the short-circuit situation of Example 25.7, find the rates of energy conversion and energy dissipation in the battery and the net power output of the battery.

SOLUTION

IDENTIFY and SET UP: Our target variables are again the power inputs and outputs associated with the battery. Figure 25.25 shows

25.25 Our sketch for this problem.

the circuit. This is the same situation as in Example 25.8, but now the external resistance R is zero.

EXECUTE: We found in Example 25.7 that the current in this situation is $I = 6$ A. From Eq. (25.19), the rate of energy conversion (chemical to electrical) in the battery is then

$$\mathcal{E}I = (12 \text{ V})(6 \text{ A}) = 72 \text{ W}$$

and the rate of dissipation of energy in the battery is

$$I^2r = (6 \text{ A})^2(2 \text{ } \Omega) = 72 \text{ W}$$

The net power output of the source is $\mathcal{E}I - I^2r = 0$. We get this same result from the expression $P = V_{ab}I$, because the terminal voltage V_{ab} of the source is zero.

EVALUATE: With ideal wires and an ideal ammeter, so that $R = 0$, *all* of the converted energy from the source is dissipated within the source. This is why a short-circuited battery is quickly ruined and may explode.

Test Your Understanding of Section 25.5 Rank the following circuits in order from highest to lowest values of the net power output of the battery. (i) a 1.4-Ω resistor connected to a 1.5-V battery that has an internal resistance of 0.10 Ω; (ii) a 1.8-Ω resistor connected to a 4.0-V battery that has a terminal voltage of 3.6 V but an unknown internal resistance; (iii) an unknown resistor connected to a 12.0-V battery that has an internal resistance of 0.20 Ω and a terminal voltage of 11.0 V. ∎

25.6 Theory of Metallic Conduction

We can gain additional insight into electrical conduction by looking at the microscopic origin of conductivity. We'll consider a very simple model that treats the electrons as classical particles and ignores their quantum-mechanical behavior in solids. Using this model, we'll derive an expression for the resistivity of a metal. Even though this model is not entirely correct, it will still help you to develop an intuitive idea of the microscopic basis of conduction.

In the simplest microscopic model of conduction in a metal, each atom in the metallic crystal gives up one or more of its outer electrons. These electrons are then free to move through the crystal, colliding at intervals with the stationary positive ions. The motion of the electrons is analogous to the motion of molecules of a gas moving through a porous bed of sand.

If there is no electric field, the electrons move in straight lines between collisions, the directions of their velocities are random, and on average they never get anywhere (Fig. 25.26a). But if an electric field is present, the paths curve slightly because of the acceleration caused by electric-field forces. Figure 25.26b shows a few paths of an electron in an electric field directed from right to left. As we mentioned in Section 25.1, the average speed of random motion is of the order of 10^6 m/s, while the average drift speed is *much* slower, of the order of 10^{-4} m/s. The average time between collisions is called the **mean free time,** denoted by τ. Figure 25.27 shows a mechanical analog of this electron motion.

We would like to derive from this model an expression for the resistivity ρ of a material, defined by Eq. (25.5):

$$\rho = \frac{E}{J} \tag{25.21}$$

where E and J are the magnitudes of electric field and current density, respectively. The current density $\vec{J}$ is in turn given by Eq. (25.4):

$$\vec{J} = nq\vec{v}_d \tag{25.22}$$

where n is the number of free electrons per unit volume, $q = -e$ is the charge of each, and $\vec{v}_d$ is their average drift velocity.

We need to relate the drift velocity $\vec{v}_d$ to the electric field $\vec{E}$. The value of $\vec{v}_d$ is determined by a steady-state condition in which, on average, the velocity *gains* of the charges due to the force of the $\vec{E}$ field are just balanced by the velocity *losses* due to collisions. To clarify this process, let's imagine turning on the two effects one at a time. Suppose that before time $t = 0$ there is no field. The electron motion is then completely random. A typical electron has velocity $\vec{v}_0$ at time $t = 0$, and the value of $\vec{v}_0$ averaged over many electrons (that is, the initial velocity of an average electron) is zero: $(\vec{v}_0)_{av} = 0$. Then at time $t = 0$ we turn on a constant electric field $\vec{E}$. The field exerts a force $\vec{F} = q\vec{E}$ on each charge, and this causes an acceleration $\vec{a}$ in the direction of the force, given by

$$\vec{a} = \frac{\vec{F}}{m} = \frac{q\vec{E}}{m}$$

where m is the electron mass. *Every* electron has this acceleration.

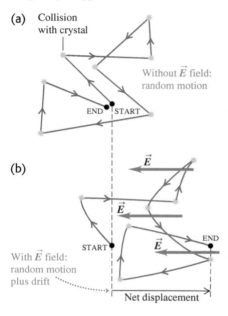

25.26 Random motions of an electron in a metallic crystal (a) with zero electric field and (b) with an electric field that causes drift. The curvatures of the paths are greatly exaggerated.

(a) Collision with crystal

Without $\vec{E}$ field: random motion

END START

(b)

$\vec{E}$

$\vec{E}$

START $\vec{E}$ END

With $\vec{E}$ field: random motion plus drift

Net displacement

Mastering**PHYSICS**

PhET: Conductivity

25.27 The motion of a ball rolling down an inclined plane and bouncing off pegs in its path is analogous to the motion of an electron in a metallic conductor with an electric field present.

Q25.13 Why does an electric light bulb nearly always burn out just as you turn on the light, almost never while the light is shining?

Q25.14 A light bulb glows because it has resistance. The brightness of a light bulb increases with the electrical power dissipated in the bulb. (a) In the circuit shown in Fig. Q25.14a, the two bulbs A and B are identical. Compared to bulb A, does bulb B glow more brightly, just as brightly, or less brightly? Explain your reasoning. (b) Bulb B is removed from the circuit and the circuit is completed as shown in Fig. Q25.14b. Compared to the brightness of bulb A in Fig. Q25.14a, does bulb A now glow more brightly, just as brightly, or less brightly? Explain your reasoning.

Figure **Q25.14**

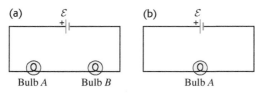

Q25.15 (See Discussion Question Q25.14.) An ideal ammeter A is placed in a circuit with a battery and a light bulb as shown in Fig. Q25.15a, and the ammeter reading is noted. The circuit is then reconnected as in Fig. Q25.15b, so that the positions of the ammeter and light bulb are reversed. (a) How does the ammeter reading in the situation shown in Fig. Q25.15a compare to the reading in the situation shown in Fig. Q25.15b? Explain your reasoning. (b) In which situation does the light bulb glow more brightly? Explain your reasoning.

Figure **Q25.15**

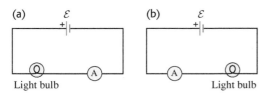

Q25.16 (See Discussion Question Q25.14.) Will a light bulb glow more brightly when it is connected to a battery as shown in Fig. Q25.16a, in which an ideal ammeter A is placed in the circuit, or when it is connected as shown in Fig. 25.16b, in which an ideal voltmeter V is placed in the circuit? Explain your reasoning.

Figure **Q25.16**

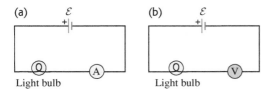

Q25.17 The energy that can be extracted from a storage battery is always less than the energy that goes into it while it is being charged. Why?

Q25.18 Eight flashlight batteries in series have an emf of about 12 V, similar to that of a car battery. Could they be used to start a car with a dead battery? Why or why not?

Q25.19 Small aircraft often have 24-V electrical systems rather than the 12-V systems in automobiles, even though the electrical power requirements are roughly the same in both applications. The explanation given by aircraft designers is that a 24-V system weighs less than a 12-V system because thinner wires can be used. Explain why this is so.

Q25.20 Long-distance, electric-power, transmission lines always operate at very high voltage, sometimes as much as 750 kV. What are the advantages of such high voltages? What are the disadvantages?

Q25.21 Ordinary household electric lines in North America usually operate at 120 V. Why is this a desirable voltage, rather than a value considerably larger or smaller? On the other hand, automobiles usually have 12-V electrical systems. Why is this a desirable voltage?

Q25.22 A fuse is a device designed to break a circuit, usually by melting when the current exceeds a certain value. What characteristics should the material of the fuse have?

Q25.23 High-voltage power supplies are sometimes designed intentionally to have rather large internal resistance as a safety precaution. Why is such a power supply with a large internal resistance safer than a supply with the same voltage but lower internal resistance?

Q25.24 The text states that good thermal conductors are also good electrical conductors. If so, why don't the cords used to connect toasters, irons, and similar heat-producing appliances get hot by conduction of heat from the heating element?

EXERCISES

Section 25.1 Current

25.1 • **Lightning Strikes.** During lightning strikes from a cloud to the ground, currents as high as 25,000 A can occur and last for about 40 μs. How much charge is transferred from the cloud to the earth during such a strike?

25.2 • A silver wire 2.6 mm in diameter transfers a charge of 420 C in 80 min. Silver contains 5.8×10^{28} free electrons per cubic meter. (a) What is the current in the wire? (b) What is the magnitude of the drift velocity of the electrons in the wire?

25.3 • A 5.00-A current runs through a 12-gauge copper wire (diameter 2.05 mm) and through a light bulb. Copper has 8.5×10^{28} free electrons per cubic meter. (a) How many electrons pass through the light bulb each second? (b) What is the current density in the wire? (c) At what speed does a typical electron pass by any given point in the wire? (d) If you were to use wire of twice the diameter, which of the above answers would change? Would they increase or decrease?

25.4 • An 18-gauge copper wire (diameter 1.02 mm) carries a current with a current density of 1.50×10^6 A/m^2. The density of free electrons for copper is 8.5×10^{28} electrons per cubic meter. Calculate (a) the current in the wire and (b) the drift velocity of electrons in the wire.

25.5 •• Copper has 8.5×10^{28} free electrons per cubic meter. A 71.0-cm length of 12-gauge copper wire that is 2.05 mm in diameter carries 4.85 A of current. (a) How much time does it take for an electron to travel the length of the wire? (b) Repeat part (a) for 6-gauge copper wire (diameter 4.12 mm) of the same length that carries the same current. (c) Generally speaking, how does changing the diameter of a wire that carries a given amount of current affect the drift velocity of the electrons in the wire?

25.6 • Consider the 18-gauge wire in Example 25.1. How many atoms are in 1.00 m^3 of copper? With the density of free electrons given in the example, how many free electrons are there per copper atom?

25.7 • **CALC** The current in a wire varies with time according to the relationship $I = 55$ A $- (0.65$ A/s$^2)t^2$. (a) How many coulombs of charge pass a cross section of the wire in the time interval between $t = 0$ and $t = 8.0$ s? (b) What constant current would transport the same charge in the same time interval?

25.8 • Current passes through a solution of sodium chloride. In 1.00 s, 2.68×10^{16} Na$^+$ ions arrive at the negative electrode and 3.92×10^{16} Cl$^-$ ions arrive at the positive electrode. (a) What is the current passing between the electrodes? (b) What is the direction of the current?

25.9 • **BIO** **Transmission of Nerve Impulses.** Nerve cells transmit electric signals through their long tubular axons. These signals propagate due to a sudden rush of Na$^+$ ions, each with charge $+e$, into the axon. Measurements have revealed that typically about 5.6×10^{11} Na$^+$ ions enter each meter of the axon during a time of 10 ms. What is the current during this inflow of charge in a meter of axon?

Section 25.2 Resistivity and Section 25.3 Resistance

25.10 • (a) At room temperature what is the strength of the electric field in a 12-gauge copper wire (diameter 2.05 mm) that is needed to cause a 2.75-A current to flow? (b) What field would be needed if the wire were made of silver instead?

25.11 •• A 1.50-m cylindrical rod of diameter 0.500 cm is connected to a power supply that maintains a constant potential difference of 15.0 V across its ends, while an ammeter measures the current through it. You observe that at room temperature (20.0°C) the ammeter reads 18.5 A, while at 92.0°C it reads 17.2 A. You can ignore any thermal expansion of the rod. Find (a) the resistivity at 20.0°C and (b) the temperature coefficient of resistivity at 20°C for the material of the rod.

25.12 • A copper wire has a square cross section 2.3 mm on a side. The wire is 4.0 m long and carries a current of 3.6 A. The density of free electrons is $8.5 \times 10^{28}/\text{m}^3$. Find the magnitudes of (a) the current density in the wire and (b) the electric field in the wire. (c) How much time is required for an electron to travel the length of the wire?

25.13 • A 14-gauge copper wire of diameter 1.628 mm carries a current of 12.5 mA. (a) What is the potential difference across a 2.00-m length of the wire? (b) What would the potential difference in part (a) be if the wire were silver instead of copper, but all else were the same?

25.14 •• A wire 6.50 m long with diameter of 2.05 mm has a resistance of 0.0290 Ω. What material is the wire most likely made of?

25.15 •• A cylindrical tungsten filament 15.0 cm long with a diameter of 1.00 mm is to be used in a machine for which the temperature will range from room temperature (20°C) up to 120°C. It will carry a current of 12.5 A at all temperatures (consult Tables 25.1 and 25.2). (a) What will be the maximum electric field in this filament, and (b) what will be its resistance with that field? (c) What will be the maximum potential drop over the full length of the filament?

25.16 •• A ductile metal wire has resistance R. What will be the resistance of this wire in terms of R if it is stretched to three times its original length, assuming that the density and resistivity of the material do not change when the wire is stretched? (*Hint:* The amount of metal does not change, so stretching out the wire will affect its cross-sectional area.)

25.17 • In household wiring, copper wire 2.05 mm in diameter is often used. Find the resistance of a 24.0-m length of this wire.

25.18 •• What diameter must a copper wire have if its resistance is to be the same as that of an equal length of aluminum wire with diameter 3.26 mm?

25.19 • You need to produce a set of cylindrical copper wires 3.50 m long that will have a resistance of 0.125 Ω each. What will be the mass of each of these wires?

25.20 • A tightly coiled spring having 75 coils, each 3.50 cm in diameter, is made of insulated metal wire 3.25 mm in diameter. An ohmmeter connected across its opposite ends reads 1.74 Ω. What is the resistivity of the metal?

25.21 • An aluminum cube has sides of length 1.80 m. What is the resistance between two opposite faces of the cube?

25.22 • You apply a potential difference of 4.50 V between the ends of a wire that is 2.50 m in length and 0.654 mm in radius. The resulting current through the wire is 17.6 A. What is the resistivity of the wire?

25.23 • A current-carrying gold wire has diameter 0.84 mm. The electric field in the wire is 0.49 V/m. What are (a) the current carried by the wire; (b) the potential difference between two points in the wire 6.4 m apart; (c) the resistance of a 6.4-m length of this wire?

25.24 • A hollow aluminum cylinder is 2.50 m long and has an inner radius of 3.20 cm and an outer radius of 4.60 cm. Treat each surface (inner, outer, and the two end faces) as an equipotential surface. At room temperature, what will an ohmmeter read if it is connected between (a) the opposite faces and (b) the inner and outer surfaces?

25.25 • (a) What is the resistance of a Nichrome wire at 0.0°C if its resistance is 100.00 Ω at 11.5°C? (b) What is the resistance of a carbon rod at 25.8°C if its resistance is 0.0160 Ω at 0.0°C?

25.26 • A carbon resistor is to be used as a thermometer. On a winter day when the temperature is 4.0°C, the resistance of the carbon resistor is 217.3 Ω. What is the temperature on a spring day when the resistance is 215.8 Ω? (Take the reference temperature T_0 to be 4.0°C.)

25.27 • A strand of wire has resistance 5.60 μΩ. Find the net resistance of 120 such strands if they are (a) placed side by side to form a cable of the same length as a single strand, and (b) connected end to end to form a wire 120 times as long as a single strand.

Section 25.4 Electromotive Force and Circuits

25.28 • Consider the circuit shown in Fig. E25.28. The terminal voltage of the 24.0-V battery is 21.2 V. What are (a) the internal resistance r of the battery and (b) the resistance R of the circuit resistor?

Figure **E25.28**

r 24.0 V
4.00 A
R
4.00 A

25.29 • A copper transmission cable 100 km long and 10.0 cm in diameter carries a current of 125 A. (a) What is the potential drop across the cable? (b) How much electrical energy is dissipated as thermal energy every hour?

25.30 • An idealized ammeter is connected to a battery as shown in Fig. E25.30. Find (a) the reading of the ammeter, (b) the current through the 4.00-Ω resistor, (c) the terminal voltage of the battery.

Figure **E25.30**

2.00 Ω 10.0 V

4.00 Ω

25.31 • An ideal voltmeter V is connected to a 2.0-Ω resistor and a battery with emf 5.0 V and internal resistance 0.5 Ω as shown in Fig. E25.31. (a) What is the current in the 2.0-Ω resistor? (b) What is the terminal voltage of the battery? (c) What is the reading on the voltmeter? Explain your answers.

Figure **E25.31**

0.5 Ω 5.0 V

2.0 Ω

25.32 • The circuit shown in Fig. E25.32 contains two batteries, each with an emf and an internal resistance, and two resistors. Find (a) the current in the circuit (magnitude *and* direction); (b) the terminal voltage V_{ab} of the 16.0-V battery; (c) the potential difference V_{ac} of point *a* with respect to point *c*. (d) Using Fig. 25.20 as a model, graph the potential rises and drops in this circuit.

Figure **E25.32**

1.6 Ω 16.0 V
a   *b*
5.0 Ω   9.0 Ω
1.4 Ω 8.0 V
                    c

25.33 • When switch S in Fig. E25.33 is open, the voltmeter V of the battery reads 3.08 V. When the switch is closed, the voltmeter reading drops to 2.97 V, and the ammeter A reads 1.65 A. Find the emf, the internal resistance of the battery, and the circuit resistance *R*. Assume that the two meters are ideal, so they don't affect the circuit.

Figure **E25.33**

r $\mathcal{E}$

R

S

25.34 • In the circuit of Fig. E25.32, the 5.0-Ω resistor is removed and replaced by a resistor of unknown resistance *R*. When this is done, an ideal voltmeter connected across the points *b* and *c* reads 1.9 V. Find (a) the current in the circuit and (b) the resistance *R*. (c) Graph the potential rises and drops in this circuit (see Fig. 25.20).

25.35 • In the circuit shown in Fig. E25.32, the 16.0-V battery is removed and reinserted with the opposite polarity, so that its negative terminal is now next to point *a*. Find (a) the current in the circuit (magnitude *and* direction); (b) the terminal voltage V_{ba} of the 16.0-V battery; (c) the potential difference V_{ac} of point *a* with respect to point *c*. (d) Graph the potential rises and drops in this circuit (see Fig. 25.20).

25.36 • The following measurements were made on a Thyrite resistor:

I (A)	0.50	1.00	2.00	4.00
V_{ab} (V)	2.55	3.11	3.77	4.58

(a) Graph V_{ab} as a function of I. (b) Does Thyrite obey Ohm's law? How can you tell? (c) Graph the resistance $R = V_{ab}/I$ as a function of I.

25.37 • The following measurements of current and potential difference were made on a resistor constructed of Nichrome wire:

I (A)	0.50	1.00	2.00	4.00
V_{ab} (V)	1.94	3.88	7.76	15.52

(a) Graph V_{ab} as a function of I. (b) Does Nichrome obey Ohm's law? How can you tell? (c) What is the resistance of the resistor in ohms?

25.38 •• The circuit shown in Fig. E25.38 contains two batteries, each with an emf and an internal resistance, and two resistors. Find (a) the current in the circuit (magnitude and direction) and (b) the terminal voltage V_{ab} of the 16.0-V battery.

Figure **E25.38**

1.6 Ω 16.0 V
a   *b*
5.0 Ω   9.0 Ω
1.4 Ω 8.0 V

Section 25.5 Energy and Power in Electric Circuits

25.39 • **Light Bulbs.** The power rating of a light bulb (such as a 100-W bulb) is the power it dissipates when connected across a 120-V potential difference. What is the resistance of (a) a 100-W bulb and (b) a 60-W bulb? (c) How much current does each bulb draw in normal use?

25.40 • If a "75-W" bulb (see Problem 25.39) is connected across a 220-V potential difference (as is used in Europe), how much power does it dissipate?

25.41 • **European Light Bulb.** In Europe the standard voltage in homes is 220 V instead of the 120 V used in the United States. Therefore a "100-W" European bulb would be intended for use with a 220-V potential difference (see Problem 25.40). (a) If you bring a "100-W" European bulb home to the United States, what should be its U.S. power rating? (b) How much current will the 100-W European bulb draw in normal use in the United States?

25.42 • A battery-powered global positioning system (GPS) receiver operating on 9.0 V draws a current of 0.13 A. How much electrical energy does it consume during 1.5 h?

25.43 • Consider a resistor with length *L*, uniform cross-sectional area *A*, and uniform resistivity ρ that is carrying a current with uniform current density *J*. Use Eq. (25.18) to find the electrical power dissipated per unit volume, *p*. Express your result in terms of (a) *E* and *J*; (b) *J* and ρ; (c) *E* and ρ.

25.44 • **BIO Electric Eels.** Electric eels generate electric pulses along their skin that can be used to stun an enemy when they come into contact with it. Tests have shown that these pulses can be up to 500 V and produce currents of 80 mA (or even larger). A typical pulse lasts for 10 ms. What power and how much energy are delivered to the unfortunate enemy with a single pulse, assuming a steady current?

25.45 • **BIO Treatment of Heart Failure.** A heart defibrillator is used to enable the heart to start beating if it has stopped. This is done by passing a large current of 12 A through the body at 25 V for a very short time, usually about 3.0 ms. (a) What power does the defibrillator deliver to the body, and (b) how much energy is transferred?

25.46 • Consider the circuit of Fig. E25.32. (a) What is the total rate at which electrical energy is dissipated in the 5.0-Ω and 9.0-Ω resistors? (b) What is the power output of the 16.0-V battery? (c) At what rate is electrical energy being converted to other forms in the 8.0-V battery? (d) Show that the power output of the 16.0-V battery equals the overall rate of dissipation of electrical energy in the rest of the circuit.

25.47 •• The capacity of a storage battery, such as those used in automobile electrical systems, is rated in ampere-hours (A · h). A 50-A · h battery can supply a current of 50 A for 1.0 h, or 25 A for 2.0 h, and so on. (a) What total energy can be supplied by a 12-V, 60-A · h battery if its internal resistance is negligible? (b) What volume (in liters) of gasoline has a total heat of combustion equal to the energy obtained in part (a)? (See Section 17.6; the density of gasoline is 900 kg/m^3.) (c) If a generator with an average electrical power output of 0.45 kW is connected to the battery, how much time will be required for it to charge the battery fully?

25.48 • In the circuit analyzed in Example 25.8 the 4.0-Ω resistor is replaced by a 8.0-Ω resistor, as in Example 25.9. (a) Calculate the rate of conversion of chemical energy to electrical energy in the battery. How does your answer compare to the result calculated in Example 25.8? (b) Calculate the rate of electrical energy dissipation in the internal resistance of the battery. How does your answer compare to the result calculated in Example 25.8? (c) Use the results of parts (a) and (b) to calculate the net power output of the battery. How does your result compare to the electrical power dissipated in the 8.0-Ω resistor as calculated for this circuit in Example 25.9?

25.49 •• A 25.0-Ω bulb is connected across the terminals of a 12.0-V battery having 3.50 Ω of internal resistance. What percentage of the power of the battery is dissipated across the internal resistance and hence is not available to the bulb?

25.50 • An idealized voltmeter is connected across the terminals of a 15.0-V battery, and a 75.0-Ω appliance is also connected across its terminals. If the voltmeter reads 11.3 V: (a) how much power is being dissipated by the appliance, and (b) what is the internal resistance of the battery?

25.51 • In the circuit in Fig. E25.51, find (a) the rate of conversion of internal (chemical) energy to electrical energy within the battery; (b) the rate of dissipation of electrical energy in the battery; (c) the rate of dissipation of electrical energy in the external resistor.

Figure **E25.51**

25.52 •• A typical small flashlight contains two batteries, each having an emf of 1.5 V, connected in series with a bulb having resistance 17 Ω. (a) If the internal resistance of the batteries is negligible, what power is delivered to the bulb? (b) If the batteries last for 5.0 h, what is the total energy delivered to the bulb? (c) The resistance of real batteries increases as they run down. If the initial internal resistance is negligible, what is the combined internal resistance of both batteries when the power to the bulb has decreased to half its initial value? (Assume that the resistance of the bulb is constant. Actually, it will change somewhat when the current through the filament changes, because this changes the temperature of the filament and hence the resistivity of the filament wire.)

25.53 • A "540-W" electric heater is designed to operate from 120-V lines. (a) What is its resistance? (b) What current does it draw? (c) If the line voltage drops to 110 V, what power does the heater take? (Assume that the resistance is constant. Actually, it will change because of the change in temperature.) (d) The heater coils are metallic, so that the resistance of the heater decreases with decreasing temperature. If the change of resistance with temperature is taken into account, will the electrical power consumed by the heater be larger or smaller than what you calculated in part (c)? Explain.

Section 25.6 Theory of Metallic Conduction

25.54 •• Pure silicon contains approximately 1.0×10^{16} free electrons per cubic meter. (a) Referring to Table 25.1, calculate the mean free time τ for silicon at room temperature. (b) Your answer in part (a) is much greater than the mean free time for copper given in Example 25.11. Why, then, does pure silicon have such a high resistivity compared to copper?

PROBLEMS

25.55 • An electrical conductor designed to carry large currents has a circular cross section 2.50 mm in diameter and is 14.0 m long. The resistance between its ends is 0.104 Ω. (a) What is the resistivity of the material? (b) If the electric-field magnitude in the conductor is 1.28 V/m, what is the total current? (c) If the material has 8.5×10^{28} free electrons per cubic meter, find the average drift speed under the conditions of part (b).

25.56 •• A plastic tube 25.0 m long and 3.00 cm in diameter is dipped into a silver solution, depositing a layer of silver 0.100 mm thick uniformly over the outer surface of the tube. If this coated tube is then connected across a 12.0-V battery, what will be the current?

25.57 •• On your first day at work as an electrical technician, you are asked to determine the resistance per meter of a long piece of wire. The company you work for is poorly equipped. You find a battery, a voltmeter, and an ammeter, but no meter for directly measuring resistance (an ohmmeter). You put the leads from the voltmeter across the terminals of the battery, and the meter reads 12.6 V. You cut off a 20.0-m length of wire and connect it to the battery, with an ammeter in series with it to measure the current in the wire. The ammeter reads 7.00 A. You then cut off a 40.0-m length of wire and connect it to the battery, again with the ammeter in series to measure the current. The ammeter reads 4.20 A. Even though the equipment you have available to you is limited, your boss assures you of its high quality: The ammeter has very small resistance, and the voltmeter has very large resistance. What is the resistance of 1 meter of wire?

25.58 • A 2.0-mm length of wire is made by welding the end of a 120-cm-long silver wire to the end of an 80-cm-long copper wire. Each piece of wire is 0.60 mm in diameter. The wire is at room temperature, so the resistivities are as given in Table 25.1. A potential difference of 5.0 V is maintained between the ends of the 2.0-m composite wire. (a) What is the current in the copper section? (b) What is the current in the silver section? (c) What is the magnitude of $\vec{E}$ in the copper? (d) What is the magnitude of $\vec{E}$ in the silver? (e) What is the potential difference between the ends of the silver section of wire?

25.59 • A 3.00-m length of copper wire at 20°C has a 1.20-m-long section with diameter 1.60 mm and a 1.80-m-long section with diameter 0.80 mm. There is a current of 2.5 mA in the 1.60-mm-diameter section. (a) What is the current in the 0.80-mm-diameter section? (b) What is the magnitude of $\vec{E}$ in the 1.60-mm-diameter section? (c) What is the magnitude of $\vec{E}$ in the 0.80-mm-diameter section? (d) What is the potential difference between the ends of the 3.00-m length of wire?

25.60 • **Critical Current Density in Superconductors.** One problem with some of the newer high-temperature superconductors is getting a large enough current density for practical use without causing the resistance to reappear. The maximum current density for which the material will remain a superconductor is called the critical current density of the material. In 1987, IBM research labs had produced thin films with critical current densities of 1.0×10^5 A/cm^2. (a) How much current could an 18-gauge wire (see Example 25.1 in Section 25.1) of this material carry and still remain superconducting? (b) Researchers are trying to develop superconductors with critical current densities of 1.0×10^6 A/cm^2. What diameter cylindrical wire of such a material would be needed to carry 1000 A without losing its superconductivity?

25.61 •• **CP** A Nichrome heating element that has resistance 28.0 Ω is connected to a battery that has emf 96.0 V and internal each bulb acts as a resistor, and from a circuit-analysis perspective the string of bulbs is simply a combination of resistors.

Suppose we have three resistors with resistances R_1, R_2, and R_3. Figure 26.1 shows four different ways in which they might be connected between points a and b. When several circuit elements such as resistors, batteries, and motors are connected in sequence as in Fig. 26.1a, with only a single current path between the points, we say that they are connected in **series.** We studied *capacitors* in series in Section 24.2; we found that, because of conservation of charge, capacitors in series all have the same charge if they are initially uncharged. In circuits we're often more interested in the *current,* which is charge flow per unit time.

The resistors in Fig. 26.1b are said to be connected in **parallel** between points a and b. Each resistor provides an alternative path between the points. For circuit elements that are connected in parallel, the *potential difference* is the same across each element. We studied capacitors in parallel in Section 24.2.

In Fig. 26.1c, resistors R_2 and R_3 are in parallel, and this combination is in series with R_1. In Fig. 26.1d, R_2 and R_3 are in series, and this combination is in parallel with R_1.

For any combination of resistors we can always find a *single* resistor that could replace the combination and result in the same total current and potential difference. For example, a string of holiday light bulbs could be replaced by a single, appropriately chosen light bulb that would draw the same current and have the same potential difference between its terminals as the original string of bulbs. The resistance of this single resistor is called the **equivalent resistance** of the combination. If any one of the networks in Fig. 26.1 were replaced by its equivalent resistance R_{eq}, we could write

$$V_{ab} = IR_{eq} \quad \text{or} \quad R_{eq} = \frac{V_{ab}}{I}$$

where V_{ab} is the potential difference between terminals a and b of the network and I is the current at point a or b. To compute an equivalent resistance, we assume a potential difference V_{ab} across the actual network, compute the corresponding current I, and take the ratio V_{ab}/I.

Resistors in Series

We can derive general equations for the equivalent resistance of a series or parallel combination of resistors. If the resistors are in *series,* as in Fig. 26.1a, the current I must be the same in all of them. (As we discussed in Section 25.4, current is *not* "used up" as it passes through a circuit.) Applying $V = IR$ to each resistor, we have

$$V_{ax} = IR_1 \qquad V_{xy} = IR_2 \qquad V_{yb} = IR_3$$

The potential differences across each resistor need not be the same (except for the special case in which all three resistances are equal). The potential difference V_{ab} across the entire combination is the sum of these individual potential differences:

$$V_{ab} = V_{ax} + V_{xy} + V_{yb} = I(R_1 + R_2 + R_3)$$

and so

$$\frac{V_{ab}}{I} = R_1 + R_2 + R_3$$

The ratio V_{ab}/I is, by definition, the equivalent resistance R_{eq}. Therefore

$$R_{eq} = R_1 + R_2 + R_3$$

It is easy to generalize this to any number of resistors:

$$R_{eq} = R_1 + R_2 + R_3 + \cdots \qquad \text{(resistors in series)} \qquad [26.1]$$

26.1 Four different ways of connecting three resistors.

(a) R_1, R_2, and R_3 in series

(b) R_1, R_2, and R_3 in parallel

(c) R_1 in series with parallel combination of R_2 and R_3

(d) R_1 in parallel with series combination of R_2 and R_3

The equivalent resistance of *any number* of resistors in series equals the sum of their individual resistances.

The equivalent resistance is *greater than* any individual resistance.

Let's compare this result with Eq. (24.5) for *capacitors* in series. Resistors in series add directly because the voltage across each is directly proportional to its resistance and to the common current. Capacitors in series add reciprocally because the voltage across each is directly proportional to the common charge but *inversely* proportional to the individual capacitance.

Resistors in Parallel

26.2 A car's headlights and taillights are connected in parallel. Hence each light is exposed to the full potential difference supplied by the car's electrical system, giving maximum brightness. Another advantage is that if one headlight or taillight burns out, the other one keeps shining (see Example 26.2).

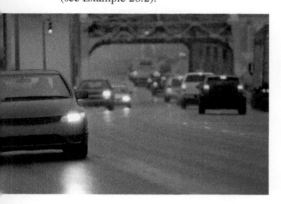

MasteringPHYSICS

ActivPhysics 12.2: DC Parallel Circuits

If the resistors are in *parallel,* as in Fig. 26.1b, the current through each resistor need not be the same. But the potential difference between the terminals of each resistor must be the same and equal to V_{ab} (Fig. 26.2). (Remember that the potential difference between any two points does not depend on the path taken between the points.) Let's call the currents in the three resistors I_1, I_2, and I_3. Then from $I = V/R$,

$$I_1 = \frac{V_{ab}}{R_1} \qquad I_2 = \frac{V_{ab}}{R_2} \qquad I_3 = \frac{V_{ab}}{R_3}$$

In general, the current is different through each resistor. Because charge is not accumulating or draining out of point *a*, the total current *I* must equal the sum of the three currents in the resistors:

$$I = I_1 + I_2 + I_3 = V_{ab}\left(\frac{1}{R_1} + \frac{1}{R_2} + \frac{1}{R_3}\right) \quad \text{or}$$

$$\frac{I}{V_{ab}} = \frac{1}{R_1} + \frac{1}{R_2} + \frac{1}{R_3}$$

But by the definition of the equivalent resistance R_{eq}, $I/V_{ab} = 1/R_{eq}$, so

$$\frac{1}{R_{eq}} = \frac{1}{R_1} + \frac{1}{R_2} + \frac{1}{R_3}$$

Again it is easy to generalize to *any number* of resistors in parallel:

$$\frac{1}{R_{eq}} = \frac{1}{R_1} + \frac{1}{R_2} + \frac{1}{R_3} + \cdots \qquad \text{(resistors in parallel)} \qquad (26.2)$$

For *any number* of resistors in parallel, the *reciprocal* of the equivalent resistance equals the *sum of the reciprocals* of their individual resistances.

The equivalent resistance is always *less than* any individual resistance.

Compare this with Eq. (24.7) for *capacitors* in parallel. Resistors in parallel add reciprocally because the current in each is proportional to the common voltage across them and *inversely* proportional to the resistance of each. Capacitors in parallel add directly because the charge on each is proportional to the common voltage across them and *directly* proportional to the capacitance of each.

For the special case of *two* resistors in parallel,

$$\frac{1}{R_{eq}} = \frac{1}{R_1} + \frac{1}{R_2} = \frac{R_1 + R_2}{R_1 R_2} \quad \text{and}$$

$$R_{eq} = \frac{R_1 R_2}{R_1 + R_2} \qquad \text{(two resistors in parallel)} \qquad (26.3)$$

Because $V_{ab} = I_1R_1 = I_2R_2$, it follows that

$$\frac{I_1}{I_2} = \frac{R_2}{R_1} \qquad \text{(two resistors in parallel)} \qquad (26.4)$$

This shows that the currents carried by two resistors in parallel are *inversely proportional* to their resistances. More current goes through the path of least resistance.

Problem-Solving Strategy 26.1   **Resistors in Series and Parallel**

IDENTIFY *the relevant concepts:* As in Fig. 26.1, many resistor networks are made up of resistors in series, in parallel, or a combination thereof. Such networks can be replaced by a single equivalent resistor. The logic is similar to that of Problem-Solving Strategy 24.1 for networks of capacitors.

SET UP *the problem* using the following steps:
1. Make a drawing of the resistor network.
2. Identify groups of resistors connected in series or parallel.
3. Identify the target variables. They could include the equivalent resistance of the network, the potential difference across each resistor, or the current through each resistor.

EXECUTE *the solution* as follows:
1. Use Eq. (26.1) or (26.2), respectively, to find the equivalent resistance for series or parallel combinations.
2. If the network is more complex, try reducing it to series and parallel combinations. For example, in Fig. 26.1c we first replace the parallel combination of R_2 and R_3 with its equivalent resistance;

this then forms a series combination with R_1. In Fig. 26.1d, the combination of R_2 and R_3 in series forms a parallel combination with R_1.
3. Keep in mind that the total potential difference across resistors connected in series is the sum of the individual potential differences. The potential difference across resistors connected in parallel is the same for every resistor and equals the potential difference across the combination.
4. The current through resistors connected in series is the same through every resistor and equals the current through the combination. The total current through resistors connected in parallel is the sum of the currents through the individual resistors.

EVALUATE *your answer:* Check whether your results are consistent. The equivalent resistance of resistors connected in series should be greater than that of any individual resistor; that of resistors in parallel should be less than that of any individual resistor.

Example 26.1   **Equivalent resistance**

Find the equivalent resistance of the network in Fig. 26.3a and the current in each resistor. The source of emf has negligible internal resistance.

SOLUTION

IDENTIFY and SET UP: This network of three resistors is a *combination* of series and parallel resistances, as in Fig. 26.1c. We determine

26.3 Steps in reducing a combination of resistors to a single equivalent resistor and finding the current in each resistor.

(a)

(b) ⇒ (c) ⇒ (d) ⇒ (e) ⇒ (f)

Continued

the equivalent resistance of the parallel 6-Ω and 3-Ω resistors, and then that of their series combination with the 4-Ω resistor: This is the equivalent resistance R_{eq} of the network as a whole. We then find the current in the emf, which is the same as that in the 4-Ω resistor. The potential difference is the same across each of the parallel 6-Ω and 3-Ω resistors; we use this to determine how the current is divided between these.

EXECUTE: Figures 26.3b and 26.3c show successive steps in reducing the network to a single equivalent resistance R_{eq}. From Eq. (26.2), the 6-Ω and 3-Ω resistors in parallel in Fig. 26.3a are equivalent to the single 2-Ω resistor in Fig. 26.3b:

$$\frac{1}{R_{6\,\Omega + 3\,\Omega}} = \frac{1}{6\,\Omega} + \frac{1}{3\,\Omega} = \frac{1}{2\,\Omega}$$

[Equation (26.3) gives the same result.] From Eq. (26.1) the series combination of this 2-Ω resistor with the 4-Ω resistor is equivalent to the single 6-Ω resistor in Fig. 26.3c.

We reverse these steps to find the current in each resistor of the original network. In the circuit shown in Fig. 26.3d (identical to Fig. 26.3c), the current is $I = V_{ab}/R = (18\text{ V})/(6\,\Omega) = 3\text{ A}$. So the current in the 4-Ω and 2-Ω resistors in Fig. 26.3e (identical to Fig. 26.3b) is also 3 A. The potential difference V_{cb} across the 2-Ω resistor is therefore $V_{cb} = IR = (3\text{ A})(2\,\Omega) = 6\text{ V}$. This potential difference must also be 6 V in Fig. 26.3f (identical to Fig. 26.3a). From $I = V_{cb}/R$, the currents in the 6-Ω and 3-Ω resistors in Fig. 26.3f are respectively $(6\text{ V})/(6\,\Omega) = 1\text{ A}$ and $(6\text{ V})/(3\,\Omega) = 2\text{ A}$.

EVALUATE: Note that for the two resistors in parallel between points c and b in Fig. 26.3f, there is twice as much current through the 3-Ω resistor as through the 6-Ω resistor; more current goes through the path of least resistance, in accordance with Eq. (26.4). Note also that the total current through these two resistors is 3 A, the same as it is through the 4-Ω resistor between points a and c.

Example 26.2 | Series versus parallel combinations

Two identical light bulbs, each with resistance $R = 2\,\Omega$, are connected to a source with $\mathcal{E} = 8\text{ V}$ and negligible internal resistance. Find the current through each bulb, the potential difference across each bulb, and the power delivered to each bulb and to the entire network if the bulbs are connected (a) in series and (b) in parallel. (c) Suppose one of the bulbs burns out; that is, its filament breaks and current can no longer flow through it. What happens to the other bulb in the series case? In the parallel case?

SOLUTION

IDENTIFY and SET UP: The light bulbs are just resistors in simple series and parallel connections (Figs. 26.4a and 26.4b). Once we find the current I through each bulb, we can find the power delivered to each bulb using Eq. (25.18), $P = I^2R = V^2/R$.

EXECUTE: (a) From Eq. (26.1) the equivalent resistance of the two bulbs between points a and c in Fig. 26.4a is $R_{eq} = 2R = 2(2\,\Omega) = 4\,\Omega$. In series, the current is the same through each bulb:

$$I = \frac{V_{ac}}{R_{eq}} = \frac{8\text{ V}}{4\,\Omega} = 2\text{ A}$$

Since the bulbs have the same resistance, the potential difference is the same across each bulb:

$$V_{ab} = V_{bc} = IR = (2\text{ A})(2\,\Omega) = 4\text{ V}$$

From Eq. (25.18), the power delivered to each bulb is

$$P = I^2R = (2\text{ A})^2(2\,\Omega) = 8\text{ W} \qquad \text{or}$$
$$P = \frac{V_{ab}^2}{R} = \frac{V_{bc}^2}{R} = \frac{(4\text{ V})^2}{2\,\Omega} = 8\text{ W}$$

The total power delivered to both bulbs is $P_{tot} = 2P = 16\text{ W}$.

(b) If the bulbs are in parallel, as in Fig. 26.4b, the potential difference V_{de} across each bulb is the same and equal to 8 V, the terminal voltage of the source. Hence the current through each light bulb is

$$I = \frac{V_{de}}{R} = \frac{8\text{ V}}{2\,\Omega} = 4\text{ A}$$

and the power delivered to each bulb is

$$P = I^2R = (4\text{ A})^2(2\,\Omega) = 32\text{ W} \qquad \text{or}$$
$$P = \frac{V_{de}^2}{R} = \frac{(8\text{ V})^2}{2\,\Omega} = 32\text{ W}$$

Both the potential difference across each bulb and the current through each bulb are twice as great as in the series case. Hence the power delivered to each bulb is *four* times greater, and each bulb is brighter.

The total power delivered to the parallel network is $P_{total} = 2P = 64\text{ W}$, four times greater than in the series case. The

26.4 Our sketches for this problem.

(a) Light bulbs in series

(b) Light bulbs in parallel

Problem-Solving Strategy 26.2   Kirchhoff's Rules

IDENTIFY *the relevant concepts:* Kirchhoff's rules are useful for analyzing any electric circuit.

SET UP *the problem* using the following steps:
1. Draw a circuit diagram, leaving room to label all quantities, known and unknown. Indicate an assumed direction for each unknown current and emf. (Kirchhoff's rules will yield the magnitudes *and directions* of unknown currents and emfs. If the actual direction of a quantity is opposite to your assumption, the resulting quantity will have a negative sign.)
2. As you label currents, it helpful to use Kirchhoff's junction rule, as in Fig. 26.9, so as to express the currents in terms of as few quantities as possible.
3. Identify the target variables.

EXECUTE *the solution* as follows:
1. Choose any loop in the network and choose a direction (clockwise or counterclockwise) to travel around the loop as you apply Kirchhoff's loop rule. The direction need not be the same as any assumed current direction.

2. Travel around the loop in the chosen direction, adding potential differences algebraically as you cross them. Use the sign conventions of Fig. 26.8.
3. Equate the sum obtained in step 2 to zero in accordance with the loop rule.
4. If you need more independent equations, choose another loop and repeat steps 1–3; continue until you have as many independent equations as unknowns or until every circuit element has been included in at least one loop.
5. Solve the equations simultaneously to determine the unknowns.
6. You can use the loop-rule bookkeeping system to find the potential V_{ab} of any point *a* with respect to any other point *b*. Start at *b* and add the potential changes you encounter in going from *b* to *a*, using the same sign rules as in step 2. The algebraic sum of these changes is $V_{ab} = V_a - V_b$.

EVALUATE *your answer:* Check all the steps in your algebra. Apply steps 1 and 2 to a loop you have not yet considered; if the sum of potential drops isn't zero, you've made an error somewhere.

26.9 Applying the junction rule to point *a* reduces the number of unknown currents from three to two.

(a) Three unknown currents: I_1, I_2, I_3

(b) Applying the junction rule to point *a* eliminates I_3.

Example 26.3   A single-loop circuit

The circuit shown in Fig. 26.10a contains two batteries, each with an emf and an internal resistance, and two resistors. Find (a) the current in the circuit, (b) the potential difference V_{ab}, and (c) the power output of the emf of each battery.

SOLUTION

IDENTIFY and SET UP: There are no junctions in this single-loop circuit, so we don't need Kirchhoff's junction rule. To apply Kirchhoff's loop rule, we first assume a direction for the current; let's assume a counterclockwise direction as shown in Fig. 26.10a.

EXECUTE: (a) Starting at *a* and traveling counterclockwise with the current, we add potential increases and decreases and equate the sum to zero as in Eq. (26.6):

$$-I(4\ \Omega) - 4\ \text{V} - I(7\ \Omega) + 12\ \text{V} - I(2\ \Omega) - I(3\ \Omega) = 0$$

Collecting like terms and solving for *I*, we find

$$8\ \text{V} = I(16\ \Omega) \quad \text{and} \quad I = 0.5\ \text{A}$$

The positive result for *I* shows that our assumed current direction is correct.

(b) To find V_{ab}, the potential at *a* with respect to *b*, we start at *b* and add potential changes as we go toward *a*. There are two paths from *b* to *a*; taking the lower one, we find

$$V_{ab} = (0.5\ \text{A})(7\ \Omega) + 4\ \text{V} + (0.5\ \text{A})(4\ \Omega)$$
$$= 9.5\ \text{V}$$

Point *a* is at 9.5 V higher potential than *b*. All the terms in this sum, including the *IR* terms, are positive because each represents an *increase* in potential as we go from *b* to *a*. Taking the upper path, we find

$$V_{ab} = 12\ \text{V} - (0.5\ \text{A})(2\ \Omega) - (0.5\ \text{A})(3\ \Omega)$$
$$= 9.5\ \text{V}$$

Here the *IR* terms are negative because our path goes in the direction of the current, with potential decreases through the resistors. The results for V_{ab} are the same for both paths, as they must be in order for the total potential change around the loop to be zero.

Continued

(c) The power outputs of the emf of the 12-V and 4-V batteries are

$$P_{12V} = \mathcal{E}I = (12 \text{ V})(0.5 \text{ A}) = 6 \text{ W}$$
$$P_{4V} = \mathcal{E}I = (-4 \text{ V})(0.5 \text{ A}) = -2 \text{ W}$$

The negative sign in $\mathcal{E}$ for the 4-V battery appears because the current actually runs from the higher-potential side of the battery to the lower-potential side. The negative value of P means that we are *storing* energy in that battery; the 12-V battery is *recharging* it (if it is in fact rechargeable; otherwise, we're destroying it).

EVALUATE: By applying the expression $P = I^2R$ to each of the four resistors in Fig. 26.10a, you can show that the total power

dissipated in all four resistors is 4 W. Of the 6 W provided by the emf of the 12-V battery, 2 W goes into storing energy in the 4-V battery and 4 W is dissipated in the resistances.

The circuit shown in Fig. 26.10a is much like that used when a fully charged 12-V storage battery (in a car with its engine running) is used to "jump-start" a car with a run-down battery (Fig. 26.10b). The run-down battery is slightly recharged in the process. The 3-Ω and 7-Ω resistors in Fig. 26.10a represent the resistances of the jumper cables and of the conducting path through the automobile with the run-down battery. (The values of the resistances in actual automobiles and jumper cables are considerably lower.)

26.10 (a) In this example we travel around the loop in the same direction as the assumed current, so all the *IR* terms are negative. The potential decreases as we travel from + to − through the bottom emf but increases as we travel from − to + through the top emf. (b) A real-life example of a circuit of this kind.

Example 26.4 | Charging a battery

In the circuit shown in Fig. 26.11, a 12-V power supply with unknown internal resistance r is connected to a run-down rechargeable battery with unknown emf $\mathcal{E}$ and internal resistance 1 Ω and to an indicator light bulb of resistance 3 Ω carrying a current of 2 A. The current through the run-down battery is 1 A in the direction shown. Find r, $\mathcal{E}$, and the current I through the power supply.

SOLUTION

IDENTIFY and SET UP: This circuit has more than one loop, so we must apply both the junction and loop rules. We assume the direction of the current through the 12-V power supply, and the polarity of the run-down battery, to be as shown in Fig. 26.11. There are three target variables, so we need three equations.

26.11 In this circuit a power supply charges a run-down battery and lights a bulb. An assumption has been made about the polarity of the emf $\mathcal{E}$ of the run-down battery. Is this assumption correct?

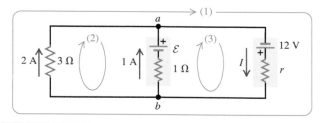

EXECUTE: We apply the junction rule, Eq. (26.5), to point a:

$$-I + 1 \text{ A} + 2 \text{ A} = 0 \quad \text{so} \quad I = 3 \text{ A}$$

To determine r, we apply the loop rule, Eq. (26.6), to the large, outer loop (1):

$$12 \text{ V} - (3 \text{ A})r - (2 \text{ A})(3 \text{ }\Omega) = 0 \quad \text{so} \quad r = 2 \text{ }\Omega$$

To determine $\mathcal{E}$, we apply the loop rule to the left-hand loop (2):

$$-\mathcal{E} + (1 \text{ A})(1 \text{ }\Omega) - (2 \text{ A})(3 \text{ }\Omega) = 0 \quad \text{so} \quad \mathcal{E} = -5 \text{ V}$$

The negative value for $\mathcal{E}$ shows that the actual polarity of this emf is opposite to that shown in Fig. 26.11. As in Example 26.3, the battery is being recharged.

EVALUATE: Try applying the junction rule at point b instead of point a, and try applying the loop rule by traveling counterclockwise rather than clockwise around loop (1). You'll get the same results for I and r. We can check our result for $\mathcal{E}$ by using the right-hand loop (3):

$$12 \text{ V} - (3 \text{ A})(2 \text{ }\Omega) - (1 \text{ A})(1 \text{ }\Omega) + \mathcal{E} = 0$$

which again gives us $\mathcal{E} = -5$ V.

As an additional check, we note that $V_{ba} = V_b - V_a$ equals the voltage across the 3-Ω resistance, which is $(2 \text{ A})(3 \text{ }\Omega) = 6$ V. Going from a to b by the top branch, we encounter potential differences $+12 \text{ V} - (3 \text{ A})(2 \text{ }\Omega) = +6$ V, and going by the middle branch, we find $-(-5 \text{ V}) + (1 \text{ A})(1 \text{ }\Omega) = +6$ V. The three ways of getting V_{ba} give the same results.

Example 26.5   Power in a battery-charging circuit

In the circuit of Example 26.4 (shown in Fig. 26.11), find the power delivered by the 12-V power supply and by the battery being recharged, and find the power dissipated in each resistor.

SOLUTION

IDENTIFY and SET UP: We use the results of Section 25.5, in which we found that the power delivered *from* an emf to a circuit is $\mathcal{E}I$ and the power delivered *to* a resistor from a circuit is $V_{ab}I = I^2R$. We know the values of all relevant quantities from Example 26.4.

EXECUTE: The power output P_s from the emf of the power supply is

$$P_{\text{supply}} = \mathcal{E}_{\text{supply}}I_{\text{supply}} = (12 \text{ V})(3 \text{ A}) = 36 \text{ W}$$

The power dissipated in the power supply's internal resistance r is

$$P_{r-\text{supply}} = I_{\text{supply}}^2 r_{\text{supply}} = (3 \text{ A})^2(2 \text{ }\Omega) = 18 \text{ W}$$

so the power supply's *net* power output is $P_{\text{net}} = 36 \text{ W} - 18 \text{ W} = 18 \text{ W}$. Alternatively, from Example 26.4 the terminal voltage of the battery is $V_{ba} = 6$ V, so the net power output is

$$P_{\text{net}} = V_{ba}I_{\text{supply}} = (6 \text{ V})(3 \text{ A}) = 18 \text{ W}$$

The power output of the emf $\mathcal{E}$ of the battery being charged is

$$P_{\text{emf}} = \mathcal{E}I_{\text{battery}} = (-5 \text{ V})(1 \text{ A}) = -5 \text{ W}$$

This is negative because the 1-A current runs through the battery from the higher-potential side to the lower-potential side. (As we mentioned in Example 26.4, the polarity assumed for this battery in Fig. 26.11 was wrong.) We are storing energy in the battery as we charge it. Additional power is dissipated in the battery's internal resistance; this power is

$$P_{r-\text{battery}} = I_{\text{battery}}^2 r_{\text{battery}} = (1 \text{ A})^2(1 \text{ }\Omega) = 1 \text{ W}$$

The total power input to the battery is thus $1 \text{ W} + |-5 \text{ W}| = 6$ W. Of this, 5 W represents useful energy stored in the battery; the remainder is wasted in its internal resistance.

The power dissipated in the light bulb is

$$P_{\text{bulb}} = I_{\text{bulb}}^2 R_{\text{bulb}} = (2 \text{ A})^2(3 \text{ }\Omega) = 12 \text{ W}$$

EVALUATE: As a check, note that all of the power from the supply is accounted for. Of the 18 W of net power from the power supply, 5 W goes to recharge the battery, 1 W is dissipated in the battery's internal resistance, and 12 W is dissipated in the light bulb.

Example 26.6   A complex network

Figure 26.12 shows a "bridge" circuit of the type described at the beginning of this section (see Fig. 26.6b). Find the current in each resistor and the equivalent resistance of the network of five resistors.

SOLUTION

IDENTIFY and SET UP: This network is neither a series combination nor a parallel combination. Hence we must use Kirchhoff's rules to find the values of the target variables. There are five unknown currents, but by applying the junction rule to junctions a and b, we can represent them in terms of three unknown currents I_1, I_2, and I_3, as shown in Fig. 26.12.

26.12 A network circuit with several resistors.

EXECUTE: We apply the loop rule to the three loops shown:

$$13 \text{ V} - I_1(1 \text{ }\Omega) - (I_1 - I_3)(1 \text{ }\Omega) = 0 \quad (1)$$
$$-I_2(1 \text{ }\Omega) - (I_2 + I_3)(2 \text{ }\Omega) + 13 \text{ V} = 0 \quad (2)$$
$$-I_1(1 \text{ }\Omega) - I_3(1 \text{ }\Omega) + I_2(1 \text{ }\Omega) = 0 \quad (3)$$

One way to solve these simultaneous equations is to solve Eq. (3) for I_2, obtaining $I_2 = I_1 + I_3$, and then substitute this expression into Eq. (2) to eliminate I_2. We then have

$$13 \text{ V} = I_1(2 \text{ }\Omega) - I_3(1 \text{ }\Omega) \quad (1')$$
$$13 \text{ V} = I_1(3 \text{ }\Omega) + I_3(5 \text{ }\Omega) \quad (2')$$

Now we can eliminate I_3 by multiplying Eq. (1′) by 5 and adding the two equations. We obtain

$$78 \text{ V} = I_1(13 \text{ }\Omega) \qquad I_1 = 6 \text{ A}$$

We substitute this result into Eq. (1′) to obtain $I_3 = -1$ A, and from Eq. (3) we find $I_2 = 5$ A. The negative value of I_3 tells us that its direction is opposite to the direction we assumed.

The total current through the network is $I_1 + I_2 = 11$ A, and the potential drop across it is equal to the battery emf, 13 V. The equivalent resistance of the network is therefore

$$R_{\text{eq}} = \frac{13 \text{ V}}{11 \text{ A}} = 1.2 \text{ }\Omega$$

EVALUATE: You can check our results for I_1, I_2, and I_3 by substituting them back into Eqs. (1)–(3). What do you find?

Example 26.7   **A potential difference in a complex network**

In the circuit of Example 26.6 (Fig. 26.12), find the potential difference V_{ab}.

SOLUTION

IDENTIFY and SET UP: Our target variable $V_{ab} = V_a - V_b$ is the potential at point a with respect to point b. To find it, we start at point b and follow a path to point a, adding potential rises and drops as we go. We can follow any of several paths from b to a; the result must be the same for all such paths, which gives us a way to check our result.

EXECUTE: The simplest path is through the center 1-Ω resistor. In Example 26.6 we found $I_3 = -1$ A, showing that the actual current direction through this resistor is from right to left. Thus, as we go from b to a, there is a *drop* of potential with magnitude $|I_3|R = (1 \text{ A})(1 \text{ }\Omega) = 1$ V. Hence $V_{ab} = -1$ V, and the potential at a is 1 V less than at point b.

EVALUATE: To check our result, let's try a path from b to a that goes through the lower two resistors. The currents through these are

$$I_2 + I_3 = 5 \text{ A} + (-1 \text{ A}) = 4 \text{ A} \quad \text{and}$$
$$I_1 - I_3 = 6 \text{ A} - (-1 \text{ A}) = 7 \text{ A}$$

and so

$$V_{ab} = -(4 \text{ A})(2 \text{ }\Omega) + (7 \text{ A})(1 \text{ }\Omega) = -1 \text{ V}$$

You can confirm this result using some other paths from b to a.

26.13 This ammeter (top) and voltmeter (bottom) are both d'Arsonval galvanometers. The difference has to do with their internal connections (see Fig. 26:15).

26.14 A d'Arsonval galvanometer, showing a pivoted coil with attached pointer, a permanent magnet supplying a magnetic field that is uniform in magnitude, and a spring to provide restoring torque, which opposes magnetic-field torque.

Magnetic-field torque tends to push pointer away from zero.

Spring torque tends to push pointer toward zero.

Spring

Magnetic field

Permanent magnet   Soft-iron core   Pivoted coil

Test Your Understanding of Section 26.2   Subtract Eq. (1) from Eq. (2) in Example 26.6. To which loop in Fig. 26.12 does this equation correspond? Would this equation have simplified the solution of Example 26.6?

26.3 Electrical Measuring Instruments

We've been talking about potential difference, current, and resistance for two chapters, so it's about time we said something about how to *measure* these quantities. Many common devices, including car instrument panels, battery chargers, and inexpensive electrical instruments, measure potential difference (voltage), current, or resistance using a **d'Arsonval galvanometer** (Fig. 26.13). In the following discussion we'll often call it just a *meter*. A pivoted coil of fine wire is placed in the magnetic field of a permanent magnet (Fig. 26.14). Attached to the coil is a spring, similar to the hairspring on the balance wheel of a watch. In the equilibrium position, with no current in the coil, the pointer is at zero. When there is a current in the coil, the magnetic field exerts a torque on the coil that is proportional to the current. (We'll discuss this magnetic interaction in detail in Chapter 27.) As the coil turns, the spring exerts a restoring torque that is proportional to the angular displacement.

Thus the angular deflection of the coil and pointer is directly proportional to the coil current, and the device can be calibrated to measure current. The maximum deflection, typically 90° or so, is called *full-scale deflection*. The essential electrical characteristics of the meter are the current I_{fs} required for full-scale deflection (typically on the order of 10 μA to 10 mA) and the resistance R_c of the coil (typically on the order of 10 to 1000 Ω).

The meter deflection is proportional to the *current* in the coil. If the coil obeys Ohm's law, the current is proportional to the *potential difference* between the terminals of the coil, and the deflection is also proportional to this potential difference. For example, consider a meter whose coil has a resistance $R_c = 20.0 \text{ }\Omega$ and that deflects full scale when the current in its coil is $I_{fs} = 1.00$ mA. The corresponding potential difference for full-scale deflection is

$$V = I_{fs}R_c = (1.00 \times 10^{-3} \text{ A})(20.0 \text{ }\Omega) = 0.0200 \text{ V}$$

Ammeters

A current-measuring instrument is usually called an **ammeter** (or milliammeter, microammeter, and so forth, depending on the range). *An ammeter always measures the current passing through it.* An *ideal* ammeter, discussed in Section 25.4, would have *zero* resistance, so including it in a branch of a circuit would not affect the current in that branch. Real ammeters always have some finite resistance, but it is always desirable for an ammeter to have as little resistance as possible.

We can adapt any meter to measure currents that are larger than its full-scale reading by connecting a resistor in parallel with it (Fig. 26.15a) so that some of the current bypasses the meter coil. The parallel resistor is called a **shunt resistor** or simply a *shunt,* denoted as R_{sh}.

Suppose we want to make a meter with full-scale current I_{fs} and coil resistance R_c into an ammeter with full-scale reading I_a. To determine the shunt resistance R_{sh} needed, note that at full-scale deflection the total current through the parallel combination is I_a, the current through the coil of the meter is I_{fs}, and the current through the shunt is the difference $I_a - I_{fs}$. The potential difference V_{ab} is the same for both paths, so

$$I_{fs}R_c = (I_a - I_{fs})R_{sh} \qquad \text{(for an ammeter)} \qquad (26.7)$$

26.15 Using the same meter to measure (a) current and (b) voltage.

(a) Moving-coil ammeter   (b) Moving-coil voltmeter

Example 26.8   Designing an ammeter

What shunt resistance is required to make the 1.00-mA, 20.0-Ω meter described above into an ammeter with a range of 0 to 50.0 mA?

SOLUTION

IDENTIFY and SET UP: Since the meter is being used as an ammeter, its internal connections are as shown in Fig. 26.15a. Our target variable is the shunt resistance R_{sh}, which we will find using Eq. (26.7). The ammeter must handle a maximum current $I_a = 50.0 \times 10^{-3}$ A. The coil resistance is $R_c = 20.0$ Ω, and the meter shows full-scale deflection when the current through the coil is $I_{fs} = 1.00 \times 10^{-3}$ A.

EXECUTE: Solving Eq. (26.7) for R_{sh}, we find

$$R_{sh} = \frac{I_{fs}R_c}{I_a - I_{fs}} = \frac{(1.00 \times 10^{-3}\,\text{A})(20.0\,\Omega)}{50.0 \times 10^{-3}\,\text{A} - 1.00 \times 10^{-3}\,\text{A}}$$

$$= 0.408\ \Omega$$

EVALUATE: It's useful to consider the equivalent resistance R_{eq} of the ammeter as a whole. From Eq. (26.2),

$$R_{eq} = \left(\frac{1}{R_c} + \frac{1}{R_{sh}}\right)^{-1} = \left(\frac{1}{20.0\ \Omega} + \frac{1}{0.408\ \Omega}\right)^{-1}$$

$$= 0.400\ \Omega$$

The shunt resistance is so small in comparison to the coil resistance that the equivalent resistance is very nearly equal to the shunt resistance. The result is an ammeter with a low equivalent resistance and the desired 0–50.0-mA range. At full-scale deflection, $I = I_a = 50.0$ mA, the current through the galvanometer is 1.00 mA, the current through the shunt resistor is 49.0 mA, and $V_{ab} = 0.0200$ V. If the current I is *less* than 50.0 mA, the coil current and the deflection are proportionally less.

Voltmeters

This same basic meter may also be used to measure potential difference or *voltage.* A voltage-measuring device is called a **voltmeter**. A voltmeter always measures the potential difference between two points, and its terminals must be connected to these points. (Example 25.6 in Section 25.4 described what can happen if a voltmeter is connected incorrectly.) As we discussed in Section 25.4, an ideal voltmeter would have *infinite* resistance, so connecting it between two points in a circuit would not alter any of the currents. Real voltmeters always have finite resistance, but a voltmeter should have large enough resistance that connecting it in a circuit does not change the other currents appreciably.

For the meter described in Example 26.8 the voltage across the meter coil at full-scale deflection is only $I_{fs}R_c = (1.00 \times 10^{-3}\,\text{A})(20.0\ \Omega) = 0.0200$ V. We can extend this range by connecting a resistor R_s in *series* with the coil (Fig. 26.15b). Then only a fraction of the total potential difference appears across the coil itself, and the remainder appears across R_s. For a voltmeter with full-scale reading V_V, we need a series resistor R_s in Fig. 26.15b such that

$$V_V = I_{fs}(R_c + R_s) \qquad \text{(for a voltmeter)} \qquad (26.8)$$

Application Electromyography
A fine needle containing two electrodes is being inserted into a muscle in this patient's hand. By using a sensitive voltmeter to measure the potential difference between these electrodes, a physician can probe the muscle's electrical activity. This is an important technique for diagnosing neurological and neuromuscular diseases.

Example 26.9 Designing a voltmeter

What series resistance is required to make the 1.00-mA, 20.0-Ω meter described above into a voltmeter with a range of 0 to 10.0 V?

SOLUTION

IDENTIFY and SET UP: Since this meter is being used as a voltmeter, its internal connections are as shown in Fig. 26.15b. Our target variable is the series resistance R_s. The maximum allowable voltage across the voltmeter is $V_V = 10.0$ V. We want this to occur when the current through the coil is $I_{fs} = 1.00 \times 10^{-3}$ A. Our target variable is the series resistance R_s, which we find using Eq. (26.8).

EXECUTE: From Eq. (26.8),

$$R_s = \frac{V_V}{I_{fs}} - R_c = \frac{10.0 \text{ V}}{0.00100 \text{ A}} - 20.0 \ \Omega = 9980 \ \Omega$$

EVALUATE: At full-scale deflection, $V_{ab} = 10.0$ V, the voltage across the meter is 0.0200 V, the voltage across R_s is 9.98 V, and the current through the voltmeter is 0.00100 A. Most of the voltage appears across the series resistor. The meter's equivalent resistance is a desirably high $R_{eq} = 20.0 \ \Omega + 9980 \ \Omega = 10,000 \ \Omega$. Such a meter is called a "1000 ohms-per-volt" meter, referring to the ratio of resistance to full-scale deflection. In normal operation the current through the circuit element being measured (I in Fig. 26.15b) is much greater than 0.00100 A, and the resistance between points a and b in the circuit is much less than 10,000 Ω. The voltmeter draws off only a small fraction of the current and thus disturbs the circuit being measured only slightly.

MasteringPHYSICS

ActivPhysics 12.4: Using Ammeters and Voltmeters

Ammeters and Voltmeters in Combination

A voltmeter and an ammeter can be used together to measure *resistance* and *power*. The resistance R of a resistor equals the potential difference V_{ab} between its terminals divided by the current I; that is, $R = V_{ab}/I$. The power input P to any circuit element is the product of the potential difference across it and the current through it: $P = V_{ab}I$. In principle, the most straightforward way to measure R or P is to measure V_{ab} and I simultaneously.

With practical ammeters and voltmeters this isn't quite as simple as it seems. In Fig. 26.16a, ammeter A reads the current I in the resistor R. Voltmeter V, however, reads the *sum* of the potential difference V_{ab} across the resistor and the potential difference V_{bc} across the ammeter. If we transfer the voltmeter terminal from c to b, as in Fig. 26.16b, then the voltmeter reads the potential difference V_{ab} correctly, but the ammeter now reads the *sum* of the current I in the resistor and the current I_V in the voltmeter. Either way, we have to correct the reading of one instrument or the other unless the corrections are small enough to be negligible.

26.16 Ammeter–voltmeter method for measuring resistance.

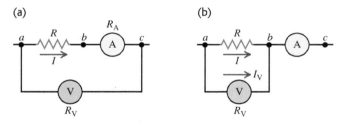

Example 26.10 Measuring resistance I

The voltmeter in the circuit of Fig. 26.16a reads 12.0 V and the ammeter reads 0.100 A. The meter resistances are $R_V = 10,000 \ \Omega$ (for the voltmeter) and $R_A = 2.00 \ \Omega$ (for the ammeter). What are the resistance R and the power dissipated in the resistor?

SOLUTION

IDENTIFY and SET UP: The ammeter reads the current $I = 0.100$ A through the resistor, and the voltmeter reads the potential difference

between a and c. If the ammeter were *ideal* (that is, if $R_A = 0$), there would be zero potential difference between b and c, the voltmeter reading $V = 12.0$ V would be equal to the potential difference V_{ab} across the resistor, and the resistance would simply be equal to $R = V/I = (12.0 \text{ V})/(0.100 \text{ A}) = 120 \ \Omega$. The ammeter is *not* ideal, however (its resistance is $R_A = 2.00 \ \Omega$), so the voltmeter reading V is actually the sum of the potential differences V_{bc} (across the ammeter) and V_{ab} (across the resistor). We use Ohm's law to find the voltage V_{bc} from the known current and ammeter resistance. Then we solve for V_{ab} and the resistance R. Given these, we are able to calculate the power P into the resistor.

EXECUTE: From Ohm's law, $V_{bc} = IR_A = (0.100 \text{ A})(2.00 \text{ }\Omega) = 0.200 \text{ V}$ and $V_{ab} = IR$. The sum of these is $V = 12.0 \text{ V}$, so the potential difference across the resistor is $V_{ab} = V - V_{bc} = (12.0 \text{ V}) - (0.200 \text{ V}) = 11.8 \text{ V}$. Hence the resistance is

$$R = \frac{V_{ab}}{I} = \frac{11.8 \text{ V}}{0.100 \text{ A}} = 118 \text{ }\Omega$$

The power dissipated in this resistor is

$$P = V_{ab}I = (11.8 \text{ V})(0.100 \text{ A}) = 1.18 \text{ W}$$

EVALUATE: You can confirm this result for the power by using the alternative formula $P = I^2R$. Do you get the same answer?

Example 26.11   **Measuring resistance II**

Suppose the meters of Example 26.10 are connected to a different resistor as shown in Fig. 26.16b, and the readings obtained on the meters are the same as in Example 26.10. What is the value of this new resistance R, and what is the power dissipated in the resistor?

SOLUTION

IDENTIFY and SET UP: In Example 26.10 the ammeter read the actual current through the resistor, but the voltmeter reading was not the same as the potential difference across the resistor. Now the situation is reversed: The voltmeter reading $V = 12.0 \text{ V}$ shows the actual potential difference V_{ab} across the resistor, but the ammeter reading $I_A = 0.100 \text{ A}$ is *not* equal to the current I through the resistor. Applying the junction rule at b in Fig. 26.16b shows that $I_A = I + I_V$, where I_V is the current through the voltmeter. We find I_V from the given values of V and the voltmeter resistance R_V, and we use this value to find the resistor current I. We then determine the resistance R from I and the voltmeter reading, and calculate the power as in Example 26.10.

EXECUTE: We have $I_V = V/R_V = (12.0 \text{ V})/(10,000 \text{ }\Omega) = 1.20 \text{ mA}$. The actual current I in the resistor is $I = I_A - I_V = 0.100 \text{ A} - 0.0012 \text{ A} = 0.0988 \text{ A}$, and the resistance is

$$R = \frac{V_{ab}}{I} = \frac{12.0 \text{ V}}{0.0988 \text{ A}} = 121 \text{ }\Omega$$

The power dissipated in the resistor is

$$P = V_{ab}I = (12.0 \text{ V})(0.0988 \text{ A}) = 1.19 \text{ W}$$

EVALUATE: Had the meters been ideal, our results would have been $R = 12.0 \text{ V}/0.100 \text{ A} = 120 \text{ }\Omega$ and $P = VI = (12.0 \text{ V}) \times (0.100 \text{ A}) = 1.2 \text{ W}$ both here and in Example 26.10. The actual (correct) results are not too different in either case. That's because the ammeter and voltmeter are nearly ideal: Compared with the resistance R under test, the ammeter resistance R_A is very small and the voltmeter resistance R_V is very large. Under these conditions, treating the meters as ideal yields pretty good results; accurate work requires calculations as in these two examples.

Ohmmeters

An alternative method for measuring resistance is to use a d'Arsonval meter in an arrangement called an **ohmmeter.** It consists of a meter, a resistor, and a source (often a flashlight battery) connected in series (Fig. 26.17). The resistance R to be measured is connected between terminals x and y.

The series resistance R_s is variable; it is adjusted so that when terminals x and y are short-circuited (that is, when $R = 0$), the meter deflects full scale. When nothing is connected to terminals x and y, so that the circuit between x and y is *open* (that is, when $R \to \infty$), there is no current and hence no deflection. For any intermediate value of R the meter deflection depends on the value of R, and the meter scale can be calibrated to read the resistance R directly. Larger currents correspond to smaller resistances, so this scale reads backward compared to the scale showing the current.

In situations in which high precision is required, instruments containing d'Arsonval meters have been supplanted by electronic instruments with direct digital readouts. Digital voltmeters can be made with extremely high internal resistance, of the order of 100 MΩ. Figure 26.18 shows a digital *multimeter,* an instrument that can measure voltage, current, or resistance over a wide range.

26.17 Ohmmeter circuit. The resistor R_s has a variable resistance, as is indicated by the arrow through the resistor symbol. To use the ohmmeter, first connect x directly to y and adjust R_s until the meter reads zero. Then connect x and y across the resistor R and read the scale.

The Potentiometer

The *potentiometer* is an instrument that can be used to measure the emf of a source without drawing any current from the source; it also has a number of other useful applications. Essentially, it balances an unknown potential difference against an adjustable, measurable potential difference.

26.18 This digital multimeter can be used as a voltmeter (red arc), ammeter (yellow arc), or ohmmeter (green arc).

26.19 A potentiometer.

(a) Potentiometer circuit

(b) Circuit symbol for potentiometer (variable resistor)

The principle of the potentiometer is shown schematically in Fig. 26.19a. A resistance wire ab of total resistance R_{ab} is permanently connected to the terminals of a source of known emf $\mathcal{E}_1$. A sliding contact c is connected through the galvanometer G to a second source whose emf $\mathcal{E}_2$ is to be measured. As contact c is moved along the resistance wire, the resistance R_{cb} between points c and b varies; if the resistance wire is uniform, R_{cb} is proportional to the length of wire between c and b. To determine the value of $\mathcal{E}_2$, contact c is moved until a position is found at which the galvanometer shows no deflection; this corresponds to zero current passing through $\mathcal{E}_2$. With $I_2 = 0$, Kirchhoff's loop rule gives

$$\mathcal{E}_2 = IR_{cb}$$

With $I_2 = 0$, the current I produced by the emf $\mathcal{E}_1$ has the same value no matter what the value of the emf $\mathcal{E}_2$. We calibrate the device by replacing $\mathcal{E}_2$ by a source of known emf; then any unknown emf $\mathcal{E}_2$ can be found by measuring the length of wire cb for which $I_2 = 0$. Note that for this to work, V_{ab} must be greater than $\mathcal{E}_2$.

The term *potentiometer* is also used for any variable resistor, usually having a circular resistance element and a sliding contact controlled by a rotating shaft and knob. The circuit symbol for a potentiometer is shown in Fig. 26.19b.

Test Your Understanding of Section 26.3 You want to measure the current through and the potential difference across the 2-Ω resistor shown in Fig. 26.12 (Example 26.6 in Section 26.2). (a) How should you connect an ammeter and a voltmeter to do this? (i) ammeter and voltmeter both in series with the 2-Ω resistor; (ii) ammeter in series with the 2-Ω resistor and voltmeter connected between points b and d; (iii) ammeter connected between points b and d and voltmeter in series with the 2-Ω resistor; (iv) ammeter and voltmeter both connected between points b and d. (b) What resistances should these meters have? (i) Ammeter and voltmeter resistances should both be much greater than 2 Ω; (ii) ammeter resistance should be much greater than 2 Ω and voltmeter resistance should be much less than 2 Ω; (iii) ammeter resistance should be much less than 2 Ω and voltmeter resistance should be much greater than 2 Ω; (iv) ammeter and voltmeter resistances should both be much less than 2 Ω.

26.4 *R-C* Circuits

In the circuits we have analyzed up to this point, we have assumed that all the emfs and resistances are *constant* (time independent) so that all the potentials, currents, and powers are also independent of time. But in the simple act of charging or discharging a capacitor we find a situation in which the currents, voltages, and powers *do* change with time.

Many devices incorporate circuits in which a capacitor is alternately charged and discharged. These include flashing traffic lights, automobile turn signals, and electronic flash units. Understanding what happens in such circuits is thus of great practical importance.

Charging a Capacitor

Figure 26.20 shows a simple circuit for charging a capacitor. A circuit such as this that has a resistor and a capacitor in series is called an *R-C* **circuit.** We idealize the battery (or power supply) to have a constant emf $\mathcal{E}$ and zero internal resistance $(r = 0)$, and we neglect the resistance of all the connecting conductors.

We begin with the capacitor initially uncharged (Fig. 26.20a); then at some initial time $t = 0$ we close the switch, completing the circuit and permitting current around the loop to begin charging the capacitor (Fig. 26.20b). For all practical purposes, the current begins at the same instant in every conducting part of the circuit, and at each instant the current is the same in every part.

CAUTION **Lowercase means time-varying** Up to this point we have been working with constant potential differences (voltages), currents, and charges, and we have used *capital* letters V, I, and Q, respectively, to denote these quantities. To distinguish between quantities that vary with time and those that are constant, we will use *lowercase* letters v, i, and q for time-varying voltages, currents, and charges, respectively. We suggest that you follow this same convention in your own work. ∎

Because the capacitor in Fig. 26.20 is initially uncharged, the potential difference v_{bc} across it is zero at $t = 0$. At this time, from Kirchhoff's loop law, the voltage v_{ab} across the resistor R is equal to the battery emf $\mathcal{E}$. The initial ($t = 0$) current through the resistor, which we will call I_0, is given by Ohm's law: $I_0 = v_{ab}/R = \mathcal{E}/R$.

As the capacitor charges, its voltage v_{bc} increases and the potential difference v_{ab} across the resistor decreases, corresponding to a decrease in current. The sum of these two voltages is constant and equal to $\mathcal{E}$. After a long time the capacitor becomes fully charged, the current decreases to zero, and the potential difference v_{ab} across the resistor becomes zero. Then the entire battery emf $\mathcal{E}$ appears across the capacitor and $v_{bc} = \mathcal{E}$.

Let q represent the charge on the capacitor and i the current in the circuit at some time t after the switch has been closed. We choose the positive direction for the current to correspond to positive charge flowing onto the left-hand capacitor plate, as in Fig. 26.20b. The instantaneous potential differences v_{ab} and v_{bc} are

$$v_{ab} = iR \qquad v_{bc} = \frac{q}{C}$$

Using these in Kirchhoff's loop rule, we find

$$\mathcal{E} - iR - \frac{q}{C} = 0 \qquad (26.9)$$

The potential drops by an amount iR as we travel from a to b and by q/C as we travel from b to c. Solving Eq. (26.9) for i, we find

$$i = \frac{\mathcal{E}}{R} - \frac{q}{RC} \qquad (26.10)$$

At time $t = 0$, when the switch is first closed, the capacitor is uncharged, and so $q = 0$. Substituting $q = 0$ into Eq. (26.10), we find that the *initial* current I_0 is given by $I_0 = \mathcal{E}/R$, as we have already noted. If the capacitor were not in the circuit, the last term in Eq. (26.10) would not be present; then the current would be *constant* and equal to $\mathcal{E}/R$.

As the charge q increases, the term q/RC becomes larger and the capacitor charge approaches its final value, which we will call Q_f. The current decreases and eventually becomes zero. When $i = 0$, Eq. (26.10) gives

$$\frac{\mathcal{E}}{R} = \frac{Q_f}{RC} \qquad Q_f = C\mathcal{E} \qquad (26.11)$$

Note that the final charge Q_f does not depend on R.

Figure 26.21 shows the current and capacitor charge as functions of time. At the instant the switch is closed ($t = 0$), the current jumps from zero to its initial value $I_0 = \mathcal{E}/R$; after that, it gradually approaches zero. The capacitor charge starts at zero and gradually approaches the final value given by Eq. (26.11), $Q_f = C\mathcal{E}$.

We can derive general expressions for the charge q and current i as functions of time. With our choice of the positive direction for current (Fig. 26.20b), i equals the rate at which positive charge arrives at the left-hand (positive)

26.20 Charging a capacitor. (a) Just before the switch is closed, the charge q is zero. (b) When the switch closes (at $t = 0$), the current jumps from zero to $\mathcal{E}/R$. As time passes, q approaches Q_f and the current i approaches zero.

(a) Capacitor initially uncharged

(b) Charging the capacitor

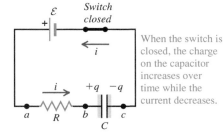

When the switch is closed, the charge on the capacitor increases over time while the current decreases.

26.21 Current i and capacitor charge q as functions of time for the circuit of Fig. 26.20. The initial current is I_0 and the initial capacitor charge is zero. The current asymptotically approaches zero, and the capacitor charge asymptotically approaches a final value of Q_f.

(a) Graph of current versus time for a charging capacitor

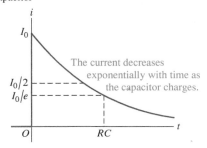

The current decreases exponentially with time as the capacitor charges.

(b) Graph of capacitor charge versus time for a charging capacitor

The charge on the capacitor increases exponentially with time toward the final value Q_f.

plate of the capacitor, so $i = dq/dt$. Making this substitution in Eq. (26.10), we have

$$\frac{dq}{dt} = \frac{\mathcal{E}}{R} - \frac{q}{RC} = -\frac{1}{RC}(q - C\mathcal{E})$$

We can rearrange this to

$$\frac{dq}{q - C\mathcal{E}} = -\frac{dt}{RC}$$

and then integrate both sides. We change the integration variables to q' and t' so that we can use q and t for the upper limits. The lower limits are $q' = 0$ and $t' = 0$:

$$\int_0^q \frac{dq'}{q' - C\mathcal{E}} = -\int_0^t \frac{dt'}{RC}$$

When we carry out the integration, we get

$$\ln\!\left(\frac{q - C\mathcal{E}}{-C\mathcal{E}}\right) = -\frac{t}{RC}$$

Exponentiating both sides (that is, taking the inverse logarithm) and solving for q, we find

$$\frac{q - C\mathcal{E}}{-C\mathcal{E}} = e^{-t/RC}$$

$$q = C\mathcal{E}(1 - e^{-t/RC}) = Q_f(1 - e^{-t/RC}) \quad \begin{array}{l}\text{(R-C circuit, charging}\\ \text{capacitor)}\end{array} \quad (26.12)$$

The instantaneous current i is just the time derivative of Eq. (26.12):

$$i = \frac{dq}{dt} = \frac{\mathcal{E}}{R}e^{-t/RC} = I_0 e^{-t/RC} \quad \begin{array}{l}\text{(R-C circuit, charging}\\ \text{capacitor)}\end{array} \quad (26.13)$$

The charge and current are both *exponential* functions of time. Figure 26.21a is a graph of Eq. (26.13) and Fig. 26.21b is a graph of Eq. (26.12).

Time Constant

After a time equal to RC, the current in the R-C circuit has decreased to $1/e$ (about 0.368) of its initial value. At this time, the capacitor charge has reached $(1 - 1/e) = 0.632$ of its final value $Q_f = C\mathcal{E}$. The product RC is therefore a measure of how quickly the capacitor charges. We call RC the **time constant,** or the **relaxation time,** of the circuit, denoted by τ:

$$\tau = RC \quad \text{(time constant for R-C circuit)} \quad (26.14)$$

When τ is small, the capacitor charges quickly; when it is larger, the charging takes more time. If the resistance is small, it's easier for current to flow, and the capacitor charges more quickly. If R is in ohms and C in farads, τ is in seconds.

In Fig. 26.21a the horizontal axis is an *asymptote* for the curve. Strictly speaking, i never becomes exactly zero. But the longer we wait, the closer it gets. After a time equal to $10RC$, the current has decreased to 0.000045 of its initial value. Similarly, the curve in Fig. 26.21b approaches the horizontal dashed line labeled Q_f as an asymptote. The charge q never attains exactly this value, but after a time equal to $10RC$, the difference between q and Q_f is only 0.000045 of Q_f. We invite you to verify that the product RC has units of time.

MasteringPHYSICS

PhET: Circuit Construction Kit (AC+DC)
PhET: Circuit Construction Kit (DC Only)
ActivPhysics 12.6: Capacitance
ActivPhysics 12.7: Series and Parallel Capacitors
ActivPhysics 12.8: Circuit Time Constants

Application **Pacemakers and Capacitors**

This x-ray image shows a pacemaker implanted in a patient with a malfunctioning sinoatrial node, the part of the heart that generates the electrical signal to trigger heartbeats. The pacemaker circuit contains a battery, a capacitor, and a computer-controlled switch. To maintain regular beating, once per second the switch discharges the capacitor and sends an electrical pulse along the lead to the heart. The switch then flips to allow the capacitor to recharge for the next pulse.

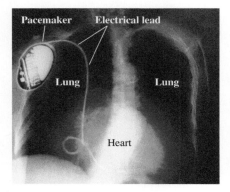